Original stories written by:

Sarah Allen

Stephen Attmore

Joan Baker

Phyllis Bampton

Graham Broach

Dennis Burley

Mae Cheeseman

Mavis Connelly

Judy Cooper

Jane Carruth

David Eden

Eugene Field

Thomas Hood

Diane Jackman

Jennifer Jordan

A. N. Keyes

Lucy Kincaid

Elizabeth Lewis

Robert Moss

Lilian Murray

Rosomond Pinney

C. M. Smith

Liz Souval

Moira Stubley

Rosalind Sutton

Jill Tomlinson

Violet Williams

June Woodman

Edited by Trevor Weston

ISBN 0 86112 365 4
© Brimax Books Ltd 1986. All rights reserved
Published by Brimax Books, Newmarket, England 1986
Printed in Hong Kong

365 BEDTIME STORIES

365
BEDTIME
STORIES

BRIMAX BOOKS · NEWMARKET · ENGLAND

JANUARY

JANUARY 1

Saved by their Tails

A family of mice lived in a large empty house. They tiptoed about in case someone found them. Then someone did: Thomas the black cat and he smelt mice! Mmm! Tasty things, mice!

After breakfast, Thomas settled down to sleep. Grandpa, the oldest mouse, called a meeting. 'We must trick this cat before he eats us all . . . Any ideas?' he asked.

'Surely,' said Pip, 'there must be one safe place?'

'Just one,' said Grandpa. 'Follow me.' While Thomas slept, they ran down passages, through rooms, and down steps to the store room. Sacks of food stood waiting.

'Well?' asked Grandpa. 'What do you think?'

'The cat might creep down those steps,' said Flip.

'Ah!' grunted Grandpa. 'The door must be shut. But how?'

'Grandpa,' said Pip, 'couldn't we each hold one another's tail and make a long mice chain? Then you wind your tail round the door handle, grip our chain and we pull,' said Pip.

Grandpa nodded. 'Very clever!' They pulled and pulled. Slowly the door moved.

'Again!' cried Pip. 'Puuuu . . . ll!' The door clicked. They were safe!

'Now we are here for ever!' said Flip sadly.

'Cheer up!' said Pip. 'We can nibble a small hole and play in the rooms upstairs when Thomas goes out.'

'We're safe from him while he's here,' smiled Grandpa, 'and while the cat's away, we mice shall play.'

JANUARY 2

The Mirror and the Moon

Long ago a lady fair
Combed her wavy golden hair;
She sat upon the silver sand,
A silver mirror in her hand.
Then up came the wind
With a whoosh and a whoo;
He laughed and grinned
With a 'How d'you do?'
And a wheel and a whoop
And a loop of the loop.

With a mighty puff and roar
He raced along the shore;
He reached the lady fair,
And pulled her golden hair.
The wind laughed, 'Ho ho ho.
You'll see your mirror soon
In the sky with a silver glow
As a shining silver moon.'
'What is a moon?' she cried.
'A bit of glass,' he replied.

JANUARY 3

The Swineherd (Part 1)

There was once a prince who lived in a small kingdom. He was strong and handsome and many princesses would have been pleased to marry him, but he cared for none of them.

He was in love with the Emperor's daughter. He decided to send her two presents. He went to his father's grave. There was a fine rose that grew there. It bloomed only once every five years. In the rose tree lived a nightingale that sang the sweetest song in the world. The prince picked the rose and put the nightingale in a cage and sent both to the princess.

When the princess saw the rose she said, 'How beautifully it is made.' Then she looked closer. 'Oh, it's only a real rose!' she cried. 'Take it away!'

'There is another present,' said the prince's messenger. He handed her the nightingale in the cage.

'What a pretty music box,' said the princess as the nightingale began to sing. Then she looked closer. 'Oh, it's a real bird!' cried the princess. 'What a nasty, dirty, feathered thing! Let it fly away. And as for the prince who sent all this rubbish, I never want to see him as long as I live!'

The messenger went back to the prince and told him what had happened. 'Well,' said the prince, 'I shall just have to try another plan.'

JANUARY 4

The Swineherd (Part 2)

The prince's presents of a rose and a nightingale had been refused by the princess he loved and so he decided on a new plan. He stained his face with brown dye, put on some old clothes and went to the Emperor's palace. 'Have you any work for a poor peasant?' asked the prince.

'The pigs need tending,' said the Emperor. 'You can be my swineherd.'

The prince agreed and went to live in a poor tumbledown hut near the pig-sties. The prince tended the pigs during the day and at night he played the flute. His favourite song was "Over the Hills and Far Away".

One evening the princess heard the sweet music. 'I know that tune,' she cried. 'It's "Over the Hills and Far Away"! I can play it too. Tell the peasant to sell me his flute,' she said to her ladies-in-waiting.

The ladies-in-waiting went over to the peasant and then came back giggling to the princess. 'He says he will sell it for fifty kisses.'

'Kiss that rough swineherd!' she cried. 'But I must have that flute . . . Tell him to approach.' The princess kissed the prince fifty times, but on the fiftieth kiss the Emperor appeared.

'How dare you kiss my daughter,' shouted the Emperor to the prince.

'I am not kissing her,' said the prince. 'She is kissing me.'

'My daughter kiss a common swineherd! I never want to see either of you ever again.'

'Oh my, what shall we do?' cried the princess.

'If you will love me,' said the prince, 'come away with me and we shall be married.'

'Marry a common swineherd?' said the princess. 'Never!'

'Well,' said the prince, wiping the dye from his face, 'you were too proud to marry an honest swineherd; but you were not too proud to kiss a stranger to get something you wanted. So you are not the wife for me.'

'Where shall I go?' wept the princess, as the prince collected his fine clothes.

'I suggest over the hills and far away,' said the prince. 'Goodbye.'

JANUARY 5

The Fable of the Fox and the Grapes

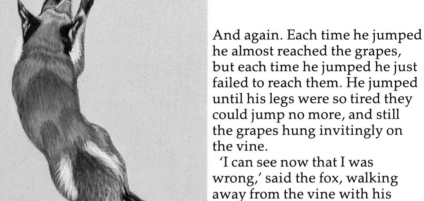

A fox saw some grapes growing on a vine. 'How delicious they look,' he said, licking his lips hungrily. 'I will eat those myself before someone else comes along and sees them.'

The grapes were hanging high on the vine. The fox stretched as tall as he could but he was not quite tall enough to reach them. He jumped. He jumped again.

And again. Each time he jumped he almost reached the grapes, but each time he jumped he just failed to reach them. He jumped until his legs were so tired they could jump no more, and still the grapes hung invitingly on the vine.

'I can see now that I was wrong,' said the fox, walking away from the vine with his nose in the air, as though he didn't care. 'I thought at first the grapes were ripe and ready to eat but now I see they are sour and not fit to eat at all.'

JANUARY 6

Eric Elf's Clever Birds

'I don't know how I shall manage until my ankle's better,' Eric Elf complained as the nurse of the fairies bandaged his sprained ankle. 'How will I feed the birds in my garden?'

'You should be able to hop around indoors if you hold on to the furniture,' said the nurse. 'You can always leave their food on the window-sill.'

As soon as the nurse left, Eric opened his window and put some crumbs on the sill. The birds soon found the crumbs and they were waiting on the sill whenever Eric opened his window to feed them.

Eric was making his bed a few days later when he noticed how dirty his pillow-case looked. 'I really must wash it,' he said, shaking his pillow from the case. 'But how will I get it dry? I can't hop all the way down the garden to peg it on the line.'

He had just finished washing his pillow-case when he heard a tapping noise at the window. He opened the window and two birds flew in. They picked up the pillow-case with their beaks and flew into the garden. They draped the pillow-case carefully over the line and then flew back indoors for the pegs.

'You really are clever birds,' Eric said, looking at his pillow-case fluttering in the breeze. 'With you to help me, I'm sure I shall manage very nicely until my ankle's better.'

JANUARY 7

A Lucky Star (Part 1)

Once there was a poor man whose only son was born under a lucky star. The King was told one day that this boy would marry his daughter.

The King was very cross when he heard this. 'A poor boy like that marry my daughter! NEVER!' he said. He went to see the boy's father. 'I want to buy your son,' he said.

The King was told the boy was not for sale; but he nagged and argued and pleaded until at last the boy's father thought, 'My son can come to no harm with the King. He will give him a better life than I can . . . I must let him go.'

The King carried the baby off. But instead of taking him home to the palace, he put him in a box and cast the box adrift on the river. With any luck it would float out to sea and the baby would never be seen again. Marry his daughter indeed!

The boy hadn't been born under a lucky star for nothing. The box was fished from the river by a miller. He took the baby home to his wife. They named him Jack and brought him up as their own son. He grew into a fine strong lad, full of mischief, but kind too.

Then one day, the King was on his travels and happened to call at the mill. 'What a handsome boy,' said the King. 'Is he your son?'

'He is now,' sighed the miller fondly. 'We found him as a baby, floating down the river in a box.'

JANUARY 8

A Lucky Star (Part 2)

The King went pale when he discovered that the boy destined to marry his daughter was still alive. He called for pen and paper and quickly wrote a letter which he sealed with bright red wax.

'Can you spare the boy to carry this letter to the Queen?' he asked the miller. 'It's very urgent.'

'Jack will be honoured to carry your letter,' said the miller, little knowing that the King had written: 'Kill the bearer of this letter. Will explain when I get home next week.'

Jack set off immediately. Towards nightfall he knocked at a cottage door and asked for shelter for the night.

'This is the home of a band of robbers,' said an old woman who answered the door. 'Are you sure you want to stay?'

'I'm carrying a letter to the Queen. They won't harm me,' said Jack. He was asleep when the robbers returned. Thinking there might be some money in the letter, they opened it.

'Look at this!' they said. 'That's disgraceful. Kill the lad, it says . . . we'll soon settle this.'

They wrote a new letter which said, 'Marry the bearer of this letter to our daughter.' They fixed the King's seal so that it looked as though it had never been broken. They burnt the letter the King had written.

That is how, when the King returned to his palace the next week, he was greeted by his daughter and her new husband Jack, who was, as Jack said himself, 'the luckiest man alive'.

JANUARY 9

The Smiling Crocodile (Part 1)

There was once a crocodile who could not find a wife. For days on end he lay in the hot sun all by himself. When he grew so lonely that he did not know what to do, he plunged into the water and floated on the surface. In the water all that could be seen was the top part of his head and the long line of his back.

One morning he was floating in the river, as still as a log, when a fish swam near his head. In a flash the crocodile opened his huge jaws and caught the fish.

Normally the crocodile would have swallowed the fish whole but he was not very hungry and he hesitated. This gave the fish time to say, 'Spare my life, Mr Crocodile, and you won't regret it.'

The crocodile carried the fish to a shallow pool and set him down. But there was no way the fish could escape back into the river. 'I have often seen you alone on the bank,' said the fish. 'You have no wife and no friends.'

'That is true,' said the crocodile in a deep voice. 'I am very lonely.'

'If I can find you a wife,' said the fish, after a long silence, 'will you free me?' The crocodile said he would.

'If you carry me back to the river and set me free,' said the fish, 'I will find you a wife by the end of the week.'

JANUARY 10

The Smiling Crocodile (Part 2)

A fish caught by a lonely crocodile promised to find the crocodile a wife if he would set him free.

'If I set you free I will never see you again,' grunted the crocodile. 'You may think I look stupid but I assure you I am not.'

'Then leave me in this shallow pool,' said the fish quickly, 'and I will tell you what you must do to find a wife. When you have found her, come back to the pool and set me free.'

'Tell me what to do,' said the crocodile.

'Swim to the far bank,' said the fish. 'Put a smile on your face and wait there . . .' The crocodile left the fish and dived into the river. He swam to the far bank. He climbed out of the water and on to the bank.

Now the fish had often seen a mother crocodile and her young daughter sunning themselves on the opposite bank. He knew very well what was in the mother's mind – a husband for her daughter.

Well, the crocodile scarcely had time to put the big smile on his face when old Mother Croc and her daughter arrived. When the mother saw the smiling stranger, she pushed her daughter towards him. And, in less time than it takes to say 'crocodile', the two had discovered they were made for each other.

In his new-found happiness, the crocodile almost forgot his promise to the fish. It was lucky he did remember for when he went back to the shallow pool he found the hot sun had almost dried up all the water, and the poor fish was gasping.

The crocodile took the fish in his strong jaws and carried him back to the deep river. 'There you go!' he said. 'Take care.' In a flash of silver, the fish swam quickly away and the crocodile went back to his new wife, smiling broadly!

JANUARY 11

Circus Stars

Petal and Poppy, two white ponies, were the stars of old Mr Bantam's little circus. All through the summer the circus moved from fair to fair. And when the business of putting up the Big Top was over, Petal and Poppy would look at each other proudly.

'We are always billed as the stars of the circus,' Petal would say.

'And so we should be,' Poppy would answer. 'The crowds love the way we dance so perfectly together.'

Then one day it happened. Minutes before the afternoon show, Petal remarked, 'By the way I thought you were a little out of step last night . . .'

Poppy snorted indignantly. 'What! Me out of step! You were the one out of step!'

They eyed each other angrily as they pranced into the ring. Petal gave Poppy a spiteful sideways glance. Poppy didn't try to match Petal's steps when it was time to waltz. The ringmaster cut short their act and they were led out of the ring in disgrace.

Poppy and Petal didn't look at each other as they waited for the evening performance. But no call came. They had been dropped.

'They say it's because we're tired,' Petal whispered to Poppy, after a long silence.

'It's never happened before!' replied Poppy.

'But then we never had a quarrel before,' Petal said. 'We'll just have to show them when we get the chance.'

The next day, Mr Bantam himself took Poppy and Petal into the ring for a rehearsal. Do you know, they were so perfect in their timing and so brilliant

in their performance that even the circus hands shouted 'Bravo!'

'Well, we've shown them!' Petal said, when they were by themselves again. 'By the way, you were absolutely splendid!'

'So were you,' said Poppy. 'So were you!'

Petal and Poppy are still the circus stars and the very best of friends.

JANUARY 12

Pixie Visitors

Pixies enjoy getting together and having fun. The trouble with pixies is they always have their parties at night when everyone else is trying to sleep.

One cold night a crowd of pixies found a nice warm farmhouse kitchen to have their party. There was shouting and singing and dancing all night long.

The farmer and his wife didn't get a wink of sleep. 'Tell them to go away,' said the farmer's wife.

'I can't do that,' said the farmer. 'If you annoy the pixies they can make everything go wrong; the hens won't lay, the milk will curdle, the crops will die.'

Unfortunately, the pixies liked the farmhouse kitchen so much they had parties in there every night. The farmer and his wife hardly slept at all.

'We must do something,' complained the farmer's wife. 'We keep falling asleep during the day.'

'I've got an idea,' said the farmer. That night he took his hay fork and shovel up to the bedroom. When the pixie party was in full swing the farmer began to lower the fork through a crack in the floor down into the kitchen. His wife began to lower the shovel on the other side of the room.

'Look!' cried one of the pixies. 'It's a giant's fork.'

'Yes, and there's his spoon,' cried another, seeing the shovel. 'He's come to eat us up. Let's run.'

Off the pixies ran and they never came back because the one thing pixies fear above all else is a hungry giant.

JANUARY 13

Rapunzel (Part 1)

One day, a prince was riding in the forest when he heard a girl singing. He got down from his horse and led it quietly along a mossy footpath until he came to a clearing. In the clearing was a tower, as round and as straight as a giant pine tree. The tower was so tall it looked as though its roof was touching the sky. At the very top of it there was a tiny window. It was from the tiny window that the sound was coming.

'It will be a long climb up the stairs to the top,' said the Prince, shading his eyes and looking upwards. 'But I must find out who is singing so sweetly.'

He looped the horse's bridle over a branch and went to look for a way in. He walked round the tower a hundred times. He could find no door . . . no window . . . no hidden entrance. It was impossible to climb up the outside for the sides were so smooth there was neither crack nor ledge where he could put his feet.

In the end the disappointed Prince had to give up his quest and ride home with the sound of the voice drifting in the wind behind him.

JANUARY 14

Rapunzel (Part 2)

The Prince could not forget the voice he had heard coming from the tower. He dreamed about it in daydreams and dreamed about it in his sleep. He rode into the forest every day, just to hear it.

One day, when he was sitting in the branches of a tree near the tower, an old witch came out of the forest. The Prince kept very quiet and watched to see what she would do.

'Rapunzel, Rapunzel, let down your hair,' she cried. Immediately, a long braid of golden hair tumbled from the window at the top of the tower. It was so long, its tip touched the ground. The old witch caught hold of it as though it was a rope and someone in the room at the top of the tower pulled her upwards until she disappeared.

The Prince was so excited he almost fell out of the tree. He waited until the old witch had come down again and hobbled away into the forest. Then he went to the foot of the tower himself.

'Rapunzel, Rapunzel,' he called. 'Let down your hair.' Again the golden hair came tumbling from the tower, but this time it was the handsome prince who used it as a rope and not an ugly old witch. In the tiny room at the top of the tower was the most beautiful girl he had ever seen.

'Who . . . who . . . are you?' she gasped. 'I thought you were the witch.'

'Don't be afraid,' said the Prince. 'I will not hurt you.' He told her his name and how he had heard her singing when he was riding in the forest.

'I sing because I am lonely,' said Rapunzel. 'I have been locked alone in this tower since I was twelve years old. My only visitor is the witch who brought me here.'

'I will help you escape,' said the Prince.

'How can you?' sighed Rapunzel. 'I cannot climb down my own hair and there is no other way in or out of the tower.'

'I will bring you a silken ladder,' promised the Prince.

JANUARY 15

Rapunzel (Part 3)

The next day the old witch visited Rapunzel in the tower again.

'You are much heavier than the Prince,' said Rapunzel, without thinking what she was saying.

The witch was so angry she almost exploded. She snatched a pair of scissors from the table and, before Rapunzel could stop her, she had cut off her long braids of golden hair.

'Now your Prince will never get into the tower,' screamed the witch. And she banished Rapunzel to a far-away place. Even if the Prince did find a way into the tower, Rapunzel would not be there.

The Prince had no way of knowing what had happened when he called Rapunzel to let down her hair. He thought it was she who threw the long golden braids from the window. But it was not. It was the witch. It was the witch who pulled the Prince up . . . and up . . . and up.

'You will never see Rapunzel again!' she screamed. And with that terrible cry, she let go the braids. The Prince fell to the ground.

The Prince lay for many hours where he fell, and when at last he opened his eyes, he could not see. He was blind.

The Prince wandered from place to place in search of Rapunzel. And then one day, he heard her singing and recognised her voice at once.

Rapunzel was overjoyed, but when she saw the Prince's poor blind eyes, she wept hot, splashing tears. Some of her tears fell on to the Prince's face. Suddenly he could see. Her tears had broken the witch's terrible spell.

Rapunzel and the Prince were married and lived happily ever after. As for the old witch, she was never heard of, or seen, again. Perhaps she is still locked in the tower. Once she had let go of the braids she had no way of getting out of the tower herself, had she?

JANUARY 16

Adventures of *The Tulip* – The Seagull

Minty, Wilbur and Thomas are three friends who live on board a boat called *The Tulip*. Thomas is in charge. Wilbur is a very good swimmer and Minty isn't. So Minty always wears a life jacket.

This is the story of the time a seagull landed on the deck of *The Tulip* and started squawking at Wilbur and Minty. Minty and Wilbur were so frightened by the seagull's squawks, they hid behind a barrel.

'Thomas!' they shouted. 'Help! Thomas!' Thomas would know what to do.

'Squawk! Squawk!' cried the seagull.

'Yes of course I will,' said Thomas.

Wilbur and Minty peeped out from behind their barrel to see who Thomas was talking to. They couldn't believe their eyes. Thomas's hand was inside the seagull's mouth.

'Don't you eat our friend!' they cried, rushing at the seagull.

'It's all right,' said Thomas calmly. 'Just watch.' And, to their amazement, Thomas pulled a large fish, tail first, from the seagull's mouth. 'He had that stuck in his throat,' Thomas explained. 'That's why he was squawking.'

The seagull squawked again, but this time in thanks. Thomas said, 'Yes, you must be getting on your way,' and with that the seagull flew off.

'Goodbye,' shouted Thomas, waving his hat.

'Goodbye,' shouted Wilbur and Minty. The seagull squawked back.

'Well,' said Minty, 'I never knew you could speak seagull, Thomas!' Thomas just smiled.

JANUARY 17

Smiling Dilly

Dilly Duck was always smiling. There was the time when the farmer's dog chased her into the pond. And the time when some naughty boys from the village threw pebbles at her. And the time when, for no reason at all, the turkey was extremely rude to her. No matter what happened to her, Dilly just went on smiling and smiling.

'I can't understand you,' Jemima, her best friend, said to her one morning. 'You always seem to be in trouble and yet you keep that silly smile on your face.'

'Well,' said Dilly, 'the sky is a beautiful blue, isn't it? The pond is a delightful place to swim and I never have to go hungry.'

Jemima showed that she didn't think much of her friend's reasons for smiling. 'One day you'll find you have nothing to smile about, you'll see. We'll be taken to market soon and you know what that means!'

When market day drew near all the ducks grew silent and sad – all except Dilly. Then came the day itself. The farmer and his little boy began driving the ducks into crates.

'Do we have to send them all away?' asked the little boy. 'Please let me keep the smiling one.'

The farmer hesitated. Then he shrugged. 'The smiling one, you say? Which duck would that be?'

'I'll show you,' said the little boy eagerly. And he went straight to Dilly and knelt down beside her. '*I* think she's smiling anyway.'

'Keep her then,' said the farmer. 'But mind you look after her properly.' The little boy began to smile. And Dilly, of course, went on smiling, with very good reason!

JANUARY 18

Bobby's Bicycle

Bobby wanted a bicycle more than anything in the world. It would be his birthday soon, but he knew his parents couldn't afford such an expensive present.

One day he took his dog, Rough, on the moor. Throwing stones, sticks and having fun, he forgot the bicycle.

Then he saw something strange. Propped against a signpost was the weirdest bicycle he'd ever seen. He walked round it, touched it and then climbed on to the saddle. Now he knew why it looked odd – it had no pedals! With his toes just reaching the ground he gave a push.

He was off! Faster and faster! Up or down hills, it made no difference. He whizzed along, legs dangling and hands gripping. Oh yes, one other thing – there were no brakes! Bobby felt scared at first but was enjoying himself so much he just shouted and laughed. A thick bush stood in his way. Suddenly the bicycle went leaping over it.

'Good old boy!' Bobby patted the handle-bars as if he was riding a horse. A wide stream stood in front of them. 'Steady, boy . . . NOW!' he cried. But the ground on the other side was boggy. The front wheel sank and Bobby was thrown over the handle-bars into the mud. He felt Rough licking his face.

'Hello, old chap! Where's the bike?' asked Bobby. It had disappeared.

Together they trudged back and at last came to the signpost. There stood a bicycle – a shining new one! A ticket on the bell said: 'Happy Birthday, Bobby, from Great Aunt Maud'. Bobby rode home bursting with excitement. 'Who's Great Aunt Maud?' he asked.

'My aunt,' said his mother. 'She lives across the moor. She used to ride an old bone-shaker bicycle like a witch riding on a broomstick. Still does, I shouldn't wonder!'

Riding his beautiful bicycle, Bobby went to find out.

JANUARY 19

The Fable of the Lion and the Mouse

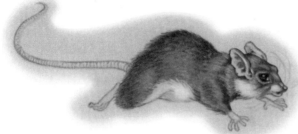

A lion was asleep one day when a mouse ran over his face. The lion woke with a snarl and scooped the mouse into his paw. The frightened mouse feared he was about to die and he pleaded for his life.

'Please, oh great and mighty lion, please let me go. Give me my freedom and one day I will repay your kindness.'

The lion was so amused to think that the tiny, shivering, frightened mouse thought he might be able to help someone as strong and big and unafraid as himself that he laughed out loud and let the mouse go.

Some days later, when the mouse was scurrying about in the undergrowth, he heard the lion roar. It sounded to the mouse as though the lion was in some kind of trouble. He went to see if he could help. The lion was trapped in a hunter's net and could find no way out.

'There is nothing *you* can do to help *me*.' said the lion sadly, when he saw the mouse. 'When the hunters return with their spears they will kill me.'

'Your last day has not come yet,' said the mouse. He began to nibble at the net with his sharp little teeth. Soon he had made a hole big enough for the lion to crawl through.

'You were right,' said the lion, as he and the mouse hurried to safety. 'There are times when the weak are able to help the strong.'

JANUARY 20

Perky and the Stopinbed

Willie Stopinbed lived in a grubby old cottage in a pine forest. He kept chickens and grew vegetables to sell in the market. But he liked staying in bed. By the time he reached the market, everybody had done their shopping. 'Days aren't long enough,' he moaned. 'It's lunch time before I've had breakfast.'

One day he exchanged his unsold vegetables for some chicks. He put them with his hens, but the wire netting was old and full of holes; the chicks flew away. The hens soon followed and Willie was alone.

'Stupid birds!' he grumbled. 'No, not really . . . I'm lazy . . . I forget to feed them . . . they need cleaning out. I'm a bad master.'

Just then a chick flew on to his shoulder. One had come back! Willie was delighted. He called his friend Perky.

Months later he asked, 'When will you lay me an egg, Perky?' Perky was puzzled. Hadn't Willie noticed his fine feathers? Hadn't he heard him trying out his voice?

So Perky practised every morning, perched on the fence. Then one day, with his feathers blowing, his bright red comb flapping on his head and his beak wide open, he made the sound he wanted.

'Cock-a-doodle-doo!
Cock-a-doodle-doo!' He crowed
again and again! Out
came Willie in his
nightshirt.

'What's all this . . .?' he started. Then he saw his friend. 'Perky!' he cried. 'You're a rooster! You're splendid! You've got me out of bed!'

Willie started work straight away. He cleaned his cottage, built a new run for some new hens and looked after them. He was always first at the market and sold all his eggs and vegetables. It was all thanks to Perky, the early bird, who woke him every morning, crowing until he was up; so never again was Willie called 'Stopinbed'.

JANUARY 21

The Lost Shoes

Jody had lost one of his shoes. He had looked everywhere for it. 'I hope it turns up tomorrow,' he said, as he climbed into bed.

Suddenly he heard a voice. It was coming from under his bed. He sat up in surprise and saw his red slippers jumping up and down. 'Come on,' they said. 'We'll go and find your shoe. Put us on.' Jody slipped his feet into

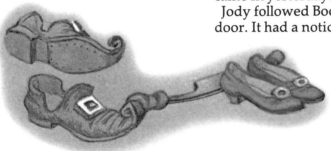

them. It was all rather strange. 'Shut your eyes,' said the slippers, 'and turn three times.'

When Jody opened his eyes he found himself in a strange room. 'Ah, there you are,' said a little old man. 'I'm Boots, the shoemender, and this is Lost Shoe Land.' Jody looked round the room. There were old shoes, new shoes, funny old-fashioned shoes, even a pair of curly-toed boots with a mouse in them.

'You'll be wanting your shoe back?' said Boots. 'I think it came in yesterday.'

Jody followed Boots to a large door. It had a notice which read,

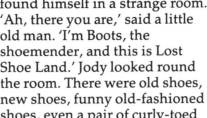

Yesterday's Shoes. Inside, the room was filled with all sorts of odd shoes, boots and slippers.

'Now, which one is yours?' asked Boots.

'It has my name in it,' said Jody nervously.

'Jody's shoe, step forward!' shouted Boots and immediately one shoe moved forward. Jody picked it up.

'Thank you,' he said.

'Not at all,' said Boots. 'But don't lose it again.' Suddenly Jody found himself back in his bedroom.

The next morning Jody went to put his slippers on and there right next to them was his missing shoe. 'Now why didn't I see that there before?' he said. Then he had a picture in his mind of a notice that read, *Yesterday's Shoes,* but it faded away as he ran downstairs for breakfast.

JANUARY 22

Just in Time

Squire George was a part-time wizard. One day he sat looking at his magic spell book for so long his head began to ache.

'I think I'll go for a gallop on my horse,' he said and he pushed the spell book to one side.

'Gee up there!' cried the Squire. The horse kicked up his heels and they were off out of the town and over the hills.

Down in the village little Billy was bent on mischief. He could see the Squire and his galloping horse up on the hill.

'He'll be up there for hours,' he said. 'Now is my chance to borrow his book of spells.' He crept up the path towards the Squire's house. He pushed open the door and crept inside. He went into the study. There was the book lying open on the desk.

Up on the hill, something made

the Squire feel prickly behind his ears. There was something wrong . . . somewhere.

'Whoa!' he cried to his horse. They pulled up sharply. He remembered he had left his book of spells open on his desk. Suppose someone got hold of it, someone who didn't understand how careful you had to be with magic spells.

He had to get home quickly. He whispered to his horse and they took the quickest way down, which was straight over the roof-tops.

The Squire and his horse landed in front of his house. He was only just in time. Little Billy was sneaking out of the front door with the spell book under his arm.

'Mine, I believe,' said the Squire. Suddenly Billy found himself sitting in the fish pond with a water-lily tucked over his ear. He decided not to 'borrow' the book again and the Squire

decided to keep it under lock and key from then on.

JANUARY 23

The Enchanted Kettle (Part 1)

Once upon a time long ago, there lived in China an old man who had a very fine kettle. It bubbled merrily on the fire and made delicious tea.

Then one day, as the kettle began to boil on the flames, it jumped from the fire. It grew four short legs and in place of the spout grew the striped head of a badger. The kettle danced round and round the room and turned the old man pale with fright.

When the kettle finally stopped and drew in its legs and head, the old man lifted it with a stick into a box and tied the lid firmly down.

The next day a tinker happened to pass that way, selling pots and pans. 'Here,' said the old man. 'You can have this beautiful kettle of mine. I have no use for it.' You can be sure he told the tinker nothing of the kettle's tricks. The tinker paid him very little and put the kettle in his sack. The old man was delighted to be rid of his mysterious kettle.

That night the tinker decided to use the kettle himself. He began to boil water for his family when suddenly the kettle jumped from the flames, sprouted legs and a badger's head and danced round the room.

'How marvellous,' cried the tinker, who liked anything out of the ordinary. 'I shall teach my kettle some tricks,' he said, and soon his children were laughing merrily at the dancing kettle. 'If this kettle makes my children laugh,' thought the tinker, 'then I have a plan to earn some money.'

JANUARY 24

The Enchanted Kettle (Part 2)

The tinker, who had bought an enchanted kettle from an old man, decided to travel with the kettle round the country. He would go from market place to market place and everywhere he went people would shout, 'Hooray, here comes the tinker with the enchanted kettle.'

As soon as the tinker set the kettle on a fire it would dance round from stall to stall and do all sorts of tricks that the tinker had taught it.

Before long, news of the kettle reached the imperial palace. One day a royal messenger came to the tinker and told him to bring his enchanted kettle to the palace to show the Emperor.

The tinker went to the palace that very day. He was amazed at how beautiful the palace was; but not as amazed as the Emperor when he saw the kettle dance. He and his courtiers laughed as loudly as the people in the market place to see its tricks.

'You must bring your kettle to see me again,' said the Emperor to the tinker. 'This bag of gold is for you. I can't remember when I laughed so much.'

The enchanted kettle made the tinker a rich man, but he often found himself thinking of the old man who had sold it to him for so little. 'I must give the kettle back and let it make a fortune for him.'

The tinker was sad to say goodbye to his dancing kettle. The old man, who had heard of the tinker's fame and fortune, was pleased to have it back.

As soon as the tinker had gone, he set the kettle on the heat. 'Grow your legs and your head,' cried the old man. 'Dance round the room.' But the kettle just sat there bubbling merrily.

For many hours the old man boiled the kettle and waited for it to dance, but it didn't move.

From that day on it never danced another step, but it did make the old man many delicious cups of tea.

JANUARY 25

The White Dove (Part 1)

Once, on a cold and blustery day, a stage-coach was travelling through the forest. It was bumping along over the ruts and through the puddles when a band of robbers ran from the trees.

'Your money or your lives!' they shouted.

As the coachman pulled hard on the reins, and the coach came to a halt, one of the doors jolted open. A slim girl, with brown hair, managed to slip unnoticed through the door and into the forest, catching her dress on brambles and losing her shoes as she went. She did not stop running until the shouts of the robbers had faded away into the distance. Then she sat on a fallen log and buried her face in her hands. She was safe from the robbers it was true, but she was alone in a deep dark wood with nowhere to go and no one to help her.

'What shall I do? I will never find my way out of the forest,' she sobbed.

Presently, between her sobs, she heard the gentle whirr of wings. She looked up and saw a white dove hovering in front of her. It was carrying a tiny key in its beak. It dropped the key on the moss at her feet and said, 'In the tree behind you, you will find a tiny lock. Open it with the key.'

Sure enough, hidden in the bark of the tree, was a tiny keyhole. She turned the key in it and a door opened to reveal a cupboard containing bread and milk.

Then the dove dropped a second key at her feet. That opened a tree door which led to a room just large enough to hold a bed.

'Sleep there, and you will be safe,' said the dove.

JANUARY 26

The White Dove (Part 2)

A girl, lost in the forest, was helped by a white dove. Each time the girl was in need of something, the dove came to her with a different key which opened a door in a different tree.

One day, the dove said to the girl, 'Will you do something for me?'

'Gladly,' said the girl.

'Follow the path that leads into the deepest part of the forest. You will come to a cottage where an old woman lives. Bring me the gold ring that she keeps on a table in her back room.'

The girl soon found the cottage. She slipped past the old woman who was sleeping. But there was no sign of the gold ring in the back room.

She peeped again at the old woman. She wasn't really sleeping. She was sneaking out of the room with a bird-cage under her shawl. The girl snatched the cage from her and gently took the gold ring that the bird was holding in its beak.

She ran into the forest looking for the dove. She waited but it didn't come. She leant against a tree. The tree felt strangely soft. It grew arms. The tree was changing into a prince. Other trees were changing into people.

'Don't be afraid,' said the prince. 'The woman in the cottage is a witch. She cast a spell on all of us turning us into trees, but she allowed me to fly as a dove for two hours a day because I am a prince.' He uncurled the girl's fingers. 'Now you have broken the spell with this ring and I want you to wear it forever as my wife.'

JANUARY 27

Ash Lodge – The Raft

Willie the Mole and his two Badger friends, Basil and Dewy, were having breakfast at Ash Lodge when Willie said, 'What shall we do today? Shall we build a boat?'

'I don't know about a boat,' said Basil, 'but we could get some logs together from the forest and build a raft.'

That sounded fine to Willie. So after breakfast Basil and Dewy dragged plenty of long logs down to the riverside. Then Basil sawed them to the same length. They found some rope in the shed and tied the logs together with a series of loops and knots.

'I'll go and find something we can use as a paddle,' said Basil, when the raft was finished.

While he was away, Dewy and Willie set the raft on the water to see if it floated. Then Willie did something quite unexpected. He gave the raft a push and jumped on to it.

'You silly mole,' shouted Dewy.

'I'm floating. Look!' cried Willie.

'But how are you going to get back?' asked Dewy. Willie hadn't thought of that. While Basil and Dewy tried to find some more rope – they had already used all they had to tie the logs together – a family of ducks came round the bend in the river.

'Can we help?' they quacked.

'Oh, yes please,' said Willie. The ducks lined themselves up behind the raft, put their heads down and paddled hard. When Basil and Dewy reached the bank, Willie had got back on dry land, and was holding on to the raft.

'No need to panic,' he said calmly. 'I've got everything under control, as usual.'

JANUARY 28

The Fable of the Travellers and the Plane Tree

Two travellers were walking along a dusty road. They had been walking since early morning. The road was long, the sun was scorching hot, and they longed for somewhere shady to sit. Presently, in the distance they saw a solitary plane tree.

'Shelter at last,' sighed one of the travellers, pointing to the distant tree.

Tired and hot though the two men were, they managed to quicken their steps until they were standing beneath the plane tree's leafy branches. They sank thankfully to the ground and lay stretched in the shade, glad to escape at last from the blazing heat.

Presently, as he lay on his back looking up into the branches of the tree, one of the travellers said to his companion, 'What a useless thing a plane tree is. It bears no fruit. It is of no use to man at all.'

The plane tree overheard the traveller's remark. 'What an ungrateful man you are,' it said. 'You take shelter from the scorching sun under my branches, and at the very moment you are enjoying the coolness and shade I have provided, you complain that I am useless.'

JANUARY 29
Bedtime

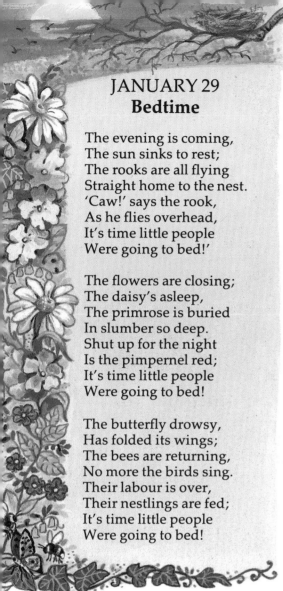

The evening is coming,
The sun sinks to rest;
The rooks are all flying
Straight home to the nest.
'Caw!' says the rook,
As he flies overhead,
It's time little people
Were going to bed!'

The flowers are closing;
The daisy's asleep,
The primrose is buried
In slumber so deep.
Shut up for the night
Is the pimpernel red;
It's time little people
Were going to bed!

The butterfly drowsy,
Has folded its wings;
The bees are returning,
No more the birds sing.
Their labour is over,
Their nestlings are fed;
It's time little people
Were going to bed!

JANUARY 30
Twirly and the Birds

Twirly was a little yellow helicopter who lived in a helicopter house called a hangar.

One morning his friend Mrs Blackbird came fluttering to his front door in a terrible state.

'Oh Twirly, please help me. They're cutting down our tree and my babies can't fly yet,' she cried.

Twirly and Mrs Blackbird set off immediately. When they got to the tree they saw that the men had sawn very nearly all the way through.

'Quick!' said Twirly to Mrs Blackbird. 'Fetch your babies from the nest and put them inside my hold.' Soon all but one of the baby blackbirds were safely aboard and Mrs Blackbird was on her way for the last one when they heard the men shout, 'Timber!' The tree began to rock.

'The tree's falling!' shouted Twirly. Mrs Blackbird swooped down, picked the last baby bird from the nest and flew clear just in time. The tree hit the ground

with a terrific CRASH!

'Oh my poor nest,' cried Mrs Blackbird when she had put her last baby in with the others. 'Never mind. I shall soon build another one and all my babies are safe thanks to you, Twirly.'

Twirly took all the blackbird family to a safe tree nearby. The little blackbirds did enjoy the ride. Mrs Blackbird built a new nest and everyone waved a happy goodbye to Twirly from their comfortable new home.

JANUARY 31
Leela's Blanket

Leela had a blanket. It was yellow and very soft and cuddly. When she was very small she took it everywhere but now that she went to school she only used it when she was sad and when she went to bed. Her brother Ali often teased her about it and sometimes tried to take it away from her.

One Saturday morning as Ali, Leela and their father came back from a morning walk, their mother said, 'Has anyone seen Honey today?' Honey was their cat. 'I've looked in all the usual places and she hasn't been in for her food.' The children went

into the garden and called her but she was nowhere to be seen.

'I expect she'll turn up soon,' said their father.

That evening Honey still hadn't come home and Leela was sad. She wanted her blanket. 'Go upstairs with her, Ali,' their mother said, 'and help her find it.'

The blanket wasn't on her bed, so they looked in the toy cupboard and the toy box. Suddenly Leela saw a piece of yellow behind the box in the corner. 'Here it is,' she called, then she stopped in surprise. There in the folds of the blanket lay Honey with four tiny kittens.

'Ooh look, Ali!' breathed Leela. Honey looked up at them; she looked so warm and comfortable

and the kittens were all cuddled up close.

'Let's go and tell Mum and Dad,' said Ali excitedly. They crept out of the room quietly.

Their mother and father were delighted and Leela was so proud that Honey had chosen her blanket for the kittens that she decided to let Honey keep the blanket for always.

FEBRUARY

FEBRUARY 1

The Princess and the Pea

One dark night, there was a dreadful storm. It rained and it thundered and bright flashes of lightning lit up the sky. There was a knock at the palace door. The Queen went to answer it.

A wet girl stood at the doorstep. 'Come in,' said the Queen. 'You must shelter here for the night.'

When the girl was dry and warm again, she told the Queen that she was a princess. Now, the Queen's son was looking for a princess to be his wife. But how could the Queen be sure this girl was a real princess?

That night, without telling anyone what she was doing, she remade the girl's bed. She put a tiny dried pea on the smooth wooden bed . . . and on top of the pea she put twenty soft mattresses . . . and on top of the mattresses she put twenty very soft feather pillows. The girl had to climb to the ceiling to get into bed!

Next morning the Queen asked her how well she had slept.

'I hardly slept at all,' sighed the girl. 'The bed was so lumpy, I tossed and turned all night.' The Queen took the girl by the hand and led her straight to the Prince.

'Only a real Princess could lie on so many soft mattresses and be unable to sleep because of one tiny pea,' she said. She explained to everyone what she had done. The Prince was overjoyed. He and the Princess were married and they lived happily ever after.

FEBRUARY 2

Toot-toot's Escape

Toot-toot was a little engine who worked in a goods yard. He pulled railway trucks carrying coal or wood. He tootled around the yard all day, only stopping for his meals of coal and water. He enjoyed his job and often gave a toot on his whistle, just for fun.

One day, three men came to look at Toot-toot. One of them peered down his funnel. 'Very nasty!' he said. The second one tapped his wheels with a hammer. 'A bad case of wheel-wobble.' The third one listened to his boiler. 'A fine old rattle here. It's no good. He'll have to be scrapped in the morning.' Then they went away.

Scrapped! Thrown away! Toot-toot wasn't going to sit there and let that happen. So when it was dark, he slipped away off the rails and hid in a wood. There he went to sleep in the moonlight.

When he woke up, the sun was shining. Toot-toot was hungry. He tootled over to a farm. 'Would you like some breakfast?' asked the farmer, when he saw Toot-toot at the door. 'I've got some coal and water over here you might like.' Toot-toot followed the farmer to a stable where he was put into a stall next to a friendly little horse called Rosie.

'Have you come to help?' asked Rosie as Toot-toot started on his coal and water. 'Can you pull things?'

'Of course I can pull things,' said Toot-toot. 'I should love to help.' And that's just what he did. He helped the farmer plough the fields. His lines weren't very straight because of his wheel-wobble but nobody minded. Toot-toot was pleased to say he wasn't ready for the scrap heap yet, and he gave a toot on his whistle, just for fun.

FEBRUARY 3

The Unexpected Rainbow (Part 1)

High above the Earth in the land of clouds there were two kingdoms, the Kingdom of Sol and the Kingdom of Splash. Both of these were ruled by powerful kings.

Now the King of Splash lived in a tall castle on top of a big black rain cloud. While not many miles away, on a big fluffy sun cloud, lived the King of Sol.

You would think that living so close to one another the two kingdoms would be friendly, but this was not so. In fact they were always quarrelling because the King of Splash always wanted it to rain and the King of Sol always wanted it to be sunny.

So, in order to make things fair, the two kingdoms agreed that one day it would be sunny and the next it would rain.

For a time this plan worked very well until one day things went wrong. The King of Splash was getting rather old and at times he was very forgetful. On this particular morning, the King woke up and forgot which day it was.

'Summon the Chief Rainmaker,' called the King. Two minutes later a little man popped his head round the door. 'What a lovely day for a downpour, Plip,' he said, smiling. 'I think we'll have a nice shower today.'

The little man scratched his head. 'Beg pardon, Your Majesty,' he said, 'but it's not supposed to rain today.'

'Not supposed to rain!' shouted the King. 'If I say it will rain then it *will* rain. Is that clear?'

The King of Sol stood at his window and watched angrily as the rain poured down on to the Earth below. 'It rained yesterday,' he complained. 'It should be sunny today. Summon the Torch Bearer,' he shouted. 'Light the biggest candle in the castle. That should put a stop to the downpour!'

FEBRUARY 4

The Unexpected Rainbow (Part 2)

The King of Splash and the King of Sol were fighting a battle of rain against sun.

'Right,' said the King of Splash. 'Time to bring out Thunder and Lightning.' The rainmaker had to do as the King ordered. Meanwhile the King of Sol had lit more candles than ever before. As for the people on Earth, they were caught in terrific storms while the sun was still beating down.

The North Wind soon got to hear of the battle. He flew off to the two kingdoms. First he blew out the candles on Sol; then he froze the water in the giant tap on Splash. The people of Earth couldn't believe it. There was no weather at all!

The King of Sol was sitting on his throne wondering if he had been too hasty, when a knock came at the door. It was the King of Splash.

'My dear fellow,' said the King of Sol.

'I've come to say how sorry I am,' said the King of Splash.

'Oh, don't mention it,' said the King of Sol. Just then the North Wind blew in.

'Aha. I see you two have made friends again,' said the Wind. The two kings looked embarrassed. 'Do you promise never to quarrel again?' asked the Wind. The two kings nodded, and as a sign that they had made friends they painted a giant rainbow across the sky.

FEBRUARY 5

The Fable of the Hare and the Tortoise

A hare was teasing a tortoise. 'You're very slow,' said the hare. 'I've never seen you hurry and I don't suppose you know how.'

'Don't mock me,' said the tortoise.

The hare wouldn't stop his teasing and at last the tortoise said, 'I'll wager that if you and I run a race I will win it.'

'Don't be silly,' laughed the hare. 'Of course you won't.'

'Try me,' said the tortoise.

'Very well,' said the hare, 'if you want to make yourself look silly.'

They asked the fox to set a course and to be judge. The fox gave the signal to start. The tortoise was soon left far behind. When the hare was within sight of the winning post he looked over his shoulder. There was no sign of the tortoise.

'I knew this would happen,' said the hare. He sat under a tree and waited for the tortoise to come. He wanted the tortoise to see *him* go past the winning post. The sun was warm and made him feel sleepy.

Meanwhile the slow old tortoise plodded steadily on. He passed the tree where the hare was resting. The hare didn't see him. He was asleep. He shouldn't have closed his eyes.

He opened them just in time to see the tortoise pass the winning post.

'Now who looks silly?' said the tortoise.

'I suppose I do,' said the hare.

FEBRUARY 6

Old Mother Hubbard

Old Mother Hubbard
Went to the cupboard,
To fetch her poor dog a bone;
But when she came there
The cupboard was bare
And so the poor dog had none.

She took a clean dish
To get him some tripe;
But when she came back
He was smoking a pipe.

She went to the tavern
For white wine and red;
But when she came back
The dog stood on his head.

She went to the fruiterer's
To buy him some fruit;
But when she came back
He was playing the flute.

She went to the tailor's
To buy him a coat;
But when she came back
He was riding a goat.

She went to the cobbler's
To buy him some shoes;
But when she came back
He was reading the news.

She went to the hosier's
To buy him some hose;
But when she came back
He was dressed in his clothes.

The dame made a curtsey,
The dog made a bow;
The dame said, 'Your servant.'
The dog said, 'Bow-wow.'

25

FEBRUARY 7

The Sultan's Problem

The Sultan was desperate to find a new tax collector. 'Is there not one honest man in this land that can collect taxes without stealing the money?' said the Sultan. He called his wisest counsellor and explained the problem.

'Announce that you are looking for a new tax collector, Your Highness,' said the counsellor, 'and leave the rest to me.'

The announcement was made and by the afternoon the palace antechamber was full. There were fat men in flowing robes, thin men in flowing robes and one man in a plain and thread-bare robe. The men in their rich robes laughed at him. 'The Sultan has more sense than to appoint a poor man as his tax collector,' they all said.

At last the wise counsellor entered. 'The Sultan will see you all at once,' he said, 'but you will have to pass one at a time through the narrow corridor leading to his apartment.'

The corridor was dark and each man had to feel his way with his hands. Finally, all were assembled before the Sultan.

'What do I do now?' whispered the Sultan.

'Order everyone to dance,' said the wise man. The Sultan thought it strange but he agreed and all the men began to dance.

'I have never seen such clumsy dancers in my life,' said the Sultan. 'Their feet are like lead.'

Only the poor man was able to dance up and down. 'This man is your new tax collector,' said the wise man. 'I lined the corridor with coins and jewels and this was the only man not to weigh down his pockets with stolen jewels.' The Sultan had found an honest man.

FEBRUARY 8

The Hungry Goldfish

The goldfish were hungry. No one had fed them for three whole days and they were getting worried. Just then a dog strolled past. 'Help! Help!' shouted the goldfish. 'No one has fed us for three days and we're very hungry.'

'Wait there,' said the dog. 'I'll bring you one of my bones.' And he rushed off.

Along the path he met a squirrel. 'I can't stop,' he panted. 'The goldfish are hungry and I'm going for some food.' And he ran off.

'Oh dear,' said the squirrel. 'Poor goldfish. I shall go and get them some of my nuts.'

At the top of the oak tree the squirrel met a bird. 'Hello, bird,' she said. 'I can't stop. The goldfish are hungry and I must find them some food.' And off she went.

'Oh dear,' thought the bird. 'Poor goldfish. I shall go and find some juicy worms for them.'

As the bird flew off he saw a small boy walking along the path with a brown paper bag. 'Hello, little boy,' said the bird. 'What have you got in that bag?'

'Food for the goldfish. I forgot to feed them, so I am bringing them some now,' said the boy.

'Oh,' said the bird. 'I was getting them some worms.'

'That's very kind, but they don't eat worms,' said the boy.

'I don't suppose they eat nuts either,' said the bird.

'No, I'm afraid not,' said the boy.

When they arrived at the pond, the boy sprinkled the goldfish food into the water.

'Thank you, thank you,' cried the goldfish, as they gobbled it greedily.

Just then the squirrel arrived with her nuts, and the dog with his bone. 'What kind animals you are to bring your own food for the goldfish,' said the boy. 'Now that I've fed them, why don't we all sit down and eat our own food?' And that's just what they did.

FEBRUARY 9

No Butter for his Bread (Part 1)

It was breakfast time and the Master wanted butter for his bread.

'Molly!' he called to the dairy maid. 'Bring me butter for my bread.'

'I can't, sir,' said Molly.

'Can't!' said the Master. 'There's no such word as can't.' Then he added, 'Why can't you?'

'Because there is no butter,' said Molly.

'No butter!' The Master jumped from his chair and knocked it with a clatter to the floor. 'No butter! What do you mean NO BUTTER!!!!'

'I've been in the dairy since six,' said Molly. 'The cream in the churn will not turn into butter.'

'Don't be ridiculous!' shouted the Master. And jumping from his chair, he marched to the dairy with Molly running after him.

'What's the matter with your milk?' he demanded of Daisy the cow as he arrived at the dairy. Daisy just mooed.

'It seems to me as though it has had a spell put on it,' said Molly.

'How do you break a spell?' asked the Master impatiently. He was getting so hungry for bread and butter he was prepared to believe anything.

'We could try holding it over running water?' said Molly.

That's how it was that the Master's wife found the Master standing in the middle of a stream holding a milk churn over his head.

FEBRUARY 10

No Butter for his Bread (Part 2)

The Master had no butter for his bread. The milk would not churn and holding the milk over running water made no difference.

'Who would want to put a spell on a churn of milk?' asked the Master.

'Molly,' said the Master's wife. 'Get your bonnet.'

'Where are you going?' asked the Master.

'To visit the witch who lives at the mill,' said his wife. 'I've heard that her butter churn fell over and broke into a hundred pieces.'

Molly and the Master's wife went straight to the mill.

'Yes,' said the witch when they questioned her, 'my butter churn is broken and I can't find the right spell to mend it. I've put a spell on all the unbroken churns. I have no butter so no one else will have any either. But I will take off the spell if you promise to bring me a large pat of freshly made butter every other day.'

When Molly and the Master's wife got home, the Master was dancing a jig in the dairy and Daisy was mooing.

'I did it . . . I found the answer . . . It's turned to butter.'

'No, you didn't,' said the Master's wife. 'Now you go this minute and take some of that butter to the witch at the mill.'

'Why? Why should I?' demanded the Master. But of course, as soon as his wife told him, he scooped some into a bowl. He ran all the way to the mill and left it on the witch's doorstep and then he ran all the way home again.

He was rather scared of the witch, to tell the truth. But at least he had some butter for his bread.

FEBRUARY 11

The Friend

The school fashion show was going to take place next week and Halima was close to tears. 'They chose Tina to model the prize dress,' she told her big brother. 'They were about to choose me but she has such a pretty face . . . I did so want to wear that dress.'

Her brother said, 'You mustn't be so jealous of your friend. She can't help being pretty, any more than you can help being clever.'

After the dress rehearsal, Tina looked down at the prize dress she was wearing. 'This dress is so beautiful,' she told Halima. 'I just hate to take if off.' And she twirled around in front of the long mirror.

Then . . . disaster! She knocked a bottle of ink off the shelf and some of it splashed over the dress. 'Oh no!' she gasped. 'The dress is ruined!' Her eyes filled with tears. 'Everybody will hate me for this!'

Halima forgot about being jealous. She felt sorry for her friend. Tina was so helpless when things went wrong. She hugged her and said, 'Don't cry, Tina. I'll help you.' And she took the dress home.

The next morning, Halima handed Tina the dress. Tina's eyes shone. 'Why . . . you've embroidered little butterflies over every ink spot! The dress is more beautiful than ever! Poor Halima! You must have been sewing all night.' She hugged her. 'What a wonderful friend! I do love you. You should wear the dress!'

Tired-eyed, Halima smiled. 'No thank you,' she said. She was happy just to be a good friend!

FEBRUARY 12

Lottie Wins the Race

Lottie Ladybird fell from the apple tree with a bump. 'I'll never learn to fly!' she sighed. 'Never!'

'Yes you will,' said Mr Woodpecker, 'when you're old enough.'

'Huh!' said Lottie. 'I can't wait that long!'

Mr Woodpecker laughed. 'The first time you fly, I'll carve the date on the tree trunk for you,' he said.

Suddenly, a handkerchief fluttered by. 'It must have blown from someone's washing line,' cried Mr Woodpecker. 'Come on, I've got an idea!' Lottie crawled up the tree after him. Then he wrapped her in the handkerchief and flew off with it. 'Come on, fly!' he cried, letting go and watching Lottie and the handkerchief flutter in the wind.

'Oh I can't!' puffed Lottie. 'My wings ache and I'm falling!' She fell, tired and frightened, on to a fluffy white cloud.

'I can't stop,' said a deep voice, 'I'm in a race.' Lottie looked around, startled. 'It's me!' said the cloud. 'It's the International Cloud Race today. I've flown round the world and the race is nearly over!'

'Well, you saved me,' said Lottie, 'so I'll help you.' She grabbed the handkerchief as it wafted by and held it in the wind like the sail of a ship. They soon passed all the other clouds and they won first prize.

'It's your prize,' said the cloud, handing Lottie the big red rosette. 'I would never have won without you. Come on, I'll give you a lift home.'

Soon Lottie said goodbye to the cloud, dropped the rosette into her apple tree and jumped off the cloud. She couldn't wait to tell Mr Woodpecker about the International Cloud Race and the rosette.

'Hey!' cried Mr Woodpecker. 'Who's a clever ladybird, then?'

'Who me?' said Lottie. 'What do you . . .?' Then she realised. She was flying! She had been too busy thinking to notice.

'Shall I carve today's date on the tree trunk then?' laughed Mr Woodpecker.

'There's no need!' said Lottie. 'This has got today's date on!' She fixed the big red rosette to the tree trunk.

FEBRUARY 13

The Magic Pot (Part 1)

Once upon a time there was a girl who lived with her mother in a tiny house on the outskirts of a small town. They were very poor and sometimes they were very hungry. They often had nothing to eat at all.

One day, when the girl was out in the woods she met an old woman who was carrying an empty iron pot.

'Take it,' said the old woman, putting the pot into her hands. 'When you are hungry, say to it, "Little pot, boil". When you have enough, say, "Little pot, stop".'

The little girl thought it very strange but she took the pot home and told her mother what the old woman had said.

'Let's see what happens,' said the mother.

'Little pot, boil,' said the girl. Soon the pot began to bubble and hiss, and steam began to rise from it. 'It's filling up,'

gasped the girl.

'Stop it before it overflows,' said her mother.

'Little pot, stop,' said the girl. The bubbling and hissing stopped at once. 'What a delicious smell!' said the girl. 'It's a kind of porrdge.'

'Bring two plates and two spoons and we'll taste it,' said

her mother.

It was the most delicious porridge either of them had ever tasted. With a magic porridge pot like that at their command, their days of being hungry were over. It didn't matter how much porridge they ate, there was always some more to be had at the command, "Little pot, boil".

FEBRUARY 14

The Magic Pot (Part 2)

A girl had been given a magic porridge pot. She and her mother had as much porridge as they wanted at the girl's command.

One day, when the girl was out, her mother set the pot on the table and said, 'Little pot, boil!' The bubbling began, the steam rose, the delicious smell of porridge filled the room. The porridge reached the brim of the pot.

The girl's mother opened her mouth to say the words to stop it and found she couldn't remember them. All she could think to say was, 'Um . . . er . . . That's enough.' A tiny trickle of

porridge began to run down the outside of the porridge pot. 'Stop! Stop!' she shouted in a panic. 'I don't want any more . . . Stop filling up . . . Go away . . .' The harder she tried to remember the right words the worse it became.

The pot bubbled and bubbled. The trickle of porridge became a stream. It spread across the table and fell to the floor.

'Whatever shall I do?' she wailed as she climbed on to a chair. The pool of porridge spread to the door and ran out into the street.

'Come back, porridge!' she shouted. The porridge pot took no notice. It would only stop when it was given the right command. But what was the right command?

The porridge was like an overflowing river running through the town. The girl was visiting at the far edge of the town. She heard the noise, and as soon as she saw the rivers of porridge oozing through the streets, she guessed what had happened. She ran home as fast as the sticky porridge would let her.

When she got home, her mother was shouting commands at the pot. 'Stop cooking! . . . Stop bubbling! . . . Stop! . . . Stop! . . .'

'Little pot, stop,' said the girl. The pot stopped instantly. 'And now, mother,' said the girl, 'we have some clearing up to do.'

FEBRUARY 15

Tug-of-War

Father Sparrow was at the water-hole trying to drink. 'Could you move over, Mr Crocodile!' he asked politely. 'I'd like to have a drink.'

'Drink somewhere else,' said the crocodile rudely.

Father Sparrow flew back to his tree. Suddenly there was a great bump. Mr Elephant had walked into the tree.

'You should look where you're going,' said Father Sparrow.

'Go away, little bird,' said Mr Elephant rudely.

'I shall have to teach you a lesson if you don't say sorry,' said the sparrow.

'You couldn't teach me a lesson,' laughed the elephant. 'You're too weak.'

'I'm as strong as you,' said the sparrow. 'I challenge you to a tug-of-war.' Father Sparrow found an extra strong, extra long vine and tied it round Mr Elephant as he stood there shaking with laughter. 'I'll just take the other end,' said the sparrow. 'When I say pull, pull.'

Father Sparrow flew to the water-hole nearby, with the other end of the vine in his beak. Mr Crocodile was still drinking. 'I'm going to teach you a lesson,' said Father Sparrow. 'Take the other end of this vine and I bet I can pull you out of that water-hole.' The crocodile laughed but agreed to let the sparrow tie the vine round his tail.

'I'll just pick up the other end behind that tree,' said the sparrow. 'When I say pull, pull.' Father Sparrow hid in the trees and shouted, 'Ready, steady, PULL!'

The elephant and crocodile began to pull. First the crocodile came slithering tail first out of the water-hole. Then he held hard and pulled the elephant back against the tree. The two were well-matched and kept pulling until sundown.

'I'm letting go now,' shouted Father Sparrow finally, as he pecked the vine in two. Mr Elephant lost his balance and fell with a bump. Mr Crocodile fell straight into the water-hole. Neither was ever rude to Father Sparrow again.

FEBRUARY 16

Chuffa and the Bandit (Part 1)

Way up in the North there is a great big fir forest, and in the forest there are many wild creatures like birds and bees, and butterflies and rabbits, and badgers and beavers and bears. There is also a railway line for carrying logs from the fir forest. On this line goes Chuffa the train, driven by old Mr Driver who is always ready to give anyone a lift. All the animals love him. They love Chuffa too! 'Chuffa-chuff, chuffa-chuff, chuffa-chuff,' goes Chuffa.

Now, one day some little birds flew up and said, 'Oh, Mr Driver, do come and have a look at Bruin the Bear. He is very poorly.'

Mr Driver jammed on the brakes. He got down from the train and the birds led him into the forest. There was Bruin the Bear propped up against a fir tree, looking very, very poorly.

'Why, what's up, Bruin?' asked Mr Driver. But Bruin could only sigh. 'Just hand me your paw,' said old Mr Driver, and he took out his watch and felt Bruin's pulse. 'My, my, that's very fast, or else my watch is slow. You certainly are a poorly bear. We shall have to get you to old Doc Sawbones. He'll fix you up in a jiffy.'

Well, it wasn't all that easy getting Bruin on the train. He was weak and limp and floppy and they had to pull him and push him and lift him.

'Gee, I feel poorly,' said Bruin.

'Never you mind, old fellow,' said old Mr Driver. 'Just a few more steps and you'll be on the train and on your way to the doctor.' At last they managed to shove him and push him and pull him into an empty truck.

'Ready?' said Mr Driver to Chuffa.

'Wooo-woooo,' replied Chuffa and off they went. 'Chuffa-chuff, chuffa-chuff, chuffa-chuff.'

FEBRUARY 17

Chuffa and the Bandit (Part 2)

Bruin the Bear was feeling ill. Chuffa had taken him to the doctor. Doctor Sawbones was very wise. He looked at Bruin and he sounded his chest and checked his tongue and felt his pulse and took his temperature. Then he said, 'Hmmm,' very wisely. 'Hmm. Had any honey lately?'

The bear groaned. 'Honey?' he said weakly. 'Did you say honey? Well, perhaps just a taste.'

'How much?' asked the doctor.

'Well, w-e-l-l, about two pounds, maybe three,' said the poor, sick bear.

'Too much honey,' said the doctor. 'Into bed for three days. That'll put you right. And no more honey for a month.'

Just as the doctor said, in a few days the bear was quite well again and fit enough to go

home. So old Mr Driver fetched Chuffa along and they took Bruin back to the fir forest.

Back at the railway station, the Sheriff had a job for Mr Driver and Chuffa. 'I want you to take this bag of money to Woodville,' said the Sheriff. 'See no one steals it. Understand?'

Mr Driver took the money in the bag and hid it under some logs in the train. Then he pulled the lever and off they went. 'Chuffa-chuff, chuffa-chuff, chuffa-chuff.'

FEBRUARY 18

Chuffa and the Bandit (Part 3)

Mr Driver and Chuffa had a job to do. They were taking money to Woodville. All was going well as they went whisking through the forest, when suddenly Chuffa saw a great pile of logs ahead – right on the railway line. He whistled and Mr Driver jammed on the brakes.

Mr Driver got down and looked at the logs. 'Something strange going on down here,' he said. Then he began to shift the logs from the line. Suddenly he heard a terrible shout.

'STICK 'EM UP!' roared a voice. There beside the track was a bad bandit with a gun. Mr Driver put his hands in the air.

'Now, where's that money?' shouted the bandit. 'I'll give you three seconds to find it.'

What could Mr Driver do but get the bag out? 'It won't do you any good, you know,' he said to the bandit.

As he said that, up popped Bruin the Bear! In a flash he seized the bad bandit's hat and pulled it down over his eyes.

At the sight of the bear, the bandit's horse bolted, and his gun went off BANG! But Bruin

held on tight until Mr Driver brought a rope. Then they tied him up so that he couldn't escape. They set him on top of some logs in one of the trucks.

'Come on, Chuffa, my lad,' said old Mr Driver. 'Off we go to Woodville as quick as we can.'

'Woo-woooo, chuffa-chuff, chuffa-chuff.'

When they reached Woodville, Mr Driver handed the money

over to the Bank Manager. Then he handed the bandit over to the Sheriff. Everyone in Woodville was delighted and there was a reward for capturing the bad bandit.

'I owe it all to Bruin,' said Mr Driver.

'And I owe it all to Chuffa,' said Bruin.

'And so do I,' said Mr Driver, proudly patting Chuffa. 'So do I.'

FEBRUARY 19

The Little Shoemakers (Part 1)

Larry and Tack were two leprechauns who lived deep in the forest in a land of little people called The Land of Joy.

Larry and Tack were expert boot and shoemakers. They had a factory where many young leprechauns helped them make dancing slippers for the fairies out of flower petals and thistledown, and boots and shoes for the other leprechauns out of nut shells and cobweb thread.

Stories of their fine work reached the ears of Giant Grumplelumpkin. He was due to visit the Land of Joy to see his cousin, Giant Funnybones, so he wrote a letter to the shoemakers telling them he wanted a new pair of boots and would be coming to see them the next day so that they could measure his feet.

Now leprechauns are very small and giants are very tall; so Larry and Tack were worried about the giant's visit. How could they possibly make boots big enough for him?

Suddenly there was the sound of thunder. All the trees of the forest were moving. It wasn't really thunder but the footsteps of the giant. He brushed the trees aside with his hand and there he stood towering above the leprechauns.

He looked down at Larry and Tack, who were shivering with fright. 'I'll sit down,' he bellowed. 'Then you can measure my feet.'

Larry and Tack got on with their measuring. The giant's toe was as big as they were but they took no notice and noted down the measurements.

'I'll come back in two days,' said the giant as he got up, pulled on his boots and set off to visit his cousin.

FEBRUARY 20

The Little Shoemakers (Part 2)

The two little shoemakers, Larry and Tack, called a meeting at their shoe factory.

'How can we make a pair of boots big enough for Giant Grumplelumpkin?' they asked.

'Well, there are piles of old plastic boxes in a dump by the river,' suggested one of the leprechauns. 'They might be made into boots.'

'The very thing,' said Larry. 'Quick! Everyone bring as many as you can and let's get to work.'

Everyone helped bring the boxes to the factory and then they all set about cutting, shaping and stitching them together into boots. After two days and nights without any rest, the shoemakers had completed the boots, and used every piece of plastic they could find.

They were just in time, because they heard a rumble of thunder, saw the trees sway and the giant appeared above them.

'Are my boots ready?' he roared.

'Yes, they're just here,' shouted Tack, trembling.

The giant looked at the boots. He tried them on. He walked up and down the forest three or four times.

'These boots,' he said to Larry and Tack, 'are fit for a king. Thank you.' Larry and Tack sighed with relief.

'My cousin wants some new boots, too,' said the giant.

'Oh no!' cried the little shoemakers.

'But I don't want him to have boots as fine as mine. So I won't let him come here.'

'Oh good,' said the shoemakers. The giant gave each of the shoemakers a little golden hammer in payment and left everyone in the Land of Joy happily in peace.

FEBRUARY 21

The Fable of
the Caged Bird and the Bat

A singing bird was kept in a cage which hung outside a cottage window. It had a beautiful voice, but unlike others of its kind it only sang when darkness fell. One night, when it was singing, a bat flew up and clung to the bars of the cage.

'I have a question to ask you,' said the bat. 'Why do you sing at night and remain silent all day, when other birds like yourself sing during the day and remain silent at night?'

'I have a very good reason for doing what I do,' said the bird sadly.

'Then please tell me what it is,' said the bat.

'When I was free to fly wherever I chose, I sang all day long,' said the bird. 'One day a birdcatcher heard me and came looking for me. He set his net and caught me. It is he who keeps me locked in this cage. I lost my freedom because I sang by day. Now I only sing when I am hidden by the darkness.'

'It seems to me,' said the bat, 'that if you had only thought of that when you were free, you would not be a prisoner now.'

FEBRUARY 22

Ash Lodge –
Willie Goes Jogging

Willie the Mole lives at Ash Lodge with his two Badger friends, Basil and Dewy. One afternoon Willie heard a noise outside his door: 'Hup, two, three, four . . .' It was Ralf Runner and the rest of his duck family out jogging.

'Why don't you join us, Willie!' said Ralf. 'You look as though you could do with losing some weight. But you're probably not fit enough to keep up.'

'Not fit enough?' cried Willie. 'I can jog as well as any duck.' Willie set off after the four ducks. 'Hup, two, three, four. Hup, two, three, four,' he puffed. But soon Willie was trailing behind.

Basil and Dewy were relaxing by the pond. 'Hello, ducks,' said Basil. 'Nice day for jogging.'

'Hup, two, three, four,' replied Ralf. 'No time to stop. One more lap.'

'Hello, Willie,' said Dewy as Willie came waddling slowly past. 'Only one more lap. We'll

get a bath ready for your feet.'

'Hup, puff, two, puff, three, puff, four,' answered Willie faintly.

Half an hour later, the ducks returned. 'Where's Willie?' asked Basil.

'Couldn't keep up,' said Ralf. 'Quite out of condition.'

'Let's get his bath ready,' said Dewy.

It was just getting dark, two hours later, when Willie crawled through the door of Ash Lodge. 'I'm not really tired,' he said feebly. 'Just my feet . . .' and he slumped into a chair and put his feet into the water. 'I could go on for miles, really . . .'

Suddenly there was a knock at the door. Basil went to answer it. 'It's Ralf,' said Basil, coming back into the room. 'He wants to know if you want to join them for an early morning jog tomorrow, Willie.' But all the reply Willie gave was a very loud snore.

FEBRUARY 23

The Ugly Duckling (Part 1)

Once there was a duck who had a clutch of eggs to hatch. Five of them hatched into fluffy little ducklings, but the sixth, which for some reason was bigger than all the others, lay in the nest smooth and unbroken.

'That's much too big to be a duck egg,' said one of the duck's friends. 'Looks more like a turkey egg to me.'

'How will I be able to tell?' asked the duck.

'It won't swim when it's hatched,' said her friend. 'Turkeys never do!'

But the egg wasn't a turkey egg because the bird that hatched from it did swim. It swam as well as any duckling.

'That last duckling of yours is very ugly,' laughed the farmyard hens. It was true. He wasn't a bit like his brothers and sisters.

'What an ugly duckling!' laughed the geese when they saw him. Somehow that name stuck. Whenever anyone wanted him they called, 'Ugly duckling, where are you?' or if they didn't want him, they said, 'Ugly ducking, go away.' He even thought of himself as "ugly duckling". He was very sad. He didn't like being so ugly. He didn't like being teased. No one would play with him. No one would swim with him. Even his mother made fun of him.

One day, the ugly ducking ran away. And I am sorry to say, no one missed him at all.

FEBRUARY 24

The Ugly Duckling (Part 2)

The ugly duckling hoped he would find someone in the big wide world to be his friend, someone who wouldn't mind how ugly he was. But the wild ducks were just as unkind as the farmyard ducks, and the wild geese honked at him and made fun, just as the farmyard geese had done.

'Will I ever find a friend? Will I ever be happy?' sighed the ugly ducking.

One day, as he sat alone and unhappy in the middle of a lake on the bleak flat marshes, he heard the steady beat of wings. When he looked up there were swans flying overhead with their long necks stretched before them and their white feathers gleaming in the sun. They were so beautiful.

The ugly duckling stayed on the lake all through the long hard winter. Food was hard to find and he was often hungry. Once he was trapped in some ice and thought he would die. He was set free, just in time, by a farmer and his dog.

Spring came and the lake where he had spent the lonely winter became a busy, exciting and noisy place. The ducks were forever quacking and the geese were forever honking. There was plenty of splashing and excitement. But not for the ugly duckling. No one quacked the latest piece of gossip to him. Sadly he spread his wings and took to the sky. He had never flown before and he was surprised how strong his wings were. They carried him away from the lake and the marshes and over a leafy garden.

On a still, clear pond in the garden, he could see the beautiful white swans, with their gracefully arched necks, and suddenly the ugly duckling felt that he did not want to live any longer.

FEBRUARY 25

The Ugly Duckling (Part 3)

The next day the ugly duckling went down to the pond. 'I will ask those beautiful birds to kill me,' he said. He went down to the water. He bent his head humbly and closed his eyes.

'Kill me,' he said to the swans. 'I am too ugly to live.'

'Ugly?' said the swans. 'Have you looked at your reflection?'

'I do not need to look. I know how ugly I am,' said the ugly duckling.

'Look into the water,' said the swans. So the ugly duckling did. What he saw made his heart beat faster and filled him with happiness. During the long winter months he had changed.

'I'm . . . I'm just like you . . .' he whispered.

When the children who lived in the garden came to feed the swans they called to one another, 'A new swan . . . a new swan . . . Isn't he beautiful?' And then the ugly duckling knew without a doubt that he really was a swan, that he had always been a swan and that his days of being lonely were over.

FEBRUARY 26

Taking a Donkey to Market

Once upon a time, there was an old man who had a donkey he wanted to sell. One fine day, he and his son and the donkey of course, set off for market. The way to market was along a winding country road. It was hot and the old man did not feel like walking.

'We might as well make use of the donkey while we have him,' he said and climbed on to the donkey's back. Young John took hold of the halter round the donkey's neck and they set off at a steady pace.

'Shame on you, old man,' said someone along the way, 'for riding when your son is walking.'

The old man blushed and looked ashamed. He slid from the donkey's back and took the halter from his son's hand. 'You ride a while and let me lead the donkey,' he said.

Soon they met some women returning from market. 'Shame on you!' they cried, shaking their fists at young John. 'A young man like you riding when your old father is walking.' John's face went as red as his father's had done.

'The women are right, father,' he said. 'I shouldn't be riding when you are walking.'

'Why don't we both ride?' said the old man.

The donkey trotted along with both men on his back. 'Shame on you!' shouted some men who were making hay in a nearby field. 'Two grown men riding on a little donkey. How can you be so cruel?' The old man and his son slid quickly from the donkey's back.

'I know what we can do,' said young John at last. 'Instead of letting the donkey carry us, we can carry the donkey.'

The men were greeted with howls of laughter as they staggered into the market place carrying the donkey. 'Fancy carrying a donkey, when the donkey should be carrying you,' shouted the people in a chorus.

'By trying to please everyone,' said the old man, 'we have pleased no one. In future we will please ourselves.'

FEBRUARY 27

Time for a Rest

Peter was struggling with his sums. 'I can't do these,' he said aloud.

'Can't do them?' said a voice close to his ear. Peter looked round in surprise. It was the old clock on the table. 'Tick-tock! Of course you can,' said the clock. 'Look at all the sums I have to do every day; seconds, minutes and hours. What's the first sum then?'

'3 plus 6,' said Peter.

'The best way is to count on,' said the clock. Peter looked puzzled. 'Watch my hand,' said the clock. The big hand was on the three. 'Now count on six,' said the clock. Peter counted on from one to six as the big hand went round. Each number gave a little wriggle and the big hand came to a stop when Peter reached six. It rested on number nine.

The nine stood up and gave a funny bow. Peter giggled.

'Pay attention,' said the clock crossly. 'Let's do another.'

'6 plus 5,' said Peter. They did this the same way, the big hand starting on the six and moving on as Peter counted to five.

'Eleven,' said Peter triumphantly. 'I understand now.' In no time at all he had finished his homework.

The clock was so pleased that it began to jump up and down and all the numbers began to dance. 'It's easy, it's easy,' they chanted. The hands whirred round so fast that Peter began to feel dizzy.

'Stop!' he shouted. Too late! There was a loud "ping" and everything stopped.

'Now look what's happened!' groaned the clock. 'Now I shall have to go to be mended. At least I shall have a rest.' His voice faded away.

Peter patted him. 'I'm sorry,' he said. 'Thank you for helping me.'

FEBRUARY 28

Twirly and the Chimney Sweep

Twirly was a little yellow helicopter. He was on his way back from seeing his friends, the Blackbird family. He was flying over the roof-tops when he spotted a man sticking out of a chimney-pot of a very large house.

Twirly flew down. 'Are you stuck?' he asked.

'No, not stuck,' said the man. 'Just tired. I've got so many chimneys to sweep on this house, I shall never finish them today.'

'I'll help you,' said Twirly. 'If you tie a heavy weight to your brush, I'll help you lower it down each chimney in turn. We'll soon have the job done.' The man hopped aboard, did as Twirly said and they swept the chimneys, all thirty-two of them, in no time.

'I wonder who owns such a big house,' said Twirly, as he set the man down outside the front door.

'I do,' said the man.

'So you're not a chimney sweep?' said Twirly.

'No, but I'll be happy to sweep your chimney any time you want,' said the man with a smile. Twirly smiled back and then, with a twirl of his blades, off he flew.

FEBRUARY 29

Peas

A gardener kneeling on his knees
Planted several rows of peas.
The sunshine shone, the breezes blew,
And all the little peapods grew.

Then, in the night, from a nearby hole,
A family of mice to the garden stole.
They climbed the stems with the greatest ease,
And that was the end of the garden peas!

MARCH

MARCH 1

The Cats of Fortune (Part 1)

The Kingdom of Bergam was divided into two parts by a huge wall. No one in Upper Bergam ever visited Lower Bergam. Indeed, the people from one part of the Kingdom had never even seen those from the other.

Not even the cats in Upper Bergam had climbed the Great Wall. Everyone in Upper Bergam thought of cats as special creatures with unusual powers. 'As long as our cats are healthy,' the wise men would say, 'Upper Bergam will be healthy.' So the cats wanted for nothing and lived a life of luxury just like their owners.

Now Palladin was a sleek, healthy cat who belonged to the First Lady of Upper Bergam. One day he spotted another cat. As we know, it was not unusual to see cats in Bergam but Palladin was surprised because this cat was so thin. It looked half-starved.

Palladin followed the creature until he saw it leap over the Great Wall. Palladin decided he must follow. So, for the first time, one of the cats of Upper Bergam leapt over the wall into the Kingdom beyond.

Palladin looked round him in amazement. The crops were flourishing, the cattle looked healthy, but the people were all shabbily dressed. Men, women and children were still working in the fields although it was late.

Palladin followed one group as they went home to a small house. There was hardly enough food to go round. Their cat sat in a corner feeding on scraps.

'This is like another world,' thought Palladin. He returned to Upper Bergam, but from that night onwards he sat in a corner and refused to eat.

'It's a very bad sign,' said the wise men. 'It means misfortune for us all.'

MARCH 2

The Cats of Fortune (Part 2)

Palladin, a cat from Upper Bergam, had followed a half-starved cat over the Great Wall into Lower Bergam. What he saw made him refuse to eat again.

Before long, the people found their crops and cattle were dying just like Palladin. One of the wisest men of the Kingdom bowed down before Palladin.

'Why has this misfortune come upon us?' he asked. Although he was weak, Palladin stood up and led the startled people to the Great Wall. He began to scratch against the wall.

'We must cross the Great Wall,' announced the Wise Man. Ladders were fetched and, for the first time, people from Upper Bergam crossed the wall into Lower Bergam. They saw what Palladin had seen: shabbily dressed people, poor houses but good crops and healthy cattle.

'We can learn from these people,' whispered the Wise Man.

'There are things we can share with them too,' said the First Lady, putting her shawl round a woman dressed in rags.

All the people began talking together, planning to create two wealthy kingdoms side by side. Then they say Palladin on top of the Great Wall scratching at the stones.

'If we pull down the wall,' cried the Wise Man, 'we shall be one kingdom.'

Everyone worked together to pull down the wall and soon the troubles in Upper Bergam were forgotten. Their streams were full again, the cattle recovered and the crops grew as before. The whole kingdom was renamed Great Bergam – a place where people achieved great things by working together.

MARCH 3

The Little Engine

The little engine sat in the attic dreaming about the old days when the little boy who had owned him used to race him round his track. They had been such good times, but now the little boy had grown up and gone away. Now the little engine lived with all the other things that were not needed any more, like the doll's house, some books, a lamp and an old clock that didn't work.

Downstairs, Paula was bored. She loved her grandparents but there wasn't anything to do. She had come to stay with them because her father had gone away on business for six months and her mother was looking after her sister, who had just come out of hospital. She missed them both, particularly her Dad because they always had such fun together.

Just then Grandpa came in. 'I've got to go up into the attic to fetch something for Grandma. Do you want to come Paula?' Paula's face brightened.

'Yes please,' she said and was soon following Grandpa up the ladder. The sun shone through the little window in the roof as Paula scrambled about looking at everything. Suddenly she came upon the little engine. 'Oh look! An engine.'

Grandpa laughed. 'Oh yes, I'd forgotten about that. It belonged to your Dad when he was small. Let's take it downstairs.'

Grandpa soon had the track laid out on the floor and Paula had a fine time sending the little engine round and round until it felt quite dizzy. But it did feel good to have its wheels turning again.

'I have some red paint in the shed,' said Grandpa. 'We'll give it a new coat tomorrow.' Paula was thrilled to be playing with Dad's engine; somehow it seemed to bring him closer.

MARCH 4

The Three Little Pigs (Part 1)

Once upon a time, there were three little pigs who lived together in one house. As they grew bigger their house seemed to grow smaller, and one day they decided to build three separate houses. The first little pig built himself a house of straw. The second little pig built himself a house of sticks. The third little pig built himself a house of bricks.

Soon after the first little pig had moved into his house, there was a knock at the door. It was a wolf who had come to call.

'Little pig, little pig, let me come in,' said the wily old wolf, thinking how nice it would be to have pig for dinner.

'No, no, by the hair on my chinny chin chin, I will not let you in,' said the first little pig.

'Then I'll huff and I'll puff and I'll blow your house in,' growled the wolf. And that is exactly what he did. The straw house blew away in the wind and the wolf gobbled up the pig.

When the wolf saw the house built of sticks, he licked his lips and said: 'Little pig, little pig, let me come in.'

'No, no, by the hair on my chinny chin chin, I will not let you in,' said the second little pig.

'Then I'll huff and I'll puff and I'll blow your house in,' growled the wolf. The house of sticks was as easy to blow down as the house of straw, and that was the end of the second little pig.

MARCH 5

The Three Little Pigs
(Part 2)

The wolf knew there was a third little pig about somewhere and when he saw the house of bricks he called through the letter-box: 'Let me in, little pig.'

'No, no, by the hair of my chinny chin chin, I will not let you in,' said the third little pig.

'Then I'll huff and I'll puff and I'll blow your house in,' said the wolf. And the wolf huffed and he puffed, and he puffed and he huffed, until he was quite out of breath, but the house of bricks stood firm. It didn't even creak.

'I can see I'll have to be clever to catch this little pig,' said the wolf. 'I'll have to lure him outside his house.' He told the little pig about a field he knew where the turnips were ready for digging, and arranged to meet him there the next morning. But the third little pig was much cleverer than the wolf realised. He knew exactly what the wolf was up to. He had been to the field, dug up the turnips and was safely back indoors before the wolf had woken up.

The wolf tried to keep his temper. He told the little pig about a tree he knew that was weighed down with juicy red apples. 'I'll meet you there in the morning,' he said slyly.

The wolf wasn't going to be caught again and next day he got up very early. When he reached the orchard the little pig was in the tree picking apples.

'I'll throw you one,' called the little pig, and he threw an apple so that it rolled into the long grass. While the wolf was looking for it, the little pig jumped from the tree and ran home. He was safely inside his brick house before the wolf realised he had been tricked.

By this time the wolf was getting very annoyed . . . and hungry. 'I'll meet you at the fair tomorrow,' he said.

MARCH 6

The Three Little Pigs
(Part 3)

The wolf was trying to catch the third little pig. He agreed to meet the little pig at the fair. The little pig went to the fair the next day and bought himself a butter churn. He was on his way home when he caught sight of the wolf. As quick as a raindrop hiding in a puddle, he hid himself in the butter churn and began to roll down the hill. He rolled right over the wolf's foot. The pig was safely inside the brick house before the wolf stopped trembling.

When the wolf discovered who had been inside the butter churn he was very angry indeed. He was determined that the little pig should not escape again. He climbed on to the roof of the brick house and began to ease himself down the brick chimney.

The little pig was very frightened when he heard the wolf mumbling and grumbling inside his chimney, but he didn't panic. He built up a fire and set his biggest cooking pot on the flames.

The wolf slithered down the chimney and fell into the pot with an enormous splash and a very loud OUCH!!! And that, I am glad to say, was the end of the wolf.

MARCH 7

Adventures of *The Tulip* – The Lock-Keeper's Wife

Thomas, Minty and Wilbur in their riverboat, *The Tulip*, were waiting with the other boats to go through the lock.

'What's the hold-up?' shouted Thomas to the boat ahead.

'It's the lock-keeper. His wife has locked him in the lodge,' came the reply.

'I think we'd better do something,' said Thomas. So he, Minty and Wilbur jumped ashore and went up to the lodge. Thomas shouted to the lock-keeper through the window, 'Why did she lock you in?'

'I only said where are the blackberries in the blackberry pie she made and then she hit me with a rolling pin and locked me in here,' replied the lock-keeper.

Thomas, Minty and Wilbur went to see the lock-keeper's wife. They found her standing guard at the back door with her rolling pin.

'Is it my fault the birds have taken all the blackberries?' she

shouted at them.

'You could always put an apple in the pie,' suggested Wilbur timidly.

'I don't suppose she knows how to make blackberry and apple pie,' whispered Minty.

'Don't know how to make blackberry and apple pie?' shouted the lock-keeper's wife, waving her rolling pin. 'We'll soon see about that,' and off she went to find some apples.

As she set off she dropped a key. 'Quick,' whispered Thomas. 'It's the key to the lodge.' They picked up the key and freed the lock-keeper. While his wife was away, he let all the boats through the lock gates.

'Now remember,' said Thomas, as *The Tulip* passed by the lock-keeper, 'say something nice about the pie she makes.' The lock-keeper smiled and waved goodbye.

MARCH 8

The Fable of the Quack Frog

One day, a frog came hobbling from his home on the marshes and set up a stall in the market place. He had blue bottles, green bottles, brown bottles, clear bottles. He had bottles of all shapes and sizes. When all was ready, he climbed on to a box so that everyone could see him and began to shout.

'Roll up! Roll up!' he cried. 'Come and consult the most famous doctor! Come and be cured!'

'What can you cure?' asked a fox.

'Any ailment you care to mention,' answered the frog. 'I have studied under all the best professors. I know all there is to know about medicines. Tell me your symptoms and I guarantee one of these bottles will have something in it to cure you.' The frog did a brisk trade. Everyone wanted to be cured of something.

Presently, the fox, who had been standing by watching, called out, 'If you are such a clever doctor, how is it you are lame and your skin is so blotchy and wrinkled?'

After a remark like that, nobody would buy another bottle. Nobody would even take a sniff from one. The frog had to pack up his wares and hobble back to his home on the marshes.

MARCH 9

Wizard Beanie

Once upon a time, there lived a good wizard. He was called Wizard Beanie because he was so tall and thin that he looked like a runner bean. Now the house where he lived was almost a ruin and everyone told him he should do something about it.

'Why don't you magic yourself a new house?' the villagers said.

'What a good idea,' said the wizard. So he set to work to make a spell. He put on his hat, nodded his head three times, waved his wand and hey presto, the ruin disappeared and a house stood there instead. But there was one thing wrong with it. The house wasn't high enough for Wizard Beanie. He was bent almost double and couldn't stand up at all.

He crawled out of the door, straightened himself and scratched his head. Now what was he to do? It looked a good strong house. It would be warm and dry in the winter, but it was no use to him if he had to be bent double all day. Then he had an idea and chuckling to himself, he crawled back in and worked another spell.

At once the spell began to work; he could feel himself shrinking and in no time at all he could stand up quite comfortably in his new home. But now instead of being tall like a runner bean he was short and fat.

'Well we can't call you Wizard Beanie, now,' said all the villagers. 'You look more the shape of a cauliflower. That's it! We'll call you Wizard Caulie.'

So that's how Wizard Beanie became Wizard Caulie. As the wizard himself said, 'It's just a matter of spelling.'

MARCH 10

Mufty's Cake

Mufty Mouse put the finishing touches to his letter and then checked it for spelling mistakes. 'Dear Mrs Squirrel,' he read aloud. 'Please would you come for a cup of tea this afternoon. From Mufty Mouse.'

Satisfied everything was neat and correct, he scampered off and popped the letter through Mrs Squirrel's door. Peeping through the letter-box he could see that Mrs Squirrel was spring-cleaning. She was scrubbing and washing and polishing everything. She looked so tired that Mufty decided he would bake her a cake to have with her cup of tea.

He raced off home and started mixing and stirring until the cake was ready to go into the oven. He had just cleared up when Mrs Squirrel arrived.

'What a fine letter, Mufty,' she said. 'Thank you for inviting me.' Mufty decided not to tell her about the cake just yet and asked about the spring-cleaning instead.

'Well, I've only the windows to do,' said Mrs Squirrel. 'But the bottom fell out of my bucket so I can't finish them.' Mufty laughed. He thought a bottomless bucket was very funny. But Mrs Squirrel was wrinkling her nose. There was an awful smoky smell coming from the oven.

'My cake!' yelled Mufty. 'I forgot about it!' It was too late. The cake was burnt black and as hard as a brick. 'Oh dear!' wailed Mufty. 'We were going to eat this with our tea!'

Mrs Squirrel couldn't help laughing. 'I've just thought of something,' she said. 'Come on, let's go back to my house and bring your cake along.'

The kettle whistled merrily on Mrs Squirrel's stove and she gave Mufty a piece of the softest cake he had ever tasted.

'Mmmm,' he said. 'This is delicious. I'm sorry my cake was so useless.'

'No, it wasn't,' laughed Mrs Squirrel. 'Look!'

Mufty watched in amazement as Mrs Squirrel hammered his hard black cake on to the bottom of her bucket. 'There,' she said. 'Now it will hold the water and I can finish my windows.' Mufty couldn't stop laughing. It was a happy ending for his cake after all.

MARCH 11

The Little Husky

Tuktu, the Eskimo boy, wanted to keep the strange little husky dog that had wandered into their village.

Akla, his father, said, 'Food is scarce, my son. A husky dog must pull the sledge and work for his food. This husky isn't strong enough to pull with the team. And the others don't like strangers.'

'But he's very clever,' said Tuktu.

Akla said, 'He is half-starved. We will feed him until he is strong enough to go on his way.'

One day, the little husky sniffed out a seal-hole in the sea ice. Tuktu caught the seal and there was a great feast. The little husky snatched a piece of seal-meat and dropped it at the feet of Fram, the lead dog.

'The clever little rascal!' laughed Akla. 'He's making friends with Fram. He knows that if Fram accepts him the other dogs will too.'

One day, Akla fell ill. 'Take me to the doctor at the Trading Post,' he told Tuktu. The little husky whined to go, so Tuktu let him run ahead of the team.

Later, they ran into a terrible snow storm and the dogs lost their way. But the little husky sniffed out the trail and led them to the Trading Post.

'Why, it's Sniffer!' the doctor cried when they arrived. 'Welcome home!' While he gave Akla medicine, the doctor explained about Sniffer. 'He's my lead dog. Thieves stole him but he must have escaped. Thank you for feeding him. Would you like one of his puppies?'

Tuktu's eyes sparkled. 'Oooh! Yes please!'

MARCH 12

Lucy and her Sticks

Lucy liked counting. She collected sticks to help her count. First she counted to ten, then to twenty, thirty, forty and fifty.

'What are you going to do with all these sticks?' her mother asked.

'I'm going to build a house in the garden with them,' said Lucy. First she used ten sticks to build one wall; ten more to build another wall; ten more for the third; and ten for the fourth. She used five sticks together for one side of the roof; five more for the other side. She had used up every stick. She had to leave a space for the door and windows. Lucy liked her house and went to see it every day.

Then her grandmother became ill. Lucy and her mother went to look after her. Lucy said goodbye to her house. When her grandmother was better they brought her back to their house for a holiday. Lucy told her all about her house in the garden.

'Shall we go and see it?' asked her grandmother. Lucy raced to find it. There it was! A bird sang

from the roof-top. A spider's web hung like a silk curtain across part of the window and inside a cat lay purring, feeding her baby kittens.

'Oh!' cried Lucy. 'My house is a real house now! . . . Come and look, everybody! Come and look!'

MARCH 13

Bessie the Elephant

Bessie the elephant blushed with shame;
She had forgotten her name, her name.
She asked the stork, but he would not tell,
The parrot he merely said, 'Well, well'.
She asked the lion, who roared with laughter,
And ten little monkeys came giggling after.

She asked the hippo, who yawned aloud.
The stately peacock was much too proud.
The donkey he merely gave a bray,
The dormouse was shy, and couldn't say.
Bess blew her trumpet: 'Oh, tell me do.'
Then all of them answered: 'You are you!'

MARCH 14

Pixie Potter's Invention

Pixie Potter was working on his invention. It was an alphabet machine. When the handle was turned, the letters of the alphabet came out of an opening in the side. They were all different colours.

Just then, his wife Hannah called out, 'For goodness sake, stop playing with that and do some gardening. The garden is like a jungle. I'm going shopping.'

Suddenly there was a knock at the door. 'Bother!' said Potter.

On the doorstep was an old fairy. 'Buy some flowers, dearie?' she whined.

Potter frowned. 'No thank you, I'm busy.' As he closed the door, he heard her muttering but he didn't hear what she said.

He had a shock when he opened the door of the workroom. All the letters from his machine were running and jumping about. Some rushed past him into the kitchen, some ran upstairs. 'Oh no!' he gasped and began to rush around catching as many as he could.

Soon his pockets were full of wriggling letters, but there were more to be caught. Suddenly everything stopped. 'That old fairy must have put a spell on my work,' Potter thought. 'Thank goodness it has worn off.'

He spent the rest of the morning looking for lost letters. There were S's in saucepans, W's in the wardrobe and B's in his bed. He had just finished and collapsed into the armchair when Hannah came in. 'Why, you lazy thing,' she said. 'What about the garden?'

Potter groaned. 'I'm going now,' he said. When he reached the bottom of the garden he made sure that Hannah couldn't see him as he sat under the shade of the mushrooms and fell fast asleep.
I wonder what she'll say when she finds him.

MARCH 15

Snow-White and Rose-Red (Part 1)

Once there was a woman who lived in a lonely cottage in the middle of a wood. She had two daughters, one called Snow-White, and the other Rose-Red. One winter evening, when they were all sitting by the fire, there was a knock at the door.

'Someone must be seeking shelter from the cold,' said the woman and she went to the door. Standing on the doorstep, his black fur sprinkled with snow, was an enormous bear. Snow-White and Rose-Red took one look at his bright shining eyes and his powerful claws, and ran to hide.

'You look very cold,' said the woman to the bear. 'Please come in and warm yourself by the fire.'

'Don't be afraid,' said the bear when he saw the children peeping at him. 'I will not harm you.'

'Will you help me brush the snow from my fur?' asked the bear, as the children crept nervously from their hiding place. They picked up the broom so that they could brush him without getting too close, but the bear was so friendly and it was such fun brushing a bear with a broom they soon forgot to be afraid.

The bear came to the house and slept by the fire every night throughout the long winter. He and the children became firm friends, and no matter how roughly the children played, the bear was always very gentle.

Then one day, as summer grew near, the bear said goodbye. 'I must go and protect my treasure from the dwarfs,' he said. 'They stay underground in winter but in summer they get everywhere. I fear they are not to be trusted.'

MARCH 16

Snow-White and Rose-Red (Part 2)

One day, later that summer, when Snow-White and Rose-Red were in the wood picking wild strawberries, they saw a dwarf themselves. He was jumping up and down in a terrible rage. The end of his beard had caught in a crack in a fallen log and he couldn't get it out.

'How did it happen?' asked Snow-White, as she and Rose-Red did their best to pull him free.

'Not that it's any business of yours,' grumbled the dwarf, 'but I was driving a wedge into the crack to keep it open. The wedge popped out and the crack closed up again over my beard . . . Ouch! Ouch! You're hurting me! Be careful!'

Snow-White took the scissors which she always carried in her pocket, and cut through the dwarf's beard. He was free, but he wasn't at all pleased. He picked up the sack of gold which was lying beside the log, and stomped off without even a thank-you.

A few days later, Snow-White and Rose-Red went to the river to catch fish. Who should they see there but the very same dwarf. He was in terrible trouble. The end of his beard had caught in his fishing line, and a fish was pulling the line and him into the river.

'Help me! Help me!' shrieked the dwarf, holding as tightly as he could to a bunch of reeds. He was slipping all the time.

'We must do something quickly or he will drown,' said Rose-Red. Snow-White took out her scissors and snipped the end off the dwarf's beard. The dwarf fell backwards into the reeds and the fish swam away. Was the dwarf grateful? Not at all! He picked up a sack of pearls which was lying in the reeds and stomped off with a bad-tempered glare.

MARCH 17

Snow-White and Rose-Red (Part 3)

Some time later, Snow-White and Rose-Red were crossing the heath when an eagle, which had been hovering over a rock, swooped low suddenly. There was a terrible cry. They ran to see what had happened. The eagle had its talons in the dwarf's coat and was lifting him off the ground.

'Help me!' shrieked the dwarf. Snow-White and Rose-Red caught hold of his legs and pulled . . . downwards. The eagle held on tight with his talons and pulled . . . upwards.

'You'll tear me in two!' shrieked the dwarf. But all that was torn was his coat, as the eagle continued to soar upwards and the dwarf fell with a thud to the ground. 'You should have been more careful, then you wouldn't have torn my coat!' he grumbled.

The dwarf picked up a sack of precious stones which was lying beside the rock and headed towards a cave. Snow-White and Rose-Red were used to the dwarf's grumpy ways by now. They didn't expect a thank-you; which was just as well, because they didn't get one.

Just then an enormous black bear came ambling along the path. The dwarf turned as pale as an uncooked pancake, and ran towards his cave. But the bear was quicker than he was and stood in his way.

'Don't eat me . . . please don't eat me!' The dwarf was shivering with fright. 'You can have all my treasure! I'm too small and thin to eat! Eat those two wicked girls!'

The bear raised his paw and knocked the dwarf to the ground. Snow-White and Rose-Red were very frightened, but the bear called to them not to be afraid and they recognised his voice. As they ran to him, his bearskin fell to the ground. He wasn't a bear at all, but a king who had been bewitched by the dwarf, and the treasure the dwarf had been gloating over was his. Now the dwarf was dead, the spell was broken.

MARCH 18

Sun and Games

'How lazy the sun is,' Katrina mewed with a shiver. 'He never wants to play. He just sits and smiles. Sometimes he goes away altogether.' Her silky grey and white fur felt cold.

'Will *you* play with me?' Katrina purred into the golden ears of corn waving gently from the field where she strolled.

'Not us,' they whispered. 'Soon the sun will ripen us for the harvest and our grain will be made into bread.'

Jumping over the garden fence and into the tall tree, Katrina playfully tried to push one of the green apples from its sturdy bough. 'Stop it!' squeaked the apple in alarm. 'We're waiting for the sun to sweeten us then we can be made into apple pie.'

Katrina leapt down among the tall flowers as they danced in the breeze near the house. 'We're waiting to blossom in the sunshine,' they murmured, slowly lifting their colourful heads. 'The bees love to collect our sweet nectar to make honey.'

Feeling thirsty, Katrina paused at one of the puddles made by the rain. She could see herself dip her pink tongue into the water. It was just like looking into a mirror. Suddenly she noticed a familiar smile peering from behind a cloud. She glanced up into the sky to see the sun beaming down again.

Katrina stretched contentedly in the warm sunshine. So the sun wasn't lazy after all. He was helping everything with his smile and he even had time to play "hide-and-seek" behind the clouds!

MARCH 19

Angry Fairies

The farmer's wife was beating her carpets. Dust was flying everywhere in the garden. Unfortunately rather a lot of it landed on a group of fairies who had chosen this particular garden to have one of their fairy meetings.

The fairies coughed and choked and shouted to her to stop, but of course humans cannot hear or see fairies. So the farmer's wife kept on beating her carpet and the fairies got dustier and angrier.

'Right,' said the head fairy, trying not to cough. 'We shall be back tonight to teach you a good lesson.' Off stamped all the fairies from the garden.

That night an army of a hundred fairies came back to the farmhouse armed with picks and shovels. They began loosening every brick and removing every nail from the bottom of the house, while the farmer and his wife slept. Finally the fairies loosened the last brick, unfolded their wings and slipped into the space they had made under the house.

'Ready, steady, heave!' cried the head fairy. Up, up, up . . . went the house as the fairies flapped their wings and lifted it into the sky.

Then suddenly a voice boomed from the sky, 'Fairies! Dawn is breaking. Return to your fairy kingdom at once.' Gently, the fairies set the house down and, having gone back to collect their tools, they all flew off to Fairyland.

The next morning the farmer's wife had a great shock when she went out to milk the cow. She was standing up to her knees in the muddiest, stickiest bog in the country, miles and miles from the nearest house, with a long, long walk to find the cow.

MARCH 20

The Walnut Tree

The bees buzzed busily among the flowers on a hot, sunny afternoon some years ago. Martin sat in his wheelchair and gazed longingly at the walnut tree at the bottom of his garden. How he wished he could climb up into its strong branches, but for now he could only sit and look at it.

He thought back to his last visit to hospital. The doctor had said: 'We can help you run about again, but a lot will depend on you.' Martin wasn't sure what he meant but he was ready to do anything to be able to walk again.

At last Martin went into hospital for his operation. He was scared but excited. After the operation he was in a lot of pain and had to lie still. Sometimes, when he was drifting off to sleep, he could see the walnut tree waiting for him.

Before long he was doing exercises every day to strengthen his legs and back. The exercises hurt and made him feel so tired that he felt like giving up. Now he knew what the doctor had meant.

Then came the great day when he took his first steps with the help of crutches. It was an even greater day when he walked on his own and went home. At the bottom of the garden the walnut tree was waiting for him and Martin knew that now it wouldn't be long before his dream came true.

MARCH 21

Puss in Boots (Part 1)

Once upon a time, there was a miller who had three sons. When he died he left his mill to his first son, his donkey to his second son, and because he had nothing else, he left his cat to his third son.

One day, the cat said, 'Master, give me a pair of boots and a sack and you will see that I am not as useless as you think.' It was a very strange request for a cat to make. The cat, or Puss in Boots as the miller's son now called him, went into the forest and caught a rabbit. He put it in the sack and then instead of taking it home to the miller's son, he took it to the King's palace.

'Please accept this small present from my master, the Marquis of Carabas,' said Puss in Boots. It was to be the first of many presents Puss in Boots took to the King, and each time he said he had been sent by his master. Though the King never actually met the Marquis of Carabas, he soon became very familiar with his name. The miller's son knew nothing of the presents, or of the Marquis of Carabas, and Puss in Boots did not tell him.

One day, when Puss in Boots was at the palace, he overheard someone say that the King was about to take his daughter for a drive in the country. Puss in Boots hurried home.

'Quick, master!' he called. 'Go and bathe in the river and I will make your fortune.' It was another strange request for a cat to make, but the miller's son was used to his pet by now and so he did as he was told. No sooner was the miller's son in the river than Puss in Boots took his clothes and threw them into the river with him.

'Puss . . . Puss . . . What are you doing?' called the miller's son. Puss didn't answer; he was watching the road. Presently he saw the King's carriage in the distance. He waited until it was close, then he ran out in the road in front of it.

'Help! Help! My master, the Marquis of Carabas, is drowning! Please save him!'

MARCH 22

Puss in Boots (Part 2)

Puss in Boots pretended that his master was the Marquis of Carabas and he told the King and the Princess that his master was drowning. His master was soon pulled from the river and given some dry clothes. He looked so handsome in the fine clothes that the Princess fell in love with him at once.

'Father dear, may the Marquis of Carabas ride with us?'

'Of course,' said the King. 'Will you ride with us, Puss?'

Puss asked to be excused. He said he had something rather important to attend to.

He ran on ahead of the carriage, and each time he saw someone at work in the fields he called: 'If the King asks who this land belongs to, tell him it belongs to the Marquis of Carabas.'

The King did stop the carriage several times, and each time he received the same answer to his question. 'The Marquis of Carabas must be a very rich man,' he thought.

Puss in Boots ran so swiftly that soon he was a long way ahead of the carriage. Presently he came to a castle, which he knew belonged to an ogre. He went straight up to the ogre and said: 'I hear you can turn yourself into any animal you choose. I won't believe a story like that unless I see it for myself.' Immediately, the ogre changed himself into a lion, and roared and growled.

'There,' he said, when he had turned himself back into an ogre. 'I hope I frightened you.'

'It must be easy to change yourself into something big,' said Puss in Boots. 'I don't suppose you can turn yourself into something as small as a . . . er . . . um . . . a mouse?'

The ogre couldn't have a mere cat doubting his special abilities. He changed himself into a tiny mouse in the twinkling of an eye. It was the last time he changed himself into anything because Puss in Boots pounced on him and ate him up before he could change back into an ogre, and that was the end of him!

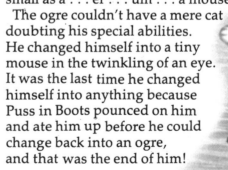

MARCH 23

Puss in Boots (Part 3)

'Hooray!' shouted the castle servants. 'We are free of the wicked ogre at last. Hooray!'

'Your new master will always be kind, you can be sure of that,' said Puss in Boots.

'Who *is* our new master?' they asked.

'The Marquis of Carabas, of course,' said Puss in Boots.

When the King's carriage reached the castle, Puss in Boots was standing at the drawbridge, with the smiling servants gathered round him. 'Welcome,' he said with a beautiful bow. 'Welcome to the home of my master, the Marquis of Carabas.'

The miller's son was too astonished to do anything except think to himself, 'Whatever is Puss up to?' Luckily Puss had time to explain while the King was getting out of the carriage.

'What a rich man this Marquis must be,' thought the King. 'And such a nice young man too.'

Not long afterwards the Princess and the miller's son were married. They, and Puss in Boots, lived happily ever after in the castle that had once belonged to the wicked ogre.

MARCH 24

King Frog

Ever since Freddy Frog had grown out of being a tadpole he had looked upon himself as something special. When he was only a little frog he longed to be as big as his hero who was huge and called Bully Frog.

'You must eat as much as I do,' advised Bully. From that moment Freddy spent all his time catching insects on his sticky tongue. Well, he grew and he grew. Soon he was as big as his hero. And then he was bigger. One day he was the biggest frog for miles around. When his friends began treating him with great respect, Freddy was delighted. After a time he decided that he was too important to be known as Freddy Frog.

'From now on you must address me as King Frog,' he announced one morning. He hopped on to a big boulder and sat there looking about him with a lordly air. Not one of his friends came near him all day and when night fell Freddy felt quite miserable. 'If this is what it is to be King,' he thought, 'I would rather just be ordinary.'

He hopped down from his boulder and went off to find his friends so that he could tell them he wasn't King Frog any more. Nowadays Freddy Frog is quite enormous but he never mentions his size to his friends in case they think he is still King Frog.

MARCH 25

Mitzy and the Mop

Mitzy lived in a big luxury flat. She had bright eyes and long silky hair. She was the pet of a rich old lady who gave her salmon for dinner and chocolate drops before she went to bed. When Mitzy wasn't playing with her expensive doggy toys, she was sitting on a beautiful velvet cushion,

being very well-behaved.

One day her mistress had to go out and leave Mitzy. 'I won't be long, my darling,' she told Mitzy. 'You stay here and play with all your toys.'

As soon as Mitzy heard the front door shut, she jumped down from her velvet cushion. This was the chance she had been waiting for! What fun it was to wander where she wanted. Mitzy gave a yelp of excitement. She jumped on and off the chairs and nibbled one of the big rubber plants

standing in the hall. Then she raced round the kitchen, upsetting her bowl of cream and knocking over her dish. But then she discovered the mop . . .

That mop was the best toy in the world. Mitzy chewed its stringy head, shook it and growled at it. It was such fun that Mitzy could not bear to leave it lying there, all by itself, on the kitchen floor. She grabbed a mouthful of its stringy head and dragged it into the sitting room where she played with it happily until her mistress came home.

'An old mop in my sitting room!' exclaimed her mistress, when she came into the room. 'What have you been up to, my darling?' Mitzy jumped

back on to her velvet cushion and put her head between her paws. With a puzzled frown, her mistress picked up the mop. 'Nasty thing!' she said. 'I'll put it away in the cupboard.'

'Nasty thing indeed!' Mitzy thought. 'But I know where it is now. Just wait until I'm left alone next time.'

MARCH 26

Noisy Neighbours

Dormouse was sleepy. He had been up all night searching for food. Now he had to go to sleep. But the birds were singing at the tops of their voices. Dormouse shouted, 'Be quiet! You're keeping me

awake!' But the singing went on.

Dormouse got very cross. 'I've had enough of this,' he grumbled. 'I shall go and complain to the God of the Woods.'

'Lord Pan,' said Dormouse to the God of the Woods, 'I am a night creature so I must sleep in the daytime, but my noisy neighbours keep me awake. Will you please order them to be quiet?'

'Dormouse,' said Pan, 'I must be fair to all creatures. Your neighbours are singing to each other. That is as it should be. Now, they have not complained to me of your noise or of any of the other night creatures. They must hear your squeaks. And what about the snorts of Badger, the hoots of Owl and Nightingale's song?' Dormouse had not thought of that. He felt ashamed.

Then Pan began to play on his magic pipes. The music wove a spell around Dormouse. He did not remember going home and he fell asleep straight away. For the magic music of Pan was in his ears . . . and it is there whenever he wants to go to sleep.

MARCH 27

The Fable of the Fisherman and the Sprat

A fisherman was at sea fishing. He cast his net into the waves over and over again, but each time he drew it back into the boat it was empty.

He was beginning to think there wasn't a single fish left in the sea when he caught a tiny little sprat. It was so small it fitted snugly into the palm of his hand.

'Please let me go,' said the sprat. 'You can see for yourself how small I am. When I have grown much bigger you can catch me again. I'll be much more use to you then. Please let me go.'

'Do you take me for a fool?' said the fisherman. 'If

I let you go I would never see you again, and well I know it. Now I have you, I intend keeping you.'

MARCH 28

Chow the Cat

Chow was an unusual cat. His thick, bushy fur was a sleek silver grey. 'How beautiful he is,' everyone said. Chow was very proud of himself. He saw the other cats – black, ginger and striped – that lived nearby.

'I'm not at all like them,' he told himself. 'I don't think I'm a cat at all.'

One day the people living next door to Chow bought an expensive silver car. It purred smoothly up their drive. Everyone admired it just as everyone admired Chow. 'How beautiful,' they all said.

'That's the answer,' said Chow. 'I'm not a cat. I'm a creature like that one.'

The next day Chow saw the car coming out of its garage backwards as far as the road. Then it turned and went forwards. Chow walked down his drive backwards. He stopped at the road and then walked smoothly forwards along the gutter.

He walked like that into the town, stopping at red traffic lights with all the other cars. Then he spotted the silver car. It had broken down.

Mechanics were trying to fix it.

It was then that Chow, not looking where he was going, caught his foot in a grid. One of the mechanics saw him and ran over with his tool bag.

'I'll soon have you out of there,' said the mechanic. Chow wondered if the silver car had the same problem. The mechanic carried Chow to the garage and bandaged his leg. Chow saw the silver car being pushed in as well. The men fitted a nozzle into its side. 'That's how it feeds,' thought Chow. Some of the liquid had spilt. Chow limped over to taste it. It was horrible!

'Here you are,' said the mechanic putting down a saucer of milk. Chow lapped it up happily.

'Maybe I am a cat after all,' he thought.

MARCH 29

The Three Wishes

There was once a poor man and his wife who were sitting by their fire one evening talking as they usually did about their rich neighbours.

'How happy we would be if we were as rich as they are,' said the wife.

'Why, if we were granted just one wish,' said the husband, 'we could be the happiest people alive.'

Suddenly, a bright light filled the room. Standing in the room was a fairy.

'You wanted one wish,' said the fairy. 'I will grant you three. The first three wishes you make will come true. Think carefully before you wish.' With that the fairy was gone.

When they recovered from the surprise the man and wife discussed what wishes to make. 'I think we should wish for great riches,' said the wife.

'But what about good health,' said the husband, 'or good looks? Let's think about it tonight and make our wishes tomorrow.'

His wife agreed and set to tending the fire. Without thinking, she said, 'I wish we had a sausage to cook on the fire.' Her wish was quickly granted. A sausage appeared in front of her.

'You've wasted a wish!' shouted the man angrily. 'I wish that sausage would grow on the end of

your nose.' And that is exactly what happened. The man had wasted their second wish.

The wife began to cry. 'What shall we do with our third wish?' she sobbed.

'We can still be rich,' said the man. 'I'd buy you a gold case to put round the sausage.'

'You can be rich,' said the wife, 'but I am going to hide myself away for ever.'

'We have one wish left,' said the man. 'You use it for whatever you want.'

'I wish,' said his wife, 'that the sausage would go from the end of my nose.'

The sausage disappeared and the man and his wife stayed poor. But they never wished for anything again and they learned to be content with what they had.

MARCH 30

The Impatient Witch

Flewella the Witch was worried,
Her pet frogs had all jumped away,
Her cauldron had rusted completely,
And her bats had flown to Bombay.

A black cat had swallowed her spiders,
And her broomstick had snapped in half,
Her rats were all playing Bingo,
And her crow was asleep in the bath.

'I'm getting too old,' she said sadly,
'I'm wrinkled and losing my brain,
I'll visit the local Witch Doctor,
He'll magic me young again.'

The Witch Doctor listened intently,
And mixed her a bright yellow brew.
'A sip a day for a week,' he said,
'And avoid carrots, doughnuts and stew.'

Now Flewella was very impatient,
She swallowed the brew in one go,
Then she settled down in the armchair,
To wait for the magic to show.

But the potion worked very quickly,
In fact, by a quarter to four,
Flewella was sitting like a baby,
Clapping her hands, on the floor.

'She should have followed instructions,'
The Witch Doctor said, aghast.
'A sipful a day, not a bottle,
No wonder it worked so fast!'

Flewella giggled and gurgled,
And waved her bottle aloft,
She stayed like that for a couple of weeks,
Until the magic wore off!

MARCH 31

The Butterfly Trees

'It's so gloomy living here this time of year,' Mrs Dumpy said, moving away from the window of her little cottage in the wood. 'The trees look so sad without their leaves.'
She stitched the wings on to a butterfly brooch she was making and went to the door to call Tabby, her cat, who was sitting in a tree in the garden.
Mrs Dumpy ran over to the tree saying, 'Come indoors, Tabby, before it gets dark.' Then she pinned the butterfly brooch to a branch of the tree and held out her arms to get Tabby down. Tabby edged herself along the branch towards the butterfly brooch and began to purr.
'So you like my butterfly brooch, Tabby,' Mrs Dumpy said, smiling. 'Come indoors quickly. I've got an idea.'
They ran indoors and Mrs Dumpy took her needlework box from the shelf. She sat in her big armchair with Tabby at her feet and stitched away all night. Early next morning, Mrs Dumpy left her cottage carrying a large cardboard box which she placed on the ground under a tree. She took a butterfly brooch from the box and carefully pinned it to a branch at the bottom of the tree. Tabby put her head in the box and pulled out another brightly coloured butterfly on a large hook. She scampered up the tree and hooked the butterfly around a top branch.
Mrs Dumpy and Tabby worked all morning, pinning and hooking butterfly brooches to all the trees round the cottage. Then Mrs Dumpy went indoors and looked out of her window. 'It's so pleasant living here now,' she said. 'The trees look so cheerful with their beautiful butterflies.'

APRIL

APRIL 1

The Nesting Place

Mrs Blackbird couldn't find anywhere to build her nest. The only place left was a large tree at the bottom of the garden, but its branches were much too wide apart. Just then she heard the children's voices.

'Where shall we build it?' called Maria.

'High up off the ground,' replied their father. He was carrying some large pieces of wood, a box of nails and a hammer.

'I know,' shouted Luke. 'That big tree at the bottom of the garden would be good with its wide branches.'

Their father climbed up into the tree. The children passed the wood and the nails up to him. Suddenly, Mrs Blackbird felt a large "plop" on her beak. 'Oh no,' she sighed. 'It's raining again. I'm going to get cold and wet.'

'Let's go inside for tea now,' said father. 'We'll finish it tomorrow.'

All night it rained very hard. 'I suppose our bird-house will be ruined inside now,' sighed Luke as they got up the next morning.

'Just look,' gasped Maria, peering out of the bedroom window. The children ran into the garden. They could scarcely believe their eyes. Their bird-house had a very smart new roof, made from leaves, twigs and grass, all cleverly woven

together. Inside, on a little nest, with a shiny egg inside, sat a very proud Mrs Blackbird. She had found the best nesting place in the garden.

APRIL 2

Chuffa in the Wild West (Part 1)

Chuffa and Mr Driver had been given the job of taking the Sheriff and his prisoner from Abilene to Deadwood City. The prisoner was the famous outlaw, Big Bad Jake.

'We've got to make it to Deadwood City by sundown,' said the Sheriff, 'before the

judge leaves town.'

'We'll never get there on time in that old wreck,' sneered Jake, pointing at Chuffa. 'Anyway, my boys will find a way to slow us down.'

Chuffa wasn't too pleased to be called an old wreck, and as they set off he wondered what Jake meant about his 'boys'.

All was going well as they chuffed along through the prairie. Mr Driver was singing a cowboy song when suddenly he jammed on the brakes.

'Tree on the line up ahead,' he shouted. 'Now how did that get there?'

'I could tell you,' said Jake.

'Your boys, I suppose, Jake?' said the Sheriff. 'Watch out for a

trap, driver.'

Finally they managed to heave the tree off the track. 'We've lost time,' said the Sheriff. 'Can we speed up?'

'We'll do what we can,' said Mr Driver. They clattered along as fast as they could over the prairie. Mr Driver started singing his cowboy song. Then suddenly he jammed on the brakes again.

'What is it this time?' complained the Sheriff.

'Look ahead!' said Mr Driver. There in the middle of the desert was a large herd of hairy, thirsty buffalo and they were all crossing the railway track.

'We'll never get to Deadwood in time,' said the Sheriff.

APRIL 3

Chuffa in the Wild West (Part 2)

Chuffa and Mr Driver were taking the Sheriff and his prisoner, Big Bad Jake, to Deadwood City. They had to get there by sundown and now there was a herd of buffalo in their way.

'They must be looking for the water-hole,' said Mr Driver. He jumped out of the driver's cab and led the leader of the herd down to the water-hole on the other side of the tracks. The rest of the herd followed.

They were very grateful to Mr Driver and they nodded their thanks. Mr Driver waited until the last one had crossed the track. Then Chuffa whistled goodbye as they set off again.

The Sheriff was getting impatient. He said, 'Can't you get this train to move any faster? The sun's starting to go down and we're still a long way from Deadwood.'

'Don't worry, Sheriff,' said Mr Driver, 'Chuffa will get us there.' They hadn't gone far when Mr Driver started singing his cowboy song and then suddenly he jammed on the brakes. 'Rocks on the line,' said Mr Driver. 'Must be an avalanche.'

'That's no avalanche!' said the Sheriff, as a group of riders appeared in the distance.

'There are my boys,' said Jake. 'Well, it looks like I shan't be coming with you to Deadwood City, after all,' he smiled.

APRIL 4

Chuffa in the Wild West (Part 3)

Big Bad Jake's outlaw gang were coming to save him from being taken for trial in Deadwood City. Chuffa gave three long blasts on his whistle. That was his distress signal.

The outlaws galloped down to the train. The Sheriff was just about to give up his prisoner when they heard the distant thunder of hooves. The outlaws looked round and in the distance they saw a cloud of dust.

'Buffalo stampede!' they cried. 'Quick! Let's get out of here.'

'What about me?' cried Jake after them.

'You're coming with us to Deadwood City,' smiled the Sheriff. The buffalo herd swooped down and chased the outlaws away, scattering them in all directions.

'They must have heard our signal, Chuffa,' said Mr Driver. 'It just shows it pays to do folks a good turn.'

Working together, Mr Driver, the Sheriff and a miserable Big Bad Jake soon cleared all the rocks blocking the line. With an extra burst of speed they neared Deadwood City. The sun was setting as Mr Driver finished his cowboy song and put on the brakes as they drew into Deadwood City station.

'Just in time, Mr Driver,' said the Sheriff. 'Well done, and well done, Chuffa.' Off he went with the prisoner.

When Mr Driver and Chuffa arrived back in Abilene the next day, the news of their journey had reached the Mayor.

'Fine work,' said the Mayor, giving Mr Driver a medal and Chuffa an enormous bow to tie round his funnel.

'Not bad,' said Chuffa to himself, 'for an old wreck!'

APRIL 5

The Fable of the Grasshopper and the Ants

One day, in the middle of winter, when the ants were putting their storehouse in order, a grasshopper came knocking at the door.

'What do you want?' asked the ants, as they carried on sweeping and tidying and sorting. The ants never stopped working just to ask questions or wait for answers.

'I am very hungry,' said the grasshopper. 'You have plenty of food in your storehouse. Please give me something to eat before I starve to death.'

The ants were so shocked they put down their rakes and their brooms and gathered round the grasshopper.

'What were you doing last summer when food was so plentiful?' they asked. 'Weren't you out collecting grain and putting it in store, so that you would have food to see you through the cold winter months?'

'Well, to tell you the truth,' said the grasshopper, 'I was so busy singing and enjoying the sun, I didn't have the time to spare.'

'If you spent the summer singing, then maybe you should spend the winter dancing, and not bother about eating at all,' said the ants. They picked up their rakes and their brooms and went back to work. They did not offer the grasshopper a single grain of wheat and he went away hungry.

APRIL 6

The Magic Combs

King Bonkers was bored. He decided to go and see his old friend Wizard Winegum to see if he could suggest something.

'Try one of my magic combs,' he said. 'They're always fun. If someone combs their hair with one, the first thing they touch will turn into something different.'

'Into what?' asked the King.

'You don't know until you touch it,' said the wizard.

'I'll have two of your combs then,' said the King and he ran home. There he found his wife brushing her hair in front of the mirror. 'Here, my dear,' said the King. 'Use this new comb.'

'Thank you, dear,' said the Queen, putting down her brush and picking up the magic comb. When she had finished combing her hair, the Queen touched her chair and it turned into a kangaroo. It hopped out of the door with the Queen clinging to its neck.

King Bonkers laughed and laughed as the Queen went bouncing off. Next he decided to play a trick on his daughter.

'Hello, Mirabelle,' said the King to the Princess. 'I've got a present for you. It's a comb.'

'That's beautiful,' said the Princess, running the comb through her hair. 'Oh, thank you, father,' she cried, running towards him.

'No, don't touch me,' protested the King. But he was too late. The Princess gave him a kiss and the King turned into a frog. The Princess gasped. She touched the frog and it turned into a bird. The King-bird flew out of the window into a tree.

Half an hour later, when he turned back into King Bonkers, he was so embarrassed at being stuck in a tree, that he decided to be a wise and sensible king from then on.

APRIL 7

Digging for Fish

One starry night, when the fishermen were getting their boats ready to go out to sea, an old woman hobbled along the beach towards them pulling a spindly-legged boy by the hand.

'What do you want, old woman?' asked the fishermen. 'Can't you see we are busy? We don't want to miss the tide.'

'Take my boy with you and teach him how to fish,' she said. The fishermen took one look at the boy, who had arms like broomsticks, and they laughed out loud.

'You can't be serious,' they snorted. 'Him . . . a fisherman! A fisherman has to battle with the sea. He couldn't battle with a kitten.'

'Please,' said the boy. 'I'm stronger than I look.'

'Get out of our way,' they said roughly. 'We haven't time to waste on the likes of you. Take the boy home, old woman,' jeered the fishermen. 'Fishing is men's work. Leave it to the men.'

'Men's work, is it?' screeched the old woman. 'Well you'll catch no fish until you bring me that!' And she pulled off the silver thimble she was wearing on her thumb and threw it on to the sand.

One of the fishermen bent to pick it up. His fingers would not close round it. It was burying itself in the sand. It was at that awful moment the fishermen realised what they had done. They left their nets and their boats and began to dig into the sand with their hands.

'Have pity on us . . .' they pleaded. 'Have pity on us . . .' But their pleas were in vain. They may be digging to this day, their boats neglected and falling to pieces, their nets tangled and rotting. All because they dared to laugh at a witch and her son.

ARPIL 8

A Little Daydream

One day Martin Mouse and his wife, Valentina, went out in the fields to pick berries. They were singing a happy song when suddenly they saw something shining in the bushes.

'Why, it's a beautiful gold ring!' cried Valentina. 'And it's studded with diamonds. It must belong to a fine lady.'

Martin Mouse picked it up and placed it on Valentina's head. 'It would make a crown for you, Valentina,' he said. 'You could be Queen of the May!'

'Yes!' cried Valentina. 'They would cover me with flowers and everyone would dance round me.' Then she placed the ring on her husband's head. 'How noble you look!' she said. 'You could be King of all the Mice!'

Martin Mouse's eyes gleamed. 'How exciting it would be to be King . . . to wear fine clothes . . . to ride by and have everyone cheering and waving at me. We could have fancy-dress balls and . . .'

'And garden parties . . . and lots of delicious food,' said Valentina. Then they both went quiet and looked into each other's eyes. 'But it wouldn't be honest to keep the ring,' said Valentina.

Martin Mouse agreed. 'Yes. We must return it to its owner.' They took the ring to the police station and left it there. Then they went back to picking berries and laughed and sang for the rest of the day.

Soon, it was time for their winter's sleep. They curled up in their cosy nest underground. 'This is the life, isn't it?' yawned Valentina. 'Nothing like a nice looooooong sleep.'

'Um hum,' murmured Martin Mouse sleepily. 'Nobody to disturb us . . . no cheering crowds . . . just you and me . . . zzzzzzzzzzzz!' Their contented snores lasted all winter.

APRIL 9

Jack and the Beanstalk (Part 1)

Jack lived with his mother in a tumbledown house. They were so poor
they never seemed to have enough to eat and one day, Jack's mother
said, 'Jack, you must take the cow to market and sell her.'

'If I do that we will have no milk,' said Jack.

'If we don't sell her we will soon have nothing to eat at all,' replied his
mother. Very sadly, Jack led the cow to market. He was about halfway
there when he met an old man.

'Is your cow for sale?' asked the old man. Jack said that she was. 'Then
I'll give you five beans for her,' said the old man.

Jack laughed. 'You can't buy a cow with five beans,' he said.

'Ah,' said the old man, 'but these are magic beans. You will make a
fortune with them.' Jack could not resist such a bargain. He gave the
cow an affectionate pat, handed her halter to the old man and took the
five beans in exchange.

Jack's mother was furious. 'We needed money to buy food,' she
scolded. 'How could you be so stupid?' She snatched the beans from
Jack's hand and tossed them out of the window. 'That's what I think of
your bargain,' she said.

Jack went sadly to bed without any supper. He supposed he *had* been
rather silly. He would have to go in search of work the following day for
he could not let his mother starve.

APRIL 10

Jack and the Beanstalk (Part 2)

Jack's mother had thrown out of the window the beans Jack had been
given for their cow. Next morning Jack woke up bright and early.
Instead of the bright rays of sunshine which usually lay across his
bedroom floor, there was a large shadow. He went to the window to see
what was blocking out the sun. Growing from the ground below his
window was the biggest beanstalk in the world. It reached up . . .
up . . . up into the sky and the top of it was lost among the clouds.

'The old man was right. They *were* magic beans,' he said. 'I'm going to
climb to the top to see what I can find.' Jack's mother begged him not to
go but Jack had made up his mind.

He climbed and climbed, up and up, and from the top of the beanstalk
he stepped into another land. It was a land just like his own except that
everything in it was three times as big. He went to the door of the only
house he could see and knocked boldly. The door was opened by a
huge woman. Jack persuaded her to give him some breakfast. He had
just finished eating when he heard footsteps as heavy as falling
boulders and then a voice as loud as thunder:

'FEE FI FO FUM, I SMELL THE BLOOD OF AN ENGLISHMAN!'

Quick as a flash, the giant woman bundled Jack into the oven. 'Sh! Be
very quiet,' she said. 'That's my husband. He eats boys like you.'

The huge woman told her husband he was mistaken and put a bowl of
porridge on the table. When he had eaten, the giant called for his hen.
'Lay!' he ordered, and the hen laid a golden egg. Jack, who could see
through a crack in the oven door, decided to have that hen for himself.

Then the giant's head began to nod. Soon he was asleep. Jack left the
oven, picked up the hen, ran to the top of the beanstalk and climbed
down to his home.

APRIL 11

Jack and the Beanstalk (Part 3)

'Mother, we are going to be rich,' said Jack, showing her the hen that laid golden eggs. A few days later he decided to pay another visit to the Land of Giants. His mother begged him not to go again, but he was determined. This time he crept secretly into the big house and hid. He watched the giant eat his breakfast.

After breakfast the giant called for his magic harp. 'Sing!' ordered the giant and the harp sang sweetly. The giant's head began to nod. Soon he was asleep. Jack jumped from his hiding place, snatched up the magic harp and started to run.

The giant woke with a roar. 'FEE FI FO FUM . . .' he bellowed, 'I SMELL THE BLOOD OF AN ENGLISHMAN . . .'

He ran after Jack with great thundering steps. Jack was small and nimble, and had a good start. When he reached the top of the beanstalk he tucked the harp inside his shirt and began to climb down. The beanstalk began to shake and creak and groan as the angry giant followed him. Faster went Jack . . . faster . . . and faster.

'Mother!' he called as he neared the bottom. 'Bring me an axe! Quickly!' He jumped to the ground and took the axe. With three hefty cuts, the beanstalk came tumbling to the ground. There was a terrible roar as the giant fell. He made a hole so big, when he hit the ground, that both he and the beanstalk disappeared into it and were lost forever. As for Jack and his mother, they lived happily ever after.

APRIL 12

Ash Lodge – A Crowded Day

Basil and Dewy, the two Badgers who live at Ash Lodge with their friend Willie the Mole, were rolling up mats and pulling furniture into the garden one morning.

'What's going on?' asked Willie.

'We're going to paint the walls and ceilings,' said Dewy, 'and you're going to help.'

'Oh no,' said Willie trying to escape. 'I always get covered in paint.'

'I'll make you a paper hat to keep the paint off,' said Dewy. In fact Dewy made a paper hat for each of them and Willie felt much happier.

They had just started painting when a voice said, 'Can anyone help?' It was Jake Squirrel standing in the doorway.

'Certainly,' said Basil. 'There are plenty of spare brushes.'

All morning people called asking to help. Somehow the word had got round. Dewy was kept so busy making paper hats he had no time to do any painting. The room became more and more crowded but the job was soon done. Basil and Dewy made a pile of sandwiches and they all had a picnic outside by the pond.

'I know,' said Willie after they had eaten. 'Let's have a hat race.' He put his hat upside down on the pond and blew it. Carried by the wind, it floated to the other side like a boat. Everyone tried to do the same. There were hats everywhere. Dewy got the raft out to collect all the soggy hats floating in the pond. By the time everyone had gone home Dewy and Basil were exhausted.

'What's the matter with you two?' said Willie. 'Some people just can't take a bit of hard work.'

APRIL 13

The Happy Traveller

Have you seen the happy traveller
Or heard his marching feet?
He sings a song and gives good luck
To everyone he meets.

He likes to walk the country lanes,
By morning and by night,
In top hat, boots, with walking stick
And flowing scarf pure white.

The country people know him well,
They give him food to eat;
A place to rest, a jug of ale,
A fire to warm his feet.

The children love to hear him.
Such tales he has to tell;
When babies cry and cannot sleep
His singing makes them well.

One day he came, how glad we were,
A wedding had begun;
The traveller sang and piped a tune,
We danced and had such fun.

He played and sang and how we danced!
He led us – one long line;
Round the houses, through the streets,
Our tapping feet kept time.

At last the traveller had to go,
The moon lit up his way,
He wished us luck and waved farewell
But he'll be back some day.

Have you seen the happy traveller,
Or heard his marching feet?
He sings a song and gives good luck
To everyone he meets.

APRIL 14

Arthur's New Friend

'Where are you, Arthur?' calls Mabel Mouse. 'The chimney is broken and needs mending.' But Arthur Mouse is going fishing. He hates mending things and he hates it when Mabel grumbles, so he sets off for the lake.

It isn't a good day for Arthur. He doesn't catch a single fish and his line gets tangled round a rock. He wades out and pushes the rock on its side. But then, all around him the water starts swirling and gurgling.

'My goodness!' he cries. 'The lake is draining away!' The big rock had been a giant plug and now the lake is almost empty! Arthur wanders among the rocks and weeds.

'Hello!' booms a voice from behind a large rock. Arthur swings round and standing next to him is a huge animal with big pink ears and a long pink tail. 'I'm a hippopotamouse,' he explains. 'I live in the water, but I'm bored down here so I'm glad you let all the water out.'

He shows Arthur where he lives. 'This is my hippopotahouse,' he says. 'I built it from all the rubbish on the lake bed.' Arthur is very impressed.

'Mabel will never believe this,' says Arthur.

'Take this old boot home with you as a souvenir,' says the hippopotamouse.

On Arthur's way home, it begins to rain. 'The lake will soon fill up again now,' he thinks.

When he gets home, Arthur tells Mabel about the hippopotamouse. 'It was so big,' he says, opening his arms as wide as he can, 'it was enormouse.'

'And I suppose it got away,' says Mabel.

'Look, if you don't believe me, here's a souvenir it gave me,' says Arthur.

'So that's all you caught,' says Mabel. 'An old boot! Now stop telling such stories and mend our chimney.'

That is what Arthur does. He turns the holey old boot upside down and makes it into a brand new chimney. Mabel is so pleased she says Arthur can go fishing again any time he likes, as long as he doesn't come home with any more silly stories.

APRIL 15

Uncama the Hunter (Part 1)

Uncama was a bold African hunter. He lived in a small village on the edge of the forest with his wife and baby son.

One harvest time, when the crops were ready to dig, a strange animal came into the village and rooted up all the vegetables in one of the vegetable patches. It came the following night and the night after that. Each time it carried off more vegetables.

'If somebody doesn't do something soon,' said Uncama, 'there will be nothing left and we will all starve.'

That night he lay in wait and watched for the strange animal. If he could catch it, he would kill it. But though Uncama kept very quiet, the strange animal heard him breathing and it fled before Uncama had time to throw his spear.

Uncama could run like the wind and he gave chase. When the animal reached the river it ran into a deep hole at the water's edge. Uncama was a brave hunter; he didn't hesitate. He followed the animal into the hole and came to an underground country. The animal disappeared and Uncama found himself in a village among a tribe of savage dwarfs who attacked him.

APRIL 16

Uncama the Hunter (Part 2)

Uncama barely escaped from the land of the dwarfs with his life. He ran back the way he had come followed by a hail of spears.

When he returned to the village no one seemed to recognise him. Uncama could see no one he knew either.

'Where are my friends?' he asked. 'And where is my wife?'

'Which wife would that be?' asked a youth.

'Do not joke . . . the wife of Uncama, of course.'

'I suppose you mean the Uncama who disappeared many years ago,' said the youth, and led him to an old woman with wrinkled face and bowed shoulders. Standing beside her was a fully grown man. The man was Uncama's son. Uncama thought he had been away for less than an hour. He did not know that an hour in the underground country of the dwarfs was as long as fifty years anywhere else.

The son, who had been a baby in his mother's arms when Uncama left in pursuit of the strange animal, was now older than Uncama himself.

APRIL 17

Mother Holle (Part 1)

Once there were two sisters, who were as different as chalk and cheese. Martha was idle and never did a thing unless she had to, which was not very often for she was her mother's favourite. Anna was always busy.

One day, Anna was sitting in the garden spinning when she pricked her finger. A speck of blood fell on to the shuttle. She was trying to wash it clean when it slipped from her finger and fell to the bottom of the well.

'You dropped it! You must go down and get it!' shouted her mother in such a rage that Anna had no choice but to do as she was told. She must have bumped her head as she fell for she remembered

nothing until she woke and found herself in a pleasant field. She got to her feet and began to walk. Presently she came to an oven.

'Take me out . . . before I burn!' cried the bread in the oven. Anna took the bread from the oven and set it to cool. A little further on she came to a tree.

'Shake me!' cried the tree. 'My apples are ripe!' Anna shook the tree. When all the apples had fallen, she piled them neatly, then went on her way until she came to the house of a witch.

APRIL 18

Mother Holle (Part 2)

Anna had fallen down a well. She found herself in a strange land, and came to a witch's house.

'You must come and work for me,' said the witch. 'Your most important task will be to shake my feather bed every morning. I am Mother Holle.'

Mother Holle was very kind to Anna. For a while Anna was happy, but then she began to feel homesick.

'You have worked very hard,' said Mother Holle, 'and I will show you the way home.' She took Anna to a hidden door. As Anna stepped through the door, a shower of golden rain fell all about her and clung to her hair and clothes.

'The gold is yours,' said Mother Holle. 'Goodbye, my dear.'

The next moment Anna found herself at home. As she ran across the yard, a cockerel sitting on the fence crowed:

'Cock-a-doodle-do!
A golden girl is come to you!'

'Where have you been, you bad girl?' shouted her mother, running to the door, but when she saw the gold she quickly changed her tune. 'Where did you get it? How did you get it?' she asked. Anna told her everything that had happened. 'Martha shall have gold too,' said her mother. 'Go, sit by the well, Martha, and spin. Do everything as Anna did.'

Martha did not like spinning and she was in a hurry to get rich. She pricked her finger on a thorn to make it bleed. She squeezed her finger so that blood fell on to the shuttle, then she threw the shuttle into the well and jumped in after it.

APRIL 19

Mother Holle (Part 3)

Anna's sister, Martha, went down the well to find Mother Holle and to become as rich as her sister. Everything happened as before until Martha reached the oven.

'Take me out before I burn!' cried the bread.

'And get my hands dirty! Certainly not!' snapped Martha.

'Shake me! My apples are ripe!' called the tree.

'What! And have one fall on my head! Certainly not!' snapped Martha. She hurried on to the witch's cottage.

'I will come and work for you,' she said to Mother Holle, without waiting to be asked. She swept the dust under the hearthrug and did not bother to shake Mother Holle's mattress at all. She stayed late in bed each day.

'It is time for you to go home,' said Mother Holle after three days.

'You must pay me first,' said Martha greedily.

'Certainly, I will pay you,' said Mother Holle. She led Martha to the hidden door. This time, instead of a shower of gold descending like rain, a shower of black pitch came pouring down. It covered Martha from head to foot.

'That is fair payment for the work you have done,' said Mother Holle sternly and she closed the door behind her. When Martha ran sobbing across the yard to the house, the cockerel sitting on the fence crowed:

'Cock-a-doodle-do!
A dirty girl is come to you!'

APRIL 20

Adventures of *The Tulip* – Are We Lost?

Thomas, Wilbur and Minty had spent several days aboard their riverboat, *The Tulip*, and now their food was running low. Wilbur and Minty volunteered to go shopping. They soon found a farm and bought everything they needed.

'Now which way is the river?' asked Minty, as they began the journey back.

'This way,' said Wilbur confidently. They set off through a field knee-deep in grass. Soon there was grass in every direction and no sign of the river.

'Are you sure this is right?' asked Minty.

'Of course I'm sure,' said Wilbur, as they squeezed through a hedge. On the other side of the hedge was a field of grazing sheep. Wilbur and Minty were halfway across the field when they had a feeling they were being followed. They looked behind and there was a flock of sheep right on their heels. Minty wondered what things sheep liked to eat and whether he was one of those things so he decided to distract them.

'Er . . . you don't happen to know where the river is, do you?' he asked. All the sheep began talking at once. Each had something quite different to say.

Meanwhile, back on *The Tulip*, Thomas had started to worry about his friends. He blew the ship's foghorn. 'Whooo . . . whooo!' The sheep stopped talking and stood still.

'Quick,' said Wilbur, 'that's *The Tulip*. This way.' Off they ran while the sheep looked on. They were delighted to see Thomas and *The Tulip* at last.

Safely aboard, Minty said to Thomas: 'You don't know what sheep like to eat, do you?'

'Grass, I think,' said Thomas.

'There you are,' said Minty. 'I knew we were safe all along.'

APRIL 21

The Homeless Elf

There was once a little elf called Spike. Spike made his home in a grocer's shop. This was a very wise choice because when the grocer put up the shutters at night, Spike had lots of space to move about. There were always tasty morsels to carry away to his little house behind the coffee beans.

Then one day, something awful happened. The grocer put up a big notice in his shop window which read: CLOSING DOWN. Soon after, men in long blue overalls came into the shop and began clearing away all the tins and bottles and packets and flour bags. It was lucky for Spike that they didn't touch the coffee beans which were on the highest shelf. But Spike knew that he must leave his little house and look for somewhere else to live.

The first night Spike left his cosy little home he slept in one of the empty boxes stacked at the back of the shop. But it was so cold and draughty that he knew he couldn't stay there.

'I'm homeless,' the little elf thought. He shed a few tears.

The next night Spike went back into the empty shop. He squeezed through a small hole at the back and found himself in a warm, well-lit room.

There was his old friend, the grocer, sitting in front of the fire. Spike felt at home at once. As quiet as a mouse, he crept into one of the cupboards where the grocer kept his old shoes and found the very thing he was looking for. Can you guess? It was a big, wide, comfortable shoe which had once belonged to the grocer's son.

'It's the very thing!' Spike thought. He settled down inside his new home and was soon fast asleep.

APRIL 22

A Pig Called Fancy

Fancy, the blue pig, opened one eye and looked out of his nest. He stretched his wings and yawned. Today was the day of his adventure. He was going to find out why he wasn't like other pigs. They were pink and lived on the ground; he was blue, had wings and lived in a tree.

Everyone who saw him said, 'Fancy, a blue pig,' and that is how he got his name. A green cat had once told Fancy that he wasn't really strange and should go north. 'That's where your answer lies,' said the cat.

Fancy set off after breakfast. On the way he met a golden bird. 'Excuse me, but am I going north?' asked Fancy.

'Yes, north. That's the place for you,' said the bird.

Fancy flew on. Suddenly there was a thundering noise. Fancy flew on to the branch of a tree. A beautiful white horse galloped through the forest.

'What are you doing up there, little blue pig?' said the horse, slowing to a trot.

Fancy noticed the horse had a single horn. It wasn't a horse; it was a unicorn. 'I'm going north,' said Fancy, 'to find out why I am not like other pigs.'

'I will carry you north,' said the unicorn. They sped on together until they reached the end of the forest. There before them lay a valley where small green cats played among groups of white unicorns and in the sky flew golden birds and flocks of blue pigs.

Without a backward glance, Fancy took off from the unicorn's back. He was home at last.

APRIL 23

The Beetle and her Nest

Dora, the dor beetle, lived in a farmer's field. She had made a ball out of earth and dung. She was going to lay an egg on it, but she needed a safe place for it first; so off she went, pushing it with her head and her legs.

She caught up with Delia, another dor beetle, who was also pushing her nest. Then Delia turned away, taking a different direction. 'Don't go that way!' Dora called. 'You'll fall off the edge of the world!'

'Fall off!' repeated Delia. 'The world is round, like our nests! I could start here and come straight home to this spot!'

'But if you go that way you'll come to an edge and if you step over it, that's the end of your dung-ball!' shouted Dora. But Delia went on her way.

Dora found a safe place for her nest and with her front legs she dug a small tunnel for the ball to rest in. Then, having laid an egg on it, she went to make another.

Delia pushed on towards a cliff. Her nest started rolling on a slope. 'Good!' she buzzed. 'Easier at last!' Suddenly the ball dropped into space! 'Oh!' screamed Delia. 'My lovely nest!' She let go and opened her wings – just in time! The dung-ball had fallen into the sea! Delia went back to find Dora who was working happily.

'Have you been round the world already?' asked Dora.

'No!' wailed Delia. 'I came to the edge and . . . I lost my nest.' Poor Delia was in tears.

'Cheer up!' said Dora. 'Let's make another one together and we'll look after it here.'

APRIL 24

Cowboy Charley

Charley wanted to be a cowboy when she grew up. She knew what cowboys wore and her mother bought her all the things; she would dress up in them every day after school.

She collected all the cowboy pictures from magazines and comics, and she never missed the cowboy films. When she played outside with her friends she was always a cowboy. Sometimes her mother would say, 'Don't you ever get tired of playing cowboys?'

But Charley always shook her head. 'I'm going to be a cowboy on a black and white horse,' she would say. That's why her father called her Cowboy Charley.

One Friday when she came home from school, the television was switched on. 'Hurry up and get changed, Charley. There's a film about real live cowboys,' said her mother. So Charley scrambled into her cowboy clothes and sat down to watch.

The film showed that the cowboy's life was very hard. He worked from dawn to dusk in the dust and heat, rounding up and branding the cattle. All the cowboys lived together in a rough wooden hut, ate very big suppers, then went to bed early so as to be up in time to start all over again next day. Nobody was shooting guns or chasing baddies. Charley was very quiet.

Next day at breakfast time, her mother asked her why she wasn't wearing her cowboy clothes. 'I don't think I like cows,' she said.

'What will you be when you grow up, then?' asked her mother.

'I think I'll be an astronaut!' said Charley.

APRIL 25

The Fable of the Foolish Frog

One day a baby frog was hop-hop-hopping through a meadow. A cow came along, munching the sweet grass. The little frog had never seen a cow before. He was very frightened, so he hop-hop-hopped home as fast as he could go.

When the baby frog reached the pond where he lived, he saw his father sitting on a lily pad, sunning himself.

'Dad,' the baby frog said, 'I've just seen the biggest animal in the *whole world*!'

The old bullfrog gloated, 'Not bigger than me.'

'Yes, much bigger,' the baby frog replied.

The old bullfrog was very *foolish* and very *vain*. He began to puff out his chest. He puffed until he was quite swollen. 'That animal,' he croaked, 'couldn't have been much bigger than *this*!'

'Yes it was, father. *Much* bigger.'

The foolish bullfrog began to get angry. He puffed some more. He puffed and he puffed. He puffed until he swelled up like a fat, frog-shaped balloon. All the puffing made it hard for him to talk. 'Now I'm the biggest,' he squeaked. 'Right?'

'Wrong,' said the little frog.

This made the foolish bullfrog *really* angry. So he puffed and puffed, and got bigger and bigger, and fatter and fatter until all at once he BURST . . . into lots of very small pieces. Which goes to prove that being foolish and vain is not very good if you're a frog.

APRIL 26

The Three Spinners (Part 1)

Once there was a girl who could not spin thread.

'You lazy, lazy girl!' her mother would shout. She would hit the girl across the shoulders.

One day, when she was shouting, and the girl was sitting crying at the spinning wheel, the Queen happened to pass by in her coach. She heard the girl crying and called to her coachman to stop the horses.

'Why are you beating your daughter?' she asked the woman.

The old woman was too ashamed to say she thought her daughter was lazy, so she said instead, 'My daughter loves to spin. I am only a poor old woman and I cannot afford to buy the flax. She cries because she wants to spin . . . I do not know what to do.'

'Your troubles are over,' said the Queen. 'I have plenty of flax at the palace. I will take your daughter home with me and she can spin as much as she likes.'

The Queen took the girl to the palace and showed her three rooms which were full from floor to ceiling with unspun flax. 'Spin all that flax into thread, my dear, and you shall marry my son,' said the Queen.

APRIL 27

The Three Spinners (Part 2)

The Queen had told a girl that if she spun a room full of flax into thread she could marry her son. But the girl didn't know how to spin. For two days she sat and wept. On the third day the Queen came to see her.

'Why are you weeping, child?' asked the Queen. 'Why haven't you started to spin?' The poor girl sobbed even harder.

'If there is no thread for me to see tomorrow you will be punished,' said the Queen and she swept from the room.

The girl stood at the window overlooking the street and cried. Presently, through her tears, she saw three strange women walking along the pavement. One of them had a very broad, flat foot; one had a lip that hung down over her chin; and the third had an enormous thumb. One of the women called up to the window and asked the girl why she was weeping.

'I must spin all this flax, and I do not know how to spin.'

'If you will call us aunt and be unashamed of our strange appearance, and if you will invite us to your wedding, we will help you,' said the three women. The girl agreed.

APRIL 28

The Three Spinners (Part 3)

Three strange women had offered to help a girl spin flax into thread. In return she agreed to invite them to her wedding when she married the Prince.

The women slipped unnoticed into the palace and set to work. The one with the broad, flat foot worked the spinning wheel; the one with the lip which hung over her chin wetted the flax; and the one with the enormous thumb twisted the thread. Together they spun the finest thread. Then they hid as the Queen admired it and said to the girl, 'My dear, you shall marry my son.'

'I have three aunts who have been very kind to me. May I invite them to the wedding?' asked the girl.

'Of course,' said the Queen.

An invitation was sent, and on the day of the wedding the three strange women arrived and were welcomed kindly by the girl and the Prince.

'Tell me, aunt,' said the Prince, 'why have you such a broad, flat foot?'

'Because I tread a spinning wheel,' said the first aunt.

'And how is it that you have such a long lip?' he asked the second aunt.

'Because I wet the spinning thread.'

'And why have you such a large thumb?' he asked the third aunt.

'Because I twist the spinning thread,' she answered.

The Prince looked at the three strange women, one with a broad, flat foot, one with a lip that hung down over her chin and one with an enormous thumb, and then he looked at his beautiful bride. 'If that is what spinning thread does to a woman,' he said to her, 'I forbid you ever to touch a spinning wheel again.'

APRIL 29

Toot-toot Goes to Town

Toot-toot is a little steam engine who escaped from his rails one night after some men said he would be scrapped. First Toot-toot worked on a farm. Then he decided to explore some more so he said goodbye to the farmer and his wife and their horse, Rosie, and he set off for the town.

As he tootled into town, Toot-toot saw some rails running along the main street. He hadn't been on rails for so long he couldn't resist having a ride along them.

'How nice,' sighed Toot-toot.

'Where do you think you're going?' said a voice suddenly. Toot-toot had come face to face with a tram.

'We don't like dirty little engines on our nice clean rails. Get off at once!' said the tram driver. Dirty? Toot-toot looked at himself. Yes, he was rather dirty after his farm work.

'Hurry up!' said the driver. 'My passengers have to get to work.' Toot-toot got off the rails, but the tram didn't move. It had broken down.

'Can I help?' asked Toot-toot. He got back on the rails and coupled himself to the tram. Off they tootled, and all the passengers cheered. The driver went red in the face. Toot-toot couldn't help giving a little toot on his whistle, just for fun.

APRIL 30

The Watchful Giant

Once I was very little
And I'm still not very big.
But I become a giant
In my garden when I dig.

I'm all alone and move around
As quiet as a mouse.
I'm careful where I tread for fear
I'll step on someone's house.

For now my feet are giant's feet
To many little eyes
And I must move with special care
Because of my great size.

I look so big to all of them
That if I sit quite still,
They think my head a mountain-top
My foot a great high hill.

They're busy little creatures
With all they have to do;
I've seen them dig and build all day
And feed their children too.

Now I must leave my insect world
To shelter from the rain,
And go back in the house to be
A little boy again.

MAY

MAY 1

Prince Peter of Porcelainia (Part 1)

Porcelainia is a pretty little town far away, where everything is made of porcelain. Porcelain is a delicate sort of china that can easily be broken, so everyone in Porcelainia has to be very careful in everything they do.

On Sundays all the people of Porcelainia hear the ringing of the porcelain bell calling them to the porcelain church. There they sit on the porcelain seats and sing from their porcelain hymn books.

Now, in the church there once lived a family of mice who were always squeaking during the church service. So the people of Porcelainia employed a cat, called Peter, to keep the mice quiet.

One evening, when Peter was out for a stroll in the porcelain woods, he overheard some voices. He crept closer, keeping out of sight.

He saw three men sitting on the porcelain grass. 'Tonight, we'll have some fun,' said one of the men. 'While everyone's asleep we'll smash up everything in Porcelainia. We'll bash and smash and crash and by the time we've finished the whole town will be in pieces.' The men all laughed. 'What fun!' they cried.

Peter rushed off to warn the town, but by the time he reached the main square everyone was in bed. How could he warn them? He rushed up on to one of the porcelain roofs and gave out the loudest 'Meow' he could. Someone woke up, opened their porcelain window and threw a porcelain bucket of water over him. How could Peter make the people understand the danger they were in?

MAY 2

Prince Peter of Porcelainia (Part 2)

Peter the cat had to warn the people of Porcelainia about the men who were coming to smash up the town. Wet through, Peter rushed to the porcelain church. He tried to pull the porcelain bell-rope but the porcelain bell was too heavy for him to move.

Peter gave up and sat down and cried. The mice family saw him crying and bravely went up to him, asking what was wrong. Peter explained all about the bandits and the father mouse said, 'Come on, we can help ring the bell.'

So Peter and all the mice held on to the porcelain bell-rope and gave a great tug. The three men had just reached the main square when suddenly 'Bong!' went the porcelain bell, and 'Bong!' it went again, and

'Bong!' it went for a third time.

Everyone came out of their porcelain houses. 'Is it Sunday?' asked someone wearing a porcelain dressing-gown. The three men were so surprised they just stood in the main square not knowing what to do. The policemen of Porcelainia soon had the men in porcelain handcuffs and took them away to the porcelain prison.

'Well done, well done,' said the Mayor to Peter. 'You've saved the town, with the help of the mice family.'

As a reward, the mice were allowed to squeak as much as they liked in the porcelain church and Peter was given a crown to wear. Can you guess what it was made of?

MAY 3

Ten Baby Birds

Ten baby birds are stretching their wings.
'You'll fly like me,' their mother sings.

'Come on, little birds. Stand in line.'
One flies off and then there were nine.

Another leaves the nest. 'This flying's great!'
He shouts goodbye to the other eight.

Two swoop and rise to show their tricks;
Those on the branch now number six.

Mother's close by and sees two more
Climb higher still to leave just four.

The smallest one flies up into a tree:
'Watch me!' he cries to the other three.

Two go west towards the sun,
Out of ten baby birds there's only one.

The last baby bird flies to join the rest,
Now Mother bird sits in an empty nest.

Ten baby birds have used their wings.
'You can all fly now,' their mother sings.

MAY 4

The Elf and the Mayflies

The new King of the Mayflies was sad. Before his subjects began their merry dance on the water he said to them, 'We have only a few hours to live. We dance and then we die!'

'Nobody will remember us,' said one little mayfly. 'We shall be forgotten at once.' The King nodded.

Mr Bug was passing and heard this. 'I'll go and see the elf of the wood,' he said to himself. 'He may be able to help.'

Mr Bug soon found the elf of the wood and told him the problem. 'We must build something so that they will be remembered,' said the elf. 'Come on. I've an idea.'

The elf began at once to collect the prettiest things he could find. He begged a bluebell here, a feather there and several glistening pebbles. His woodland friends were pleased to give. Then he took these treasures to a secret place by the pond and set to work.

He had soon finished and Mr Bug brought all the mayflies to the secret place. There they saw a tiny garden that the elf had made.

'This is Mayfly Garden,' said the elf.

'It's beautiful,' said the King of the Mayflies. 'Now we shall be remembered. You shall have a pair of lace wings as a gift,' he said to the elf. 'Then you will be able to fly and dance as we do.'

'In return,' said the elf, 'I shall tend your garden for ever.'

The King looked at the garden with pride and smiled as the mayflies began their happy dance over the water.

MAY 5

Ash Lodge – Something Prickly

Willie the Mole, and his two Badger friends, Basil and Dewy, were out collecting chestnuts one day in the woods near Ash Lodge.

'What do you do with them?' asked Willie as he picked up one of the prickly balls.

'You peel them and roast them,' said Dewy. 'They taste delicious.'

The badgers collected as many chestnuts in their prickly shells as they could fit into Basil's hat and then they all set off home. Willie lagged behind and then he stopped. He had seen the most enormous chestnut ever. Wouldn't Basil and Dewy be jealous when he peeled it and ate the great big chestnut inside all to himself.'

Willie had trouble picking up the big chestnut it was so prickly. It made him go 'Ooh' and 'Aah' all the way home as its prickles stuck into his paws. But it would be worth it. Finally Willie got his prickly chestnut home.

'What have you got there, Willie?' asked Dewy, who was standing in the doorway.

'I've got the biggest chestnut in the world,' cried Willie. 'Look,' he said proudly as he put it on the ground. Then, to Willie's surprise, the chestnut ran away.

'Come back!' Willie shouted after it. 'Where are you going?'

'Back to its mother, I should think,' laughed Dewy. 'Don't you know a young hedgehog when you see one?'

'Of course I do,' said Willie, pretending he had known all along. 'But I'm really glad I didn't try to peel it!'

MAY 6

The Fable of the Greedy Fox

Some shepherds found what they thought was a safe hiding place for their dinner. They put it in the bottom of a hollow tree and went off with their sheep. They planned to return for it later in the day.

A hungry fox happened to pass by that particular hollow tree that morning. It didn't take him long to smell out the hidden food. He pulled in his sides and squeezed through the narrow gap that opened into a hollow inside the trunk. He gobbled up every scrap of food there was. He didn't leave a single crumb. And then he tried to squeeze back the way he had come. He couldn't. He had eaten so much, he found it impossible to pull his sides in far enough to squeeze back through the narrow gap. He was stuck inside the tree.

When the shepherds returned, they decided to leave the greedy fox stuck there until he grew thin again.

MAY 7

A Saying from Siam (Part 1)

In olden times in the Kingdom of Siam, the people had a saying or proverb: 'Take care! For who can tell an honest man from a poisonous snake?' The saying was made up by a wise King and there is a story which explains it.

The King had six sons, all of them strong young men. One day the son who proved himself the best prince would rule over the largest portion of the Kingdom. Four of the sons were happy with this arrangement, but two were angry.

'We could take as much land as we wanted if our father didn't stop us,' they complained. So, strolling in the palace gardens, they plotted ways to kill the King.

Now, curled around the trees and creeping through the undergrowth in the gardens was a pink and black snake called Singalu. He had a vicious-looking tongue and a sharp eye but really he was harmless. When he heard the plans of the wicked princes he decided to protect the King.

The next night the snake lay in wait and soon heard voices whispering. The two princes were bringing a tree into the King's fruit garden. Singalu watched while they dug up an orange tree and planted another tall shrub in its place.

'There,' they whispered. 'Father will see this new tree and try the fruit. The poison will work quickly and kill him. Then we may take all the land we want.'

When the princes left, Singalu slithered up to the tree. It had small yellow fruits, like tropical oranges. People would surely want to taste them and Singalu wondered how he could save the King's life.

MAY 8

A Saying from Siam (Part 2)

Two princes were plotting to kill their father, the King. The snake, Singalu, overheard their plan to poison the King with the fruit from a shrub they had planted.

Walking in his garden the next morning, the King saw the new shrub. 'I must try this golden fruit,' he cried. As he stretched out his hand he saw a snake curled round the tree. Singalu's tongue shot out and the King drew back. Then the clever snake knocked some fruit off the tree. It split open and the juice ran out on to the ground. The green grass shrivelled up where it fell.

'Good snake,' exclaimed the King. 'I believe you have saved me from harm.' He ordered his gardeners to remove the tree at once.

Singalu followed the wicked princes and listened to their plans. The next night, when he retired to his bedroom, the King had another surprise. His room was the highest in the palace and looked out over all the Kingdom. There was a balcony where the King liked to enjoy the view. That night, he saw the pink and black snake curled round the rail of the balcony.

'Have you come with another warning?' the King asked. At once, Singalu unwound himself and the King looked closely at the rail. It had been carefully cut in two pieces. If the King had leant against it, he would surely have fallen to his death.

'You have saved my life again,' the King said. 'But who, I wonder, is planning to harm me? I believe that you, my good snake, must know the answer. I shall call my sons to help me solve this dreadful puzzle.'

Singalu lay quietly on the floor. What trouble might follow when the King sent for his sons? The snake knew he must think quickly and make a plan.

MAY 9

A Saying from Siam (Part 3)

Singalu the snake had twice saved the King's life. Now the King planned to bring his sons together to find out who was trying to kill him.

In the Great Hall of the palace, the six princes came to meet the King. They stood before him in line and he told them of the danger he was in. The two wicked princes pretended to be astonished like the rest. As they talked angrily amongst themselves, Singalu slid quietly across the floor and in a flash twisted himself round the feet of the two evil sons.

At once, the other princes drew their swords and would have cut off Singalu's head. But the King raised his hand. 'Stop!' he cried aloud. 'This is a good and loyal snake.' Then he thought for a moment and continued speaking: 'But it is a most poisonous creature. One touch of its tongue and you will certainly die.'

'Forgive us, father, forgive us,' cried the wicked princes in terror. 'We made evil plans against you. But you cannot let this poisonous snake kill us.'

'He is not poisonous,' replied the King slowly,

'although he appears to be. You are not honest, although you appeared to be. I say to all my people: Take care! For who can tell an honest man from a poisonous snake?'

At that moment Singalu untwisted himself from the legs of the two princes. They fell to the ground, weeping like the cowards they were.

'Good snake, you are more of a son to me than these two villains,' cried the King. 'They are banished from Siam. I shall never look on their faces again.' So it was. The two sons left Siam and Singalu lived a happy life in the palace gardens for the rest of his days.

MAY 10

Parsley the Singing Pig

Parsley Pig packed his belongings and waved goodbye to his friends. 'If you won't let me sing,' said Parsley, 'then I shall leave home and go where no one will hear me.'

'We do love you, Parsley,' said his friends. 'We just can't stand your awful singing.'

Parsley headed for the forest and as he walked he started to sing. His awful voice carried through the trees. All the birds put their wings over their ears.

Suddenly Parsley spotted a key by the side of the forest path. 'A key,' he sang. 'I've found a key down by a tree.' The forest animals dived underground to muffle the noise. Then Parsley came to a house. 'A house,' Parsley sang. 'What a fine house for a pig or a mouse.'

'What's that terrible noise?' said a voice from inside the house.

'I was only singing,' said Parsley, rather hurt.

'Well stop it and bring me that key,' said the voice. Parsley went inside the house and there he saw an old woman.

'Come with me,' she said. 'That's the key to my attic. I've been looking for it for ages.'

The old woman opened the attic door. 'Here's a reward for finding the key,' she said and gave Parsley a wooden box. 'Take it home and you can sing as much as you like. No one will mind.'

Parsley took the box home and opened it up. It was a record-player. Now Parsley buys records and, though he still sings as badly as ever, no one can hear him over the sound of the music.

MAY 11

The Fable of the Spendthrift and the Swallow

Once there was a man who was a spendthrift. He had wasted a fortune by spending foolishly and never gave a thought to what the future might bring. All he had that he could call his own were the clothes he stood up in.

One day, in early Spring, when the sun was shining and the air felt warm, he saw a solitary swallow.

'The swallows are here. That means Summer is coming,' he said. He took off his coat and sold it to the first person who came along. 'Nobody needs a coat in the Summer,' he said. He spent the money he received for it at once.

But then, as so often happens in early Spring, when the weather changes from warm to cold, and back again like a see-saw, there was a sharp and bitter frost. It turned everything white and froze the ponds. The cold was so severe it killed the swallow.

The spendthrift saw the bird's frozen body lying on the ground. 'Miserable bird,' he shivered, as he tried to keep himself warm. 'Because of you I sold my coat and now I am freezing too.'

MAY 12

Hansel and Gretel (Part 1)

Once upon a time there was a girl called Gretel and a boy called Hansel. One night they overheard their father and stepmother talking.

'We would be much better off if we only had two mouths to feed,' said their stepmother. 'Tomorrow you must take the children to the forest and leave them there.' She grumbled so much about being poor that their father agreed to do as she asked. Gretel began to cry.

'I'll take care of you,' whispered Hansel and when everyone was asleep he crept outside and filled his pockets with white pebbles.

The next day their father left them in the forest, saying he would come back for them later. The children waited and waited. They waited so long that the moon rose above the trees and cast a blue light across the ground, and then Gretel saw a trail of white pebbles leading from the clearing. Unnoticed, Hansel had dropped them, one by one, along every path they had followed and now the way home was clear.

That night they heard their stepmother talking to their father again. 'A fine mess you made of that,' she said. 'Make sure you take them to the very heart of the forest tomorrow. We don't want them finding their way home again.'

'I'll gather more pebbles,' whispered Hansel, but when he went to fill his pockets he found the door of the cottage locked and bolted.

The next day everything happened as it had done before, except that this time, instead of pebbles, Hansel left a trail of white bread crumbs. But when the moon rose and the children looked eagerly for the crumbs to show them the way home, they discovered the birds had eaten every one. Now they were really lost!

MAY 13

Hansel and Gretel (Part 2)

Hansel and Gretel had been in the forest three days when they came upon a very strange house. Its walls were made of gingerbread. Its roof was covered with biscuit tiles. Its windows were made of clear toffee. The children broke off pieces of the house and ate them. The old woman who lived there invited them inside.

'How kind you are,' said Gretel. But Gretel didn't realise the woman was a witch. Once inside, the witch pushed Hansel into a cage and locked him in.

'Hee . . . hee . . .' said the witch. 'Now, little girl, you can feed your brother until he is fat enough to eat.' Every day the witch made Hansel eat pies and cakes and custard. She gave Gretel nothing but crusts and gravy.

'Don't worry,' whispered Hansel. 'I won't let her eat me.'

Every day, when the witch ordered him to put out his finger so that she could see how fat he was getting, Hansel pushed a stick through the bars instead. The witch couldn't understand why he stayed so thin and bony. Then one morning she said crossly, 'Get the oven ready, girl. I'm tired of waiting.'

Poor Gretel. The tears rolled down her cheeks as the witch made her stoke up the fire. The oven got hotter and hotter. Poor Hansel. What could she do to save him?

'Climb into the oven and test the temperature,' the witch told Gretel.

'I can't reach,' said Gretel.

'Look. Like this,' said the witch impatiently, getting into the oven. Gretel slammed the oven door shut behind her.

'Let me out!' screamed the witch. Gretel pretended not to hear. She let Hansel out of the cage and they ran into the wood.

They found a path which led them home. Their father was overjoyed to see them and he told them that their stepmother had gone. So the three of them lived happily together.

MAY 14

The Naughty Kittens

Mother Puss was so proud of her three kittens that she decided to take them out for a walk in the park. She groomed them carefully and then she said, 'Now then, Floey, Zoey, Cloey! Pay attention, please! Today we are going for a walk in the park. You must promise me that you'll behave. You must stay close and on no account lose sight of me!'

The kittens gave their promise that they would behave. But once they found themselves in the park, they soon forgot all their promises.

Floey began chasing after the butterflies and Zoey and Cloey scampered away through the long grass in a game of hide-and-seek. In no time at all the three naughty kittens were nowhere to be seen!

When, at long last, Floey grew tired of chasing butterflies and Zoey and Cloey grew tired of hiding from each other in the long grass, they all came together again.

'Where's Mama?' Floey asked. 'Where is she?'

'We don't know,' said her sisters. 'We haven't seen her!'

'Then we're lost,' said Floey. 'We might never see her again!' And she began to cry.

Zoey and Cloey looked at each other and *they* began to cry. Then the rain started to fall and they cried and whimpered louder than ever. Soon Mother Puss heard their cries and came running towards them.

'Naughty kittens!' she said crossly. 'Just look at you! Now follow me closely and I'll take you home.'

Do you know those naughty kittens didn't look to the left or to the right as they went across the park? They never took their eyes away from Mother Puss until they were safely home.

MAY 15

McTavish's Moustache

McTavish had decided to grow the longest moustache in the world. He would stroke it and wax it and curl it as it grew longer and longer.

His wife would say, 'When will you shave off that silly moustache? It'll bring you nothing but trouble.'

McTavish's friends would laugh at the moustache. 'How is your scarf growing?' they would ask, as the moustache reached down to his knees.

One day two birds, looking for something to make their nests with, picked up one end of the moustache each and flew in opposite directions. McTavish howled with the pain. He decided to carry the ends of the moustache in his pockets. 'It will save them catching in my shoe laces,' he said, as the moustache continued to grow.

Then one day there was a great commotion outside. 'A rope . . . a rope . . . someone fetch a rope . . .'

A small boy had fallen down the cliff-side and was hanging on for his life. McTavish rushed to the cliff top and dropped both ends of his moustache over, shouting, 'Grab hold of that, boy.'

While the boy's father held McTavish's ankles, McTavish held his moustache and pulled the boy up to safety. McTavish was a hero and as Mrs McTavish was quick to admit, so was his moustache.

MAY 16

Hidden Magic (Part 1)

The mist was lying over the fields as John the Ploughman took his plough from the barn and set off with his two horses to plough a field that was

overgrown with grass and weeds.

John enjoyed ploughing. He liked to see the plough turn the earth and cut brown furrows that were as straight as lines ruled on paper. As the sun rose higher in the sky, the mist cleared. John whistled happily with the birds.

He had reached the halfway mark and was turning his plough when he heard a strange sound. John knew all the sounds of the fields and anything unusual caught his attention. 'I can hear someone crying,' he said to himself. He left his plough and walked along the hedge, parting the branches and looking deep into it. He could find nobody, but the sound of crying continued. He went

backwards and forwards along the field but no one was to be seen.

'It's not often someone can stay hidden from me,' said John. 'You're a clever rascal wherever you are.' John was about to give up the search when he saw something unusual on a flat stone by the hedge. It was a tiny shovel with a long handle. Picking it up carefully, he saw immediately that the handle was broken.

'Ah, now I understand,' said John. 'A little boy has broken his shovel and he's too shy to ask me to mend it.' John mended the shovel by cutting and stripping a twig with his knife and then fitting it in place of the broken handle. 'I'll just leave it here, and wait to see who comes for it.'

MAY 17

Hidden Magic (Part 2)

John the Ploughman had heard crying in the field where he was ploughing. Then he had found a tiny shovel with a broken handle. He had mended the shovel. Now he waited to see who would collect it.

He waited for half an hour. Now whether it was the heat of the midday sun or whether it was some invisible sleeping powder sprinkled on his eyes, John fell fast asleep.

By the height of the sun when he woke up, John knew he had been asleep only a short time. He yawned, stretched, got up to get on with his ploughing and then remembered about the tiny shovel. He glanced down at the flat stone. Of course, the shovel was gone and he noticed there was no sound of crying.

John smiled to himself as he walked back to his plough. The sleep helped John get on well with his work that day. By evening, the whole field was finished.

He looked on the neatly turned furrows by the light of the setting sun. 'Looks like a bed with a brown corduroy cover,' he said. 'Good enough to sleep in.' He smiled with satisfaction to himself.

On his way home, John happened to walk past the hedge with the flat stone by it. He glanced down at the stone. There, lying in the place where the shovel had been, was a tiny loaf of bread. It smelled so delicious he couldn't resist popping the loaf into his mouth. He couldn't remember eating a tastier morsel.

As he walked home, John started wondering. 'That shovel was rather like ones that bakers use to get bread out of the oven,' he thought. 'Surely it couldn't have been a pixie baker who was crying because he had broken his shovel. I wonder if that loaf was my reward for mending it.'

John never found out whether he was right or wrong, but he smiled at the memory each Spring as he went to plough that field.

MAY 18

The Fable of a Wolf in Sheep's Clothing

A wicked old wolf disguised himself in a sheepskin, then crept amongst a flock of sheep as they were grazing in a field. He planned to wait until it was dark, and then take the fattest sheep for his supper.

The sheep eyed him distrustfully. They knew he wasn't the same as themselves, though they couldn't understand why. The shepherd himself suspected nothing, and when he drove his flock into a pen and shut them up for the night, he drove the wolf in with them.

The wolf waited patiently for darkness to fall. He had already decided which sheep he was going to steal.

As luck would have it, they wanted fresh meat at the farmhouse that night. One of the men was sent to kill a sheep. The wicked old wolf was waiting for it to get a little darker, before he threw off his disguise and stole away with his supper. He was still dressed in his sheep's clothing. The man took him for a real sheep, so it was the wolf who was served for supper that night.

MAY 19

Adventures of *The Tulip* – A Cheeky Cygnet

While Thomas and Wilbur were busy inside their riverboat, *The Tulip*, Minty was outside painting the hull.

Mama Swan and her four baby cygnets were swimming nearby when the last little cygnet saw Minty sitting on the platform with his tail almost touching the water. He paddled off to have a closer look. He couldn't resist pecking Minty's tail.

'You naughty bird,' said Minty. 'Go away!' He prodded the cygnet gently with the end of his paintbrush.

'Mama!' squawked the cygnet.

'Mama!' he cried again.

'Shhhh!' said Minty. 'Stop making such a fuss.'

But Mama Swan had heard. She came paddling up to Minty. 'Don't push my cygnet,' she said, pushing Minty's platform with her bill.

'Don't you push our brother,' said the other little cygnets who had also swum up. Then they pushed the platform from the other side. Minty tried to stand up on the rocking platform and made things worse. First the paintpot fell off, then the paintbrush fell off and then Minty fell off. Splash!

'That's enough, now,' said Mama Swan, picking a waterlogged Minty out of the water and putting him back on the platform. 'Let that be a lesson to you. Come, children.' And off they swam.

Minty heard some giggling above his head. He looked up to see Thomas and Wilbur leaning over the rail.

'Have you been there all the time?' he asked. They didn't reply. They just smiled.

MAY 20

The Owl and the Pussy-cat

The Owl and the Pussy-cat went to sea
In a beautiful pea-green boat.
They took some honey, and plenty of money,
Wrapped up in a five-pound note.
The Owl looked up to the stars above,
And sang to a small guitar,
'O lovely Pussy! Pussy, my love.
What a beautiful Pussy you are,
   You are,
   You are!
What a beautiful Pussy you are!'

Pussy said to the Owl, 'You elegant fowl!
How charmingly sweet you sing!
O let us be married! Too long we have tarried.
But what shall we do for a ring?'
They sailed away, for a year and a day,
To the land where the Bong-tree grows,
And there in a wood a Piggy-wig stood
With a ring at the end of his nose,
   His nose,
   His nose,
With a ring at the end of his nose.

'Dear Pig, are you willing to sell for one shilling
Your ring?' Said the Piggy, 'I will.'
So they took it away, and were married next day
By the Turkey who lives on the hill.
They dined on mince, and slices of quince,
Which they ate with a runcible spoon;
And hand in hand, on the edge of the sand,
They danced by the light of the moon,
   The moon,
   The moon,
They danced by the light of the moon.

MAY 21

The Brave Little Tailor (Part 1)

One day a tailor was sitting at his bench, sewing with his needle and thread. Beside him was a plate and on the plate was a slice of bread and jam. It was his lunch and the sooner he finished sewing the sooner he could eat it. He liked jam spread on bread. He wasn't the only one.

'Jam . . .' buzzed the greedy flies. 'We smell jam.'

'Don't you dare!' shouted the little tailor. He picked up a piece of cloth. 'Take that!' he shouted, and he swatted at the flies as hard as he could. Seven of them fell dead on the table.

'How clever I am!' said the tailor. 'I have killed seven with one blow. I must tell the world about this.' So that the whole world could see how clever he was, he made himself a belt, and on the belt he embroidered the words SEVEN WITH ONE BLOW.

He put some cheese in his pocket in case he got hungry and then he set off. Beside the door, as he went out, was a small brown bird caught in a bush. He untangled it and put it in his pocket with the cheese.

He followed a road that wound round the side of a mountain. At the fourth turn in the road he met a giant carrying a tree.

'Would you like to walk with me and keep me company?' he called.

'Ho ho,' laughed the giant who was as tall as a tree. The brave little tailor barely reached his knees. 'Ho ho. ME walk with YOU. Ho ho ho.'

'Read that!' said the brave little tailor, pointing to his belt. 'And then see if you feel like laughing.'

'SEVEN WITH ONE BLOW,' read the giant. He thought that meant the brave little tailor had killed seven ogres or maybe seven dragons, and he was very impressed. Nonetheless, he decided to test the brave little tailor. After all, it is easy enough to *say* you are brave and strong.

MAY 22

The Brave Little Tailor (Part 2)

A giant decided to test a brave little tailor to see how strong he was. The giant picked up a rock that would have squashed the little tailor had it fallen on him.

'Can you do this?' asked the giant. He squeezed the rock very hard, and finally a tiny trickle of water ran from it.

'That's easy enough,' said the little tailor. He pretended to pick up a stone but he took the cheese out of his pocket. It was soft, squashy cheese. One tiny squeeze and it ran between his fingers in a milky stream.

'Oh!' said the giant. Then he said, 'Can you throw as far as this?' He picked up a small boulder and hurled it with all his might. It flew through the air like a thunderbolt and landed with a thud on the grass, at least half a mile away.

'Easily,' said the little tailor. This time he took the little brown bird from his pocket. It had got over its fright at being tangled in the bush and was glad to be free. When the little tailor tossed it into the air, it flew and flew until it was just a tiny speck in the distance. 'It will fall to the ground sooner or later,' said the tailor.

'If you're that strong,' said the giant, 'you can help me carry this tree home.'

'Glad to,' said the tailor. 'You go in front and take the roots, I'll follow behind and carry the heavy branches.'

The giant lifted the heavy trunk back on to his shoulder. The knobbly roots stuck out in front of him and he didn't see the little tailor leap into the branches behind him.

'Ready when you are!' called the little tailor. He rode all the way to the giant's cave. When they got to the cave the giant lowered the tree and sat down. He didn't see the little tailor jump to the ground. The brave little tailor wasn't a bit out of breath. The giant couldn't believe his eyes. *He* was out of breath. If this little tailor was as strong as he seemed to be then he could be dangerous. He would have to get rid of him.

MAY 23

The Brave Little Tailor (Part 3)

A brave little tailor had tricked a giant into thinking he was strong. The giant decided to get rid of him. 'Come to the cave and meet my brothers,' said the giant slyly. 'You can spend the night with us.'

That night the giant let the brave little tailor sleep in his own bed while he slept on the floor. The bed was just the right size for a giant, but for the brave little tailor it was too big and far too uncomfortable. Each lump in the mattress felt like a small mountain. He could not get to sleep.

At last he crawled into a corner of the cave and fell asleep there. What a good thing he did, for in the night all the giants hit the bed with iron bars. If the brave little tailor had been sleeping in it he would surely have been killed.

The next morning the giants were having breakfast, happy in the thought that the brave little tailor who had killed seven with one blow

was now dead himself. They had the surprise of their lives when the brave little tailor called for his breakfast.

They bellowed with fright and ran from the cave. They ran until they came to the sea and they splashed through that until they reached the land on the far side and they are probably still running.

MAY 24

The Song Contest

Two little birds sat on their favourite stone and had a conversation.

'What do you think?' said one. 'Who's going to win the King's Song Contest?'

'I don't know,' said the other. 'Lark told me he was going to win. He said the King would be certain to choose him. And he is so very handsome!'

'That's funny,' said his friend. 'Warbler told me he was going to win. He went on boasting about his singing for so long that I had to make an excuse and fly away.'

After some more talk the two friends flew off in different directions. Then they met again on the day of the contest.

'There's Warbler,' said one. 'He does look proud and confident.'

'So does Lark,' said the other. 'Sh! We'd better keep quiet. Lark is going to start singing.'

Lark sang quite beautifully. So did Warbler who followed him. The King showed his approval by bowing to each bird in turn. Then, to the audience's surprise, a very ordinary little brown bird asked if she might be allowed to sing.

'Of course,' said the King graciously. The little brown bird opened her mouth and sang with such charm and beauty that there was a stunned silence after she had finished.

'Who is she? Where does she come from?' the two friends asked each other in a whisper.

Then the King spoke. 'The prize goes to my little friend here,' he said. 'Her name is Nightingale and she has just flown in from over the sea. You must agree there is no other who can sing quite like her!'

After that the two little friends flew back to their favourite stone. They had plenty to talk about.

MAY 25

The Piglet and the Gnome

One night a thief stole a fat piglet and put it in a sack. The piglet was heavy and soon the thief was tired and needed a rest. He set the sack down by a tree and soon the thief fell asleep and was snoring loudly.

Now the thief had put the sack right by a hole where a gnome had his house. What with the piglet's squealing and the thief's snoring, the gnome couldn't sleep so he decided to see what was going on.

He untied the sack and the piglet jumped out and ran away. 'I think I'll have some fun here,' said the gnome to himself. He jumped into the sack and waited for the thief to wake up. The thief soon awoke, picked up the sack and set off on his way.

'Well this is a bumpy ride,' said the gnome from inside the sack.

'Who said that?' cried the astonished thief.

'The one riding piggyback inside your sack,' said the gnome. Of course, the thief thought it was the piglet who was speaking.

'I'll have nothing to do with a talking pig,' said the thief, dropping the sack. He ran off, frightened out of his wits.

'I don't think he'll be stealing another piglet in a hurry,' laughed the gnome as he got out of the sack and set off back home.

MAY 26

The Three Billy Goats Gruff (Part 1)

It had been a long winter. Food had been hard to find and the three Billy Goats Gruff were very thin. But now the snow had gone from the pasture and the grass was looking fresh and green.

'I shall go to the top pasture today,' said Little Billy Goat Gruff. 'The grass is always much greener and sweeter up there.'

'Take care the troll doesn't catch you,' said his brother. 'We'll follow you later.'

The only way to reach the top pasture was to cross a stream, and the only way over the stream was by the humpy-backed bridge. Underneath the bridge lived a bad-tempered troll. He had eyes as big as saucers and a nose as long and as sharp as a poker. Everyone was afraid of him, and there was nothing he liked better than eating goat for dinner.

The troll was splashing his feet in the stream when he heard 'tip . . . tap . . . tip . . . tap . . .' above his head.

'Who is that walking over MY bridge?' he shouted.

'It's Little Billy Goat Gruff,' called Little Billy Goat Gruff, trembling like a leaf.

'Then I will have you for my dinner!' roared the troll.

'Don't do that,' pleaded Little Billy Goat Gruff. 'I'm very small and thin. My brother is coming and he is much fatter than I am.'

'Then I will wait and have him for my dinner,' said the troll. 'Be on your way before I change my mind.' Little Billy Goat Gruff did not need telling twice. He skipped off to the pasture as fast as his legs would take him.

The bad-tempered troll went back under the bridge and waited for his dinner to come. Presently, he heard more footsteps tapping across the bridge: 'tip . . . tap . . . tip . . . tap . . .'

'Who is that walking over MY bridge?' he shouted.

'It's Middle Billy Goat Gruff.'

'Then I will have you for my dinner!' roared the troll.

'Don't do that,' pleaded Middle Billy Goat Gruff. 'My brother is coming and he is much fatter than I am.'

'Then I will wait and have him for my dinner,' said the troll. 'Be on your way before I change my mind.'

Middle Billy Goat Gruff didn't need to be told twice either. He quickly joined Little Billy Goat Gruff in the top pasture.

MAY 27

The Three Billy Goats Gruff (Part 2)

The troll was waiting under his bridge for Big Billy Goat Gruff to arrive. The troll sat in the damp and the dark and waited. He was getting very hungry and more and more bad-tempered. At last, he heard footsteps above his head. 'Tip . . . tap . . . tip . . . tap . . .'

'Who is that walking over MY bridge?' he shouted.

'It's Big Billy Goat Gruff.'

'Then I am coming to eat you!' roared the troll.

'Come and try,' shouted Big Billy Goat Gruff.

Out rushed the troll. But what a surprise he had! Big Billy Goat Gruff had long curly horns and a bushy beard hanging from his chin and he was afraid of no one. He caught the troll with his horns and tossed him up into the air. Up . . . up . . . up went the troll. He tossed him so high he almost reached the moon.

Then, while the troll was tumbling through the sky, Big Billy Goat Gruff went to the top pasture and joined his brothers. The troll never came back and from that day onwards it was quite safe to cross the humpy-backed bridge.

MAY 28

The Poor Farmer and his Horse (Part 1)

One evening, Simon's horse lay on the ground, too tired to move. He was still harnessed to the harrow for they had been raking all day.

'Oh, Barney,' said his master, 'get up, old fellow. It'll freeze tonight. I can't leave you here!'

A voice called: 'Simon! Are you there, man?'

'I'm over here! Who is it?' Simon answered. A figure came towards him. It was his old friend Gustav. The two friends hugged one another. They had been through the war together and then had become separated.

'Gustav! Am I glad to see you! Come and help me get my old horse back to the shed.' They put sacks under Barney, so thin and weak, and lifted him on to the harrow. Gustav harnessed Bella, his mare, to the rake and gently they dragged him home.

Simon shared his last crust and piece of cheese with Gustav.

Bella's feed was divided between her and Barney. Over a cup of acorn-coffee, the two friends talked.

'When I came back from the war,' said Simon, 'my land was covered with weeds and thorn bushes. Barney helped me clear it. I thought we'd sow this Spring, but now . . .'

'Yes, things are bad for me too. I'm looking for work. At least Bella is young and strong. Maybe we should team up? What do you say?' They shook hands on it and slept until dawn.

MAY 29

The Poor Farmer and his Horse (Part 2)

Two old friends, Simon and Gustav, had decided to team up and work together. In the morning, Barney seemed a little better. Gustav set off to find some food.

Along the road Gustav met an old woman. 'Good morning,' he called.

'Good morning to you,' she answered. 'Have you seen a donkey anywhere? She's always running off and I need her to get to market.'

'I'll take you to market,' Gustav

offered. 'We might find your runaway.' They soon found the donkey. Gustav tempted her with a carrot, and tied her to the cart. The old woman was delighted. Gustav helped her set out the chickens, butter and eggs. Then he helped serve her customers.

Mother Marley's stall was soon sold out; they were back at the cottage by lunch time. She gave Gustav a good meal and packed food for him to take away – even hay and carrots for the horses. 'You've done more for us than you know,' said Gustav. 'Thank you.'

'If you could help me sometimes, you'd never go

without,' she said.

'I'll come every market day,' promised Gustav, as he waved goodbye. A bright fire welcomed him home. Simon liked hearing about Mother Marley. The food she had sent was delicious. Barney's eyes sparkled as he and Bella crunched their carrots.

Later, rolling into his blanket, Gustav said: 'Simon, if Mother Marley can grow food, so can we. I'll dig a vegetable patch tomorrow, while you knock up a chicken-run.'

'Then we just need hens and seeds,' Simon reminded him. They laughed and went to sleep.

MAY 30

The Poor Farmer and his Horse (Part 3)

Simon was happy to see his horse, Barney, improving each day. He would soon be able to walk up the field. Market day came again. Simon's friend, Gustav, was off to help Mother Marley. He found her sprawled on the floor surrounded by broken eggs. He picked her up.

'Oh, young man,' she sighed, 'I'm too old for this work. What's to become of me?'

'Don't you worry,' he said kindly. 'Something will turn up.' Gustav went to market and sold her goods. She gave him a meal and packed him two sacks of food to take home.

Leading Bella into the shed, Gustav heard Simon shouting: 'Bring a spade, Gustav!' Barney was pawing the ground. 'He's trying to tell me something,' said Simon, starting to dig.

'This is where he lay that evening I came,' said Gustav.

'So it is!' said Simon. 'Hello! What's this?' A coin! . . . Gold! . . . And more! A leather bag spilling treasure! 'I don't believe it!' whispered Simon.

'How did you know, Barney?'

'Where was he during the war?' asked Gustav.

'Here,' Simon answered, 'with an old friend, minding the place. The enemy took over, stealing everywhere. Perhaps Barney saw someone bury all this for safe keeping. Well, it's oats for you tomorrow, Barney,' promised Simon.

'How about buying up Mother Marley's chicken farm?' Gustav suggested. 'She might stay on and cook for us.'

'That's a great idea,' said Simon, and the two friends danced round like children.

MAY 31

Snip and Snap

Early one morning two young mice found themselves stuck in a very small hole. Their names were Snip and Snap and until then they had been the very best of friends. Now, all in a flash, they began blaming each other for the trouble they were in.

'This is all your fault,' said Snip. 'You said the hole would take us into the larder.'

'You saw the hole first,' said Snap. 'You said it must lead somewhere . . .'

After a moment Snip said, 'I always considered you were on the fat side. Why don't you breathe in and make yourself thinner?'

Snap said, 'You give yourself such airs with that fancy necktie, but you haven't got the brains of a beetle!'

Soon, instead of trying to think of a way to escape, the two silly mice were trying to think up clever things to say about each other. And they might have gone on insulting each other if they had not heard a noise they both recognised. They stared about them anxiously.

'Ssh!' whispered Snip. 'It's the cat!' He jerked his head with such force that he suddenly found he could squeeze backwards out of the hole. Shivering with fright, he waited for Snap to join him.

When they were safely back in the cellar, the two looked at each other. 'Best forget what I said,' Snip murmured. 'Didn't mean any of it, of course!'

'I didn't either,' said Snap. 'Let's share that tasty morsel of cheese I stored away for my birthday.' The cheese was very tasty indeed and soon the two were the best of friends again!

JUNE

JUNE 1

The Garden Party

Mogaldy was the most popular elf in Littletown. He was always helping people and cheering them up with his dancing and singing. One morning he was happier than usual. He had received an invitation to the Queen's Garden Party. The Mayor had recommended him as being the most helpful elf in town. In his excitement he leapt on to a wall, lost his balance and fell into a flower bed, twisting his leg. 'Oh dear!' said Fairy Marigold. 'I must call an ambulance.'

'A week in hospital,' said Dr Shinbone, 'and you'll be as good as new.'

Mogaldy groaned, 'What about the Queen's Garden Party?' Dr Shinbone shook his head.

'Never mind,' said Nurse Rosemary, as a big tear slid down Mogaldy's cheek.

The next day Mogaldy wrote a letter to the Queen to say he wouldn't be able to come and then he settled down and tried to be a helpful patient.

The day of the Garden Party came and Mogaldy tried not to think about it but suddenly, at four o'clock exactly, the doors flew open and in stepped the Fairy Queen and all the party-goers, wearing paper hats and party clothes. Some carried large trays of delicious party food.

'You couldn't come to my party,' said the Queen, 'and you are such a good elf that I have brought my party to you.' Mogaldy couldn't believe his eyes; it was so exciting. Everyone joined in and it was such a success that the Queen promised that she would have a party at the hospital every year.

JUNE 2

Chuffa to the Rescue (Part 1)

'Come on, men. We've got to get this load to Woodville,' says Mr Driver as Chuffa is being loaded with logs of wood. Chuffa wonders if he will be able to pull such a weight. At least he'll try.

'Ch-uffa-chuff, ch-uffa-chuff.' Very slowly Chuffa pulls out and chuffs his way along the track. It's a strain, but in the end they make it to Woodville station, with Chuffa's boiler nearly bursting.

'Well done, Chuffa,' says Mr Driver, as the logs are unloaded and at last they can rest.

So the days passed, with Chuffa working hard and feeling happy because he was useful. But then he came home from work one day to see a brand new engine in his siding. It was a huge, gleaming, powerful engine and it was much too important to speak to little Chuffa.

'That's Samson,' said the signalman. 'He's going to take old Chuffa's place.'

JUNE 3

Chuffa to the Rescue (Part 2)

Chuffa had been replaced by a powerful new engine called Samson. Samson could pull ten times the weight of logs that Chuffa could pull. Samson was never late; he didn't spend time saying hello to the birds and animals or stopping to give anyone a lift as Chuffa did.

Chuffa just stayed in his siding all summer. There he stood as the rains came. The rivers were beginning to fill and overflow with all the rain. The wood-cutters were sheltering in a log cabin. Suddenly the foreman burst in. 'Hey fellas,' he cried. 'We've been called out for an emergency. The bridge at Redwood River is being washed away by the floods. If it goes, we'll all be cut off. We've got to try and fix it.'

The woodcutters ran down to the railway sidings and loaded up Samson's trucks with logs.

The rain poured and poured, covering the railway track in water. 'Come on, men, hurry!' shouted the foreman. Finally Samson was loaded. Mr Driver started him up. Samson's wheels turned and turned, but the engine wasn't moving.

'We're skidding in all this water,' shouted Mr Driver. Try as he might, Samson couldn't move backwards or forwards. His wheels just went whizzing round. The huge, gleaming, powerful engine was completely stuck.

JUNE 4

Chuffa to the Rescue (Part 3)

'Suppose we ask Chuffa to help,' suggested Mr Driver as Samson, the super new engine that had replaced Chuffa, was stuck in the rain.

'All right,' said the foreman, 'but hurry.'

Mr Driver went over to Chuffa and explained what had happened. 'It's an emergency, old friend. Do you think you can help?' Chuffa gave a whistle, which meant he would try. The men quickly uncoupled the trucks full of logs, attached them to Chuffa and, slowly to start with, Chuffa moved off. Samson was so cross he blew up his boiler! What a shame!

Chuffa went along faster and faster with his load. They soon reached Redwood Bridge. It had nearly collapsed. The men set to work. First they had to fix the supports, then they had to repair the railway track on top. It was hard and dangerous work; they might have been washed away by the river at any time. Finally they fixed it and the bridge was strong enough to take the weight of a small engine like Chuffa.

Chuffa was told to take Samson's place. 'We can't have an engine we can't rely on,' said the signalman. 'Anyway, Chuffa's just right for this line.'

'Chuffa-chuff,' said Chuffa, as he chuffed along the track and all his friends waved to him. He was so pleased to be back.

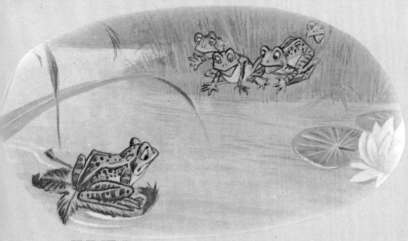

JUNE 5

Freddy Frog

A little frog upon a leaf
Went sailing down the river;
His friends all playing on the bank
Saw Freddy shake and shiver.

He knew the river's water fast
Would take him to the sea.
'Jump, jump!' they cried. 'You silly frog!
It's easy as can be.'

'I can't, I can't!' he cried in fear,
'I'm scared and I'm not clever.'
'You must, you must!' they called again.
'Make haste! It's now or never!'

A handsome swan, quite fond of frogs,
Came gliding close to catch him;
'A tasty morsel, I declare!'
And stretched his neck to snatch him.

Then Freddy knew he had to jump.
'I will not be his dinner!'
He flung himself into the air –
His leap, it was a winner.

'I can, I can,' he laughed with glee
And swam and swam delighted,
Back to his friends upon the bank
All dancing and excited.

JUNE 6

The Fable of the Mice and the Weasels

There was a war going on between the mice and the weasels. The mice lost every battle they fought, and their ranks were getting smaller and smaller.

'We must do something before we are all killed,' said one of those who were left. 'We never win a battle because we never plan our action. We need generals to tell us what to do, and generals to lead us when we go into battle.'

The other mice agreed that he was right and they elected four generals. The generals decided to wear plumed helmets and large badges of office so that everyone knew who they were. They looked very grand and they felt very important.

The generals plotted and planned, and the next time the weasels attacked, they put on their plumed helmets and led the mice into battle.

The mice fought better than they had ever done before, but the weasels were far too clever for them and the generals had to give the order to break ranks and run. The mice ran quickly to their holes and were safe. The generals ran too, but they were so weighed down by their plumed helmets and badges of office that they were the last to reach the holes. The weasels caught them all and the generals wished they had not been so vain.

JUNE 7

The New Coat (Part 1)

Pimm Pixie was rolling up cobweb thread in the brambles one day, when his coat caught on a thorn and tore from the collar right down to the hem. It was as open down the back as it was down the front.

'I suppose I could put some buttons on it,' he said, 'but then everyone would think I had my head on back to front. I think it's time I had a new coat.'

He went to see the pixie tailor. 'I want a new coat, exactly like this one,' said Pimm.

'I'll be glad to make it for you,' said the tailor.

'But I would like it made up in a different shade of green this time . . . I like the shade you are wearing.' The tailor wrote, 'Colour, emerald green,' on his note pad.

'When will it be ready?' asked Pimm.

'Tomorrow, if I start straight away,' said the tailor, and he went to the shelf and took down a roll of emerald green cloth.

'Ummmm,' said Pimm thoughtfully. 'Perhaps that blue would be better.'

The tailor put down his scissors. 'If you want your coat finished by tomorrow,' he said, 'you must make up your mind quickly.'

'I'll go away and think about it,' said Pimm. Before he reached the door he turned and said, 'I've thought already. Make it in red.'

'Very well . . . if you're quite sure,' said the tailor.

Pimm said he was sure, but five minutes later he was back. 'I've changed my mind. I'll have it made in yellow.'

'I do wish you'd make up your mind,' sighed the tailor.

'I am making up my mind,' said Pimm. 'I've made it up four times already.'

The tailor put all the rolls of cloth on the table. 'Now which is it to be?' he said.

'The trouble is,' wailed Pimm, 'I like all the colours. It really is very difficult to choose just one.'

'Then leave the choice to me,' said the tailor, 'and come back in the morning.'

JUNE 8

The New Coat (Part 2)

Pimm the pixie hardly slept a wink all night wondering what colour cloth the tailor would use to make his new coat. Next morning, as soon as it was light, he went and stood on the tailor's doorstep. It was hours before the tailor opened the door. At nine o'clock precisely, by the dandelion

clock, he unbolted the door and let Pimm in.

'Is it finished? What colour did you use? Let me see it. Oh, I do hope you used the right colour!'

'Which colour is the right colour?' asked the tailor.

'I don't know . . . if only I did know . . .' wailed Pimm. He could hardly bear to look as the tailor uncovered the coat. What could he say if he didn't like the colour the tailor had chosen? But what a surprise he had. He gasped. He clapped his hands together in joy. He jumped on to the table and danced a jig. He beamed from ear to ear. The point on his hat curled and uncurled by itself. The tailor looked pleased.

'Oh, what a clever tailor you are!' exclaimed Pimm. The tailor blushed with pleasure.

'Try it on for size,' the tailor said. It fitted perfectly.

'Thank you . . . thank you . . . thank you . . .' sang Pimm, as he danced off down the street. The clever tailor had used a piece of cloth from each roll and had made him a coat that was all the colours of the rainbow!

JUNE 9

Adventures of *The Tulip* – A Swimming Lesson

Thomas, Wilbur and Minty decided to pull their riverboat, *The Tulip*, into the bank and stop for a swim. Now, Thomas and Wilbur are very good swimmers but Minty can't swim a stroke and always wears his yellow life jacket aboard *The Tulip*.

'Will you teach me to swim?' asked Minty.

'You'll have to take your life jacket off,' said Wilbur.

They found some shallow water and while Thomas held Minty round his middle, Wilbur showed him how to kick his legs.

'I'm swimming,' cried Minty. 'Let me go, Thomas. I'm swimming.' Thomas let go. Minty sank like a stone. Thomas pulled Minty out of the water.

They tried again and again and again but each time, Minty sank to the bottom.

'At least you're not frightened of getting wet all over,' said Thomas. 'But I don't think you were meant to swim.'

'Perhaps he could swim with his life jacket on,' suggested Wilbur. Minty buckled on his life jacket and waded straight into the water.

'I'm floating! I'm floating!' he cried as the water lifted him off his feet.

'Kick your legs!' said Thomas. Minty made a terrific splash and for some reason he began to turn round in a circle.

'I'm swimming,' cried Minty.

'That's not what I call swimming,' laughed Thomas. 'That's what I call bobbing!' Minty didn't care if it was bobbing. Now he could have as much fun as the others.

JUNE 10

Little Red Hen

Little Red Hen lived on a farm. One day she found some grains of wheat. She was just about to gobble them up when she had an idea. She would turn the grains of wheat into a loaf of bread.

'Who will help me plant these grains of wheat?' asked Little Red Hen.

'Not I,' said her friend the duck. 'I want to swim in the pond.'

'Not I,' said her friend the pig. 'I want to roll in the mud.'

'Not I,' said her friend the cat. 'I want to sleep in the sun.'

'Then I will do it alone,' said Little Red Hen.

Soon, the thin green buds changed into plump golden grains of wheat.

'Who will cut the wheat?' asked Little Red Hen.

'Not I,' said the duck.

'Not I,' said the pig.

'Not I,' said the cat.

'Then I will do it alone,' said Little Red Hen. 'Who will grind the wheat into flour?'

'Not I,' said the duck.

'Not I,' said the pig.

'Not I,' said the cat.

'Then I will do it alone,' said Little Red Hen. 'Who will make the flour into bread?'

'Not I,' said the duck.

'Not I,' said the pig.

'Not I,' said the cat.

'Then I will do it alone,' said Little Red Hen.

The wheat was ground into flour. The flour was made into bread.

'Who will help me eat the bread?' asked Little Red Hen.

'I will,' said the duck.

'I will,' said the pig.

'I will,' said the cat.

'Oh no, you won't,' said Little Red Hen. 'I found the grains of wheat. I cut the wheat when it was ready. I ground the ripe wheat into flour. I made the flour into bread and I am going to eat the bread myself.'

And so she did.

JUNE 11

The Princess
and the Parasol (Part 1)

What would Princess Sing Cha Lu want for her tenth birthday? Her parents, the King and Queen of Tai Tuan, loved her dearly and would give her anything but she seemed to care for no one but herself.

When she went anywhere in her rickshaw she made her servants race as fast as they could. As they ran through the market place the stalls would be knocked to the ground, their fruit and flowers trampled underfoot.

When the Princess went to the rice fields with her pet dogs she would let them run among the growing shoots. The rice crops were ruined.

'One day,' the people would say, 'one day little Sing Cha Lu will grow into a fine princess.'

Sing Cha Lu's birthday drew near. She was walking in the royal gardens wondering whether she would ask for a gown of peacock feathers or a fine golden chain for her hair, when she felt the heat of the sun. She raised her parasol to shade her head and to her surprise the parasol turned inside out. A great gust of wind lifted her off her feet and high into the air. She held on tightly to the parasol as she sailed over the palace walls.

'Let me down!' she cried. 'I'm the Princess of Tai Tuan. Let me down!' Then she heard strange voices.

'We are the Spirits of Earth, Air, Fire and Water. We shall take you where we will.'

JUNE 12

The Princess
and the Parasol (Part 2)

Princess Sing Cha Lu had been whisked off into the sky by the Spirits of Earth, Air, Fire and Water.

'Let me go home,' she cried, as she and her parasol flew over a little wooden house. Sitting outside was a girl of her own age, very thin and pale.

'Who is that little girl?' said the Princess.

'She is not well,' said the Spirit of the Air. 'She has had no food since her parents' market stall was destroyed by a rickshaw racing through the market place.'

'That was my rickshaw,' thought the Princess.

'She does not complain,' said the Spirit.

Then the wind lifted the Princess away until she circled over an old man. 'He looks very weak,' said the Princess.

'He lives on rice,' said the Spirit of the Earth, 'but the rice crop failed this year. Some dogs got into the fields.'

'Those were my dogs,' thought the Princess.

'He does not complain,' said the Spirit.

The wind blew the Princess and the parasol back to the palace. As soon as her feet touched the ground the Princess ran to the King. 'Father,' she said, 'I want three things for my birthday.'

The King's heart sank. Whatever treasures would she request? 'Yes, my dear?'

'I want a new market stall for the parents of a little girl I know, a sack of rice for an old man I've met, and a day's holiday for everyone in Tai Tuan.'

When the people of Tai Tuan heard of the birthday plans they all agreed: 'Now we can say our little Sing Cha Lu has grown into a fine princess.'

JUNE 13

Muff and Fluff

Muff and Fluff were two tiny kittens. They lived in one room and they loved the soft red carpet. They were used to the patterned wallpaper on the walls. They liked to lie and look up at the clean white ceiling above their heads.

Their mistress would say, 'You'll love it when you can go outside. Soon you will be big enough.' What would it be like "outside", they wondered.

At last, the back door was opened. Muff and Fluff were let out into the yard. 'I don't like it,' whispered Muff. 'There's no carpet, just stones under our paws.'

'There are no patterns on the walls,' complained Fluff.

'And look,' cried Muff in surprise. 'The ceiling is moving. And it keeps changing colour from blue to white!'

The kittens were frightened. Then Muff had an idea. 'The walls don't reach the ceiling,' she said to Fluff. 'We could climb over the walls and then we'd be really outside.' So they climbed over the garden fence and into the field beyond.

This was much better. They ran to play on a soft green carpet of grass. They saw the patterns made by the flowers. They sharpened their paws on tree trunks. Then they saw a stream. 'It's water!' cried Fluff. 'But it's moving. Our drinking water always sits still in our bowls. Shall we see where it's going?' The two kittens ran down the hill beside the stream.

Then it began to rain. 'Oh dear,' Fluff complained. 'The ceiling's leaking and we're getting wet.' So they hurried back home to dry by the fire.

'Did you like it outside?' their mistress asked.

'If only we could explain,' thought Muff. 'It would be fine outside if someone would mend the ceiling!'

JUNE 14

The Fable of the Trees and the Axe

A woodman went into a forest and asked the trees if he could cut one of them down to make a handle for his axe.

Most of the trees had been in the forest a long time. They were sturdy and strong, and so big that no one had arms long enough to go round them. They considered themselves noble and important. It was they who made the decision.

'Yours is a very modest request,' they said. 'You may take that young sapling which stands by itself.' They nodded towards a young ash tree which had not had time to grow to the thickness of a man's wrist. The ash was not given a chance to speak for itself.

The woodman thanked the trees for their kindness and cut down the ash before they had time to change their minds. He made a fine strong handle for his axe.

No sooner was the new handle fixed to his axe than he set to work. This time he did not ask for permission and showed no mercy. He cut down every tree that stood in his path – big and small alike.

At that very moment, when they saw what was about to happen to them, the trees said sadly, 'It is our own fault that we are to die. By sacrificing the life of a tree smaller and weaker than ourselves we have lost our own lives. Had we defended the sapling's right to live, we would have lived on for years ourselves.'

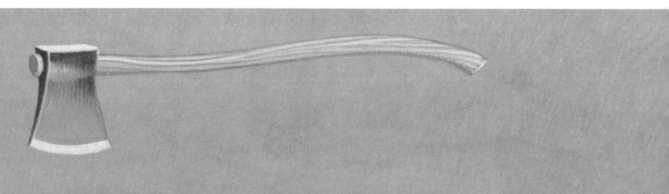

JUNE 15

The Silly Billies

'Some creatures make me laugh,' said Brown Bird to Lord Pan, the God of the Woods. 'They are never content. They always want to be someone else.'

'Yes,' grinned Pan. 'I call them the silly billies. Look! Here they come now.'

Leading them all was Mouse who wanted to be a squirrel and had stuck a brush to his tail. Then Cat arrived wearing striped pyjamas. He wanted to be a tiger.

Brown Bird laughed. 'Ha! Ha! There goes Donkey with an ice-cream cornet stuck to his forehead. He wants to be a unicorn.'

'Look up in the air!' cried Pan. 'It's Bald Eagle wearing a lady's wig!'

Then they saw Parrot up in a tree with a feather duster tied to his tail. Brown Bird laughed even louder. 'Ha! Ha! She thinks she's a fan-tailed pigeon.'

'And here comes the funniest one of all.' said Pan. 'A man waddling over to the lake wearing black flippers on his feet. There he goes under the water. He thinks he's a duck. The ducks will die laughing.'

When they had all gone, Brown Bird said, 'I'm perfectly happy to be as I am. No one can call me a silly billy. I mean, I always behave in a very normal way.' Then he yawned. 'Oh well. It's time to rest. I must have my beauty sleep.' And he hung upside down on his branch and went to sleep.

'Well! Bless my soul!' laughed Pan. 'He thinks he's a bat! What a silly billy!'

JUNE 16

Moving Castles

King Merry and King Mean-and-lazy lived on opposite sides of the world but they had one thing in common: they both wanted a new castle. King Merry had so many children that they had nowhere to play in his neat, clean, little castle in Brightshine Land; while King Mean-and-lazy's big castle was falling apart. The roof leaked, the doors were hanging off their hinges and, because he was too lazy to do any housework and too mean to pay servants, it was very dirty with cobwebs everywhere.

One day King Mean-and-lazy found a very old book in a cupboard. He brushed the dust from the cover and read the title: 'How To Move Castles By Magic'.

'What a lucky find,' he said. 'With this book I shall be able to magic this horrible, dirty, old castle to Brightshine Land and magic King Merry's nice, little castle here in its place. Then I'll burn the book and King Merry won't be able to magic them back again.' King Mean-and-lazy sat on his throne and spent the whole night reading the book from cover to cover.

The next morning King Merry and his children were eating their breakfast when their castle rose into the air and flew away, leaving them sitting round the table in the open air. But before they had time to gasp in surprise they found King Mean-and-lazy's castle had arrived in its place.

'Ugh! What a horrible, dirty, old castle!' all the children cried, when they had recovered from the shock.

King Merry looked round the castle. 'There'll be plenty of room for you to play in,' he said cheerfully. 'All it needs is cleaning and mending.'

King Merry and his children set to work with hammers and nails, scrubbing-brushes, paint-brushes and pots of paint. In no time at all the castle was as neat and clean as their old one. The children were delighted.

King Mean-and-lazy's little castle soon began to fall apart. He was too lazy to do any work himself and too mean to pay servants. Before long the roof leaked, the doors were hanging off their hinges and it was very dirty with cobwebs everywhere. What's more, he had burnt the book so he couldn't magic his old castle back.

89

JUNE 17

Hans and the Magic Sticks

Hans lived in a hut near the forest on the mountain slopes. Holiday visitors came to buy his soup and famous flip-flaps. These were cookies, baked over an open wood fire. No one made flip-flaps like Hans .

One day his fire wouldn't burn – it stayed dull and smoky. 'Come on!' he grumbled. 'What's wrong?'

'Wrong sticks, perhaps,' said a voice. An old traveller stood in the doorway.

'Wrong sticks?' Hans repeated. 'I always use these . . . But come in. Have some soup.' The old man sat down.

'Try these,' he said, giving Hans a small bundle of sticks. Immediately they made the fire clear and red-hot. The old man finished his soup and ate several flip-flaps.

'Are your sticks magic?' Hans asked. 'They last so long!'

'Maybe,' chuckled the traveller. 'I'll tell you where to find them; but you must tell me how to make flip-flaps.'

'Oh no, sir!' cried Hans. 'I can't! The recipe is a family secret. I promised my father I'd only ever tell my son.' The old man walked out.

The next day Hans's fire smoked even worse. Again the traveller came offering sticks. Again the fire cleared and Hans gave him soup and flip-flaps.

'Have you changed your mind?' asked the man.

'No, sir,' said Hans. 'A promise is a promise. I'll make *you* a promise. Every time you bring sticks I'll give you a good meal. How's that?'

They agreed and every week the traveller brought sticks. Suddenly his visits stopped; but Hans found his bundle near the hut. Inside was a note: 'These sticks will last, Hans. I keep promises too.'

So, if you ever find Hans's hut, you'll see his fire burning brightly and you'll love his buttered flip-flaps.

JUNE 18

Carlo's Panda

This story is about a little boy called Carlo who wanted a big teddy bear for his birthday.

'You will just have to wait and see,' said his father. 'But I'm sure your Aunt Petra said she was going to give you a teddy bear.'

Well, at his birthday party there were all kinds of packages for Carlo to open.

'I'll open Aunty Petra's present last,' he told his friends. 'It's going to be a teddy bear. It's the right shape. And it feels soft and cuddly.' When Carlo opened the parcel it wasn't a teddy bear at all! It was a panda! Carlo was so disappointed that he threw the panda on a chair and wouldn't look at it.

As soon as his father came home that night, Carlo told him all about his disappointment. His father got out a big book about wild animals and he showed Carlo a picture of a real giant panda.

'Pandas are really very special,' said his father. 'I'll take you to see a panda one day when we visit the zoo. Their real home is in the bamboo forests of China.'

'And they eat bamboo shoots,' said Carlo, suddenly remembering something he had learnt at school. Carlo picked up his panda and cuddled it. 'Do you think pandas are as special as teddy bears?' he asked.

'Of course they are,' said his father smiling. 'They're just as special.'

'Then I'm glad I've got a panda after all!' said Carlo happily. 'I'll probably take him to school tomorrow and show him to everyone.'

JUNE 19

The Giant and the Cobbler (Part 1)

Once there was a grumpy giant who didn't like anyone very much. More than anyone else he disliked the people who lived in the town of Shrewsbury. One day, he made up his mind he would get rid of them all.

Running close by the town of Shrewsbury there was a river. 'I'll dam the river,' said the giant, 'and flood the town. Then everyone who lives there will drown.'

It is very easy indeed for someone as big as a giant to dam a river. All he has to do is lift a spadeful of earth – a giant spade of course – and drop the earth in the right place. The giant was really rather stupid. Instead of waiting until he got to Shrewsbury before filling his spade with earth, he filled it with earth outside his own cave.

It was a hot day, and even giants get tired, especially when they are carrying a lot of crumbly earth they are trying hard not to spill. Somehow he lost his way. He sat down beside the road, holding the spade of earth, and waited for someone to come and tell him which direction to take.

Presently, a cobbler, who had been to Shrewsbury himself to collect all the boots and shoes that needed mending, came by.

'Hello there!' boomed a voice high above the cobbler's head. 'How far is it to Shrewsbury?'

The cobbler was surprised, but he wasn't one to frighten easily and he thought to himself, 'What can a giant like that be doing with a spadeful of earth like that . . . he's up to no good, I'll be bound.' Aloud he said, 'Why do you want to know?'

'I'm going to dam the river and flood the town so that all the people who live there will drown,' said the giant.

JUNE 20

The Giant and the Cobbler (Part 2)

A cobbler had met a giant who had lost his way. The giant was carrying a spadeful of earth and was on his way to build a dam to flood the town of Shrewsbury. 'Something must be done about this . . . and quickly,' thought the cobbler.

'Do you know how far it is to Shrewsbury?' he asked.

'I do not,' said the giant.

'I've just come from there myself,' said the quick-witted cobbler. 'It' been a very tiring journey I must say.' He opened his sack and tipped out all the worn boots and shoes he had collected for mending. 'That's how many boots and shoes I've worn out since I left Shrewsbury,' he said. The cobbler crossed his fingers behind his back because he wasn't telling the truth. The town of Shrewsbury was really just over the next hill.

'I can't possibly carry a spadeful of earth *that* far,' complained the giant.

'If I were you I'd leave it here and go home,' said the cobbler, putting the boots and shoes back into his sack.

'That's good advice,' said the giant, and he tipped the earth off his spade. It fell with a roar, like a cloud-burst of dark brown rain, and when the brown dust had cleared, the cobbler was standing beside a new hill. The giant was scraping his boots with the spade. There was enough earth sticking to them to make a small hill beside the big one. Then the giant went home.

The two hills the giant made are there to this day. So is the town of Shrewsbury, thanks to the quick thinking of a quick-witted cobbler.

JUNE 21

Andora

There was once a horse-thief called Snatcher. He travelled the country stealing and selling horses. One day he saw a poster on a wall announcing that the circus was coming. It showed a pretty lady on a beautiful white horse.

Snatcher thought, 'I could sell a horse like that for a lot of money.' He attached an empty horse-box to his old grey van and drove to the circus.

That night, Andora, the white horse, pranced around the circus ring with Rosie on his back doing tricks that delighted the crowd. But Rosie was sad because the circus boss had decided to sell Andora the next day.

During the night Rosie got up to say a last goodbye to Andora. Snatcher was standing nearby. He saw Rosie coming. He crept up behind her, put a gag in her mouth and tied her to a post. Then he led Andora into the horse-box and drove away.

Rosie soon struggled free and raised the alarm. 'He's in an old grey van with a horse-box,' she told the police.

When Snatcher saw the police coming he stopped the van and led Andora down the ramp. Then he jumped on. 'Get going!' he snarled. 'Get me out of here!'

But Andora, knowing something was wrong, kept running round and round in a circle. Snatcher became so dizzy that he fell off Andora into the arms of a policeman.

When the circus boss heard about it all, he decided to keep Andora. Now everyone wants to see the clever horse that outwitted the famous horse-thief.

JUNE 22

The Fine Balloon

Jeremy Jakes and Jock McClune
Went flying off in their fine balloon;
They had a passenger – fancy that!
With ears perked up – the next-door cat.

The wind blew fresh out over the sea.
'This basket doesn't agree with me,'
Said the cat as she climbed up, paw on paw;
Spread out on top she saw much more.

Then, suddenly, they shot up high
Through mist and cloud to an empty sky;
They twirled in a world of outer-space
And then bounced down on the moon's rough fac

The next-door cat, she made a move;
Here was something she'd like to prove,
To be the cat, the very first,
To find moon-milk and quench her thirst.

But try as she would, she never could
Make her legs go where they should;
She hovered, bothered, unable to think;
Oh, how she needed a good long drink!

And how would they get their fine balloon
Into the air to leave the moon?
A spaceship arrived marked USA.
A voice called: 'Leave it! . . . Come on! . . . OK?'

So, Jeremy Jakes and Jock McClune
Reached home quite safely one afternoon;
They fried fish fingers – fancy that!
And an extra one for the next-door cat.

JUNE 23

Jumping Jack (Part 1)

Jack started jumping as soon as he could walk; little jumps at first, then bigger and bigger. By the time he had grown up he found it easier and quicker to jump everywhere. 'There goes Jumping Jack,' they would say. 'It's no good trying to keep up with him.'

One day, he made up his mind to leave the village where he had lived all his life and go off into the world. He decided to walk and walk for miles and miles and cure himself of jumping. He said goodbye to his parents.

'I'll be back, mother! I'll make my fortune and get rid of this jumping disease. I don't want to be called Jumping Jack all my life.'

After several miles, Jack saw a stretch of water in front of him. Leaving his shoes on the bank, he paddled in the cool waves. Imagine his horror when he saw, swimming towards him, a huge crocodile! What could he do? There was only one thing he could do – he jumped!

With one leap Jack landed on the other side. Suddenly soldiers advanced from all directions, each armed with a sword. He took another jump – right over their heads! They gazed up in amazement. Jack looked down towards the courtyard where he would land; it stood in front of a splendid palace.

More soldiers rushed up, grabbed him and marched him off to the King. Jack begged His Majesty's pardon and explained that he'd only jumped because he'd been in great danger.

'Quite! Quite!' agreed the King. 'You're the first one Camilla has missed.' Jack gave a shudder at the thought of that terrible crocodile.

Just then the beautiful Princess Arabella entered and spoke to her father. He turned to Jack: 'We have other visitors here, competing for my daughter's hand in marriage. Would you care to join them?'

Jack bowed, first to the Princess and then to the King. 'I would be honoured, Your Majesty.'

JUNE 24

Jumping Jack (Part 2)

Jumping Jack was competing for the hand of the beautiful Princess Arabella. A contest was arranged for that very evening. Jack would have to fence with a prince, in front of the royal family and hundreds of people. It would be difficult and very dangerous.

At first, Jack pranced around keeping himself safe. Then he gave some jumps. The crowd thought him clever and funny. People began to laugh. Soon they were all doubled up with laughter. The King held his sides. He nearly collapsed when Jack leapt over the Prince's head.

'Stop! Stop!' he cried. 'That's enough . . . I can't laugh any more!'

Would the King have Jack thrown to Camilla for making the Prince look stupid? No, Arabella gave him her hand and they danced round the ballroom. She glanced at his feet. 'They're very nimble, but wouldn't they be more comfortable in shoes?' Jack felt ashamed but then he saw her smile.

'Come!' he said and they danced out of the palace to the water's edge. There, Jack lifted Arabella up in his arms and made a flying leap. Camilla's eye gleamed in the light of the moon as she watched them pass over. They landed safely, by the side of Jack's shoes. He put them on and once more jumped his princess back over the water.

Back in the palace, the King made a speech announcing the wedding. Invitations were to be sent to Jack's parents. Jack was to receive a title and the King asked him what name he would like to be called.

'Any name you wish, Your Majesty. I am so happy you could even call me Jumping Jack!'

JUNE 25

Spike in the Wood

One day Spike, the friendly little elf, went for a walk in the woods. He was looking for a friend to have fun with. 'It's such a fine day,' Spike said, 'I'm sure to find a friend who wants to play.'

The very first friend he met was Squirrel. 'Stop and play with me, Squirrel,' Spike said.

'Too busy,' said Squirrel. 'Gathering nuts, you see . . .' And away he ran. Spike tried to chase after him but he got so out of breath that he had to stop. Then he saw Badger snuffling among the leaves.

'Will you stop and play with me, Badger?' Spike said.

'Too tired,' said Badger in a grumpy voice. 'Must get on with making a bed so that I can take a long sleep.'

Just then Mouse ran over his feet, her whiskers twitching. 'Will you play with me?' Spike asked hopefully.

'Certainly not,' Mouse squeaked, looking round nervously. 'Can't you see I'm r-running away?'

'Oh!' said Spike disappointed. 'If you're running away from Owl, it's too early for his supper. He only eats at night . . .' But Mouse had already scampered off.

Spike was sad and on the point of going home when he heard

lots of squeals and giggles and thumps. The rabbit children greeted Spike with cries of delight. 'Come and play with us!' they squealed. 'Show us some new games! Mama doesn't know any!'

Spike began to smile. Now, at last, he had found some friends to play with. He set about teaching the little rabbits one of his favourite games . . . Hide-the-Nut

---

JUNE 26

Cinderella (Part 1)

There was once a girl called Cinderella. She lived with her father and her stepsisters in a huge house. Cinderella was beautiful. Her stepsisters were ugly. Cinderella was kind and gentle. Her stepsisters were unkind. They spent their time trying to make themselves look pretty and they made sure Cinderella spent her time cleaning and washing and

scrubbing so that no one would notice how beautiful she was.

One morning, when Cinderella was scrubbing floors, there was a great commotion. 'Look what we've got,' cried the ugly sisters, dancing round and round the kitchen. 'We've been invited to the King's Ball. We're going to meet the Prince. I dare say he will want to marry one of us.'

'Oh, please may I go to the Ball?' asked Cinderella. The ugly sisters hooted with laughter.

'You? Go to the Ball? How silly you are! You haven't a thing to wear.' That was perfectly true. Poor Cinderella only had a brown, ragged dress and a sackcloth apron. 'And besides, we will need you to help us get ready.'

On the night of the Ball they ordered poor Cinderella this

way and that. 'Fetch that . . . alter this . . . press that . . . tie this . . . find that . . . do it this way . . . undo it . . . do it up . . . stop pulling . . . pull it tighter . . .' Poor Cinderella felt quite dizzy by the time they were ready to go to the Ball.

'Wash the dishes . . . make up the fire . . . have supper waiting,' they called as they swept grandly to their waiting carriage, looking not the tiniest bit beautiful.

Poor Cinderella. She did the chores, then sat beside the fire and wept. She did so want to go to the Ball.

JUNE 27

Cinderella (Part 2)

Cinderella sat crying because she couldn't go to the Ball. Suddenly there was a flash of light and she saw a strange little woman wearing a pointed hat and carrying a wand of dancing stars.

'Do not be afraid,' she said. 'I am your Fairy Godmother. You *shall* go to the Ball.'

'But I have no dress to wear,' said Cinderella sadly. 'I cannot go to the Ball wearing rags.'

'You are not wearing rags now,' said the fairy. She touched Cinderella's tattered brown dress with her wand. She changed it into a beautiful ball-gown and put glass slippers on Cinderella's bare feet.

The fairy called for a pumpkin. She touched that with her wand and turned it into a coach. She turned eight white mice into eight white horses, and six green lizards into six liveried footmen. She turned a rat into the coachman.

'You must be home by midnight,' said the fairy as Cinderella stepped into the coach. 'My magic stops at midnight and your ball-gown will become rags again.'

At the Ball, Cinderella danced with the King's son all evening. He couldn't take his eyes off her. He thought her the most beautiful girl he had ever seen. Cinderella had never been so happy in her life. She was so happy she forgot time was

ticking away and it wasn't until the clock began to strike twelve that she remembered the fairy's warning.

'Wait . . . ' cried the Prince, as she slipped from his arms. 'You haven't told me your name . . . ' There was no time to stop. Cinderella ran from the ball-room without a backward glance. Seven . . . eight . . . nine . . . she lost a slipper as she ran down the palace steps. She did not dare stop to pick it up . . . ten . . . eleven. On the twelfth stroke her beautiful ball-gown became rags and her coach turned back into a pumpkin.

JUNE 28

Cinderella (Part 3)

Cinderella ran home from the Ball, her dress once more in rags. But one thing hadn't changed and that was the glass slipper which lay on the palace steps. It was the Prince himself who found it. He recognised it at once.

'I will marry the girl who can wear this slipper,' he said. 'No matter who she is.' He sent messengers across the land with orders that every girl in the kingdom was to try the slipper. Eventually they came to the house where Cinderella and her stepsisters lived. The ugly sisters were so excited. They snatched the glass slipper from the messenger before he could say a word.

'Look . . . it fits me . . . ' said the first.

'But your heel is hanging out,' said the messenger.

'It fits me . . . it fits me . . . ' said the second ugly sister.

'But your toes are bent double,' said the messenger. Then he asked, 'Is there anyone else who would like to try the slipper?'

Before Cinderella could answer, one of the ugly sisters clapped a hand over her mouth. 'She's only a serving maid . . . the slipper won't fit her.' But the messenger had his orders. Of course the slipper fitted Cinderella perfectly.

'Cinderella shall marry the Prince,' said the messenger.

'It was you . . . it was you who stole the Prince from us!' shouted the ugly sisters, their eyes nearly popping out of their heads. 'It's not fair . . . it's not fair . . .!' They stamped their feet and pouted and sulked. No one took any notice of them at all. There was a royal wedding to plan and that was far more important.

JUNE 29

Twirly Catches the Train

On his way home one day, Twirly, the yellow helicopter, was flying over the railway station when he noticed a lady on the platform waving her arms at him. Twirly went down to see what was wrong.

'Can you help me?' said the lady. 'My little girl, Emma, has just gone off in the train and she has left her suitcase behind. Can you catch up with the train?'

'I'll do my best,' said Twirly, taking the case. Off he flew as fast as he could, following the railway line. Soon he spotted the train. The train guard opened a window as Twirly came near.

'What are you doing up there?' he asked.

'I've got a suitcase for a little girl on the train. Can you give it to her? Her name's Emma.'

The guard took the suitcase and went off with it down the train. Twirly followed the train and as he pulled alongside one of the carriages he saw someone waving at him. It must be Emma. Yes, it was. There was the suitcase beside her. She was shouting something. Twirly couldn't hear her very well through the window but it sounded like 'Thank you'. Emma was smiling up at Twirly.

Twirly smiled back and then off he flew, giving a little twirl in the sky, pleased he had been able to help.

JUNE 30

The Cheeky Little Birds

The little birds couldn't find anything to eat. 'Mother!' they cried. 'We're so hungry and the ground is too hard to find any worms.'

'There! There!' said Mother Bird. 'The lady in the house will soon throw out some crumbs.' Sure enough, when the lady saw the hungry birds, she threw out some crumbs.

The little birds were just about to eat the crumbs when Greedy Dog rushed at them. 'Woof! Woof!' he barked, scaring them away. Then he gobbled up all the crumbs.

The next day the lady threw out some more crumbs. But watchful Mother Bird spotted two staring eyes underneath a bush. 'Look out! It's Fat Cat!' she cried. 'Stay up in the tree!' The hungry little birds had to watch while Fat Cat crept over to the crumbs and ate them all.

Every day the lady threw out crumbs, but if Greedy Dog didn't get them first, Fat Cat gobbled them up. And the little birds grew hungrier and hungrier.

One day when Mother Bird saw Greedy Dog in the garden, she had an idea. She went to look for Fat Cat. When she found her, she pretended to have a broken wing and fluttered about on the ground.

'Aha!' grinned Fat Cat. 'I'll soon catch her now!' But Mother Bird was too quick for Fat Cat, and too clever! She led Fat Cat right back to Greedy Dog who bristled when he saw her.

'Grrr!' snarled Greedy Dog.

'Yeow!' screeched Fat Cat, claws ready.

Well! You never saw such a fight! There were screeches and howls and tufts of fur everywhere! While they fought, those cheeky little birds flew down and ate up all the crumbs. Fat Cat and Greedy Dog never came into the garden again.

JULY

JULY 1

The Bean Pole

Laurie was a happy little girl until she started growing. She grew so tall that everybody thought that she was a grown-up. Laurie didn't like being so tall. She was a young girl. She wanted to play with her toys. But people kept saying, 'You're too big to play with toys.' At parties, all her little friends had dancing partners. But no one wanted to dance with Laurie because she was too tall.

One day, someone said, 'Look at that walking bean pole!' When Laurie began to cry they said, 'Big girls don't cry!'

'But I'm only a little girl inside!' said Laurie. She tried to make herself smaller by pushing her head down and leaning forward. But that only made people laugh. Sometimes she dreamed she was small and had lots of dancing partners. She sighed when she woke up and saw her long legs.

She decided to make the best of it. 'If I can't dance, then I shall learn to play games,' she said. One day, in the park, she saw an old shopping bag hanging from a tree. Laurie threw a ball into the bag and it fell out of the bottom. 'I'll see how many times I can get the ball into the bag,' she said. She got better and better and soon she could throw the ball into the bag every time.

One day, a tall girl said to Laurie, 'You'd make a good basketball player. Will you join our team?' Laurie was very happy because the girls on the team were as tall as she was. She began to straighten up and walk tall. Now she doesn't mind being tall at all!

JULY 2

Little Boots

Little Boots, the Eskimo girl, had gathered some seeds. Her mother painted them with berry juice and sewed them in a pretty design on her new boots. 'Thank you, mother,' said Little Boots.

'I think I'll take my new boots for a walk.'

'Don't get lost!' warned her mother. Little Boots was always getting lost. She loved to chase wild creatures. As soon as she was out of sight, she forgot her mother's warning and chased a white fox. The fox escaped. When Little Boots looked around her, she knew she was lost. It was dark and bitterly cold. She found a hole in the snow and crawled into it. It was the winter home of the snow bird.

'You look so hungry,' said Little Boots to the bird. 'I'm sorry I have no food.' Then she remembered the seeds on her boots. She unpicked every seed and fed them to the snow bird.

Little Boots' mother found her the next morning. Little Boots told her about the hungry bird and the seeds. Her mother smiled. 'I'll sew some new seeds on your boots. I found these ones on our sledge last night.'

Little Boots' eyes shone. 'Perhaps they came from the sky!' she said. It was true. To reward her kindness the Star Spirits had put magic in the seeds. They glowed like the stars, always lighting her way home and she never got lost again!

JULY 3

The Pedlar of Swaffham (Part 1)

Once, long ago, when London Bridge was lined with shops, a pedlar living in the country, far away from London, had a strange dream. He dreamed that if he went to London Bridge he would hear some good news. The first time he had the dream he didn't take much notice of it. The second time he had the dream he began to wonder and the third time he had the dream he decided to make the trip to London Town.

He was too poor to hire a horse and it was a very long walk. His shoes had almost worn out by the time he got there. He walked up and down the bridge for three days waiting to hear what the good news might be. On the third day, one of the shopkeepers who kept a shop on the bridge could bear it no longer.

'I've watched you walk up and down for three days,' he said. 'Have you something to sell?'

'No,' said the pedlar.

'Then are you begging?' asked the shopkeeper, looking at his worn shoes and dusty coat.

'Certainly not,' said the pedlar.

'Then what are you doing?' asked the shopkeeper. The pedlar told him about his dream.

JULY 4

The Pedlar of Swaffham (Part 2)

A poor pedlar had a dream that if he went to London Bridge he would here some good news. He told a shopkeeper on the bridge about his dream.

The shopkeeper hooted with laughter. 'Do you mean to say you have come all this way because of a dream? I dream myself. Why only last night I dreamed that in an orchard behind a pedlar's house in Swaffham, which is a place I've never even heard of, there is an oak tree, and under the oak tree there is buried treasure . . . now do you think I would be so foolish as to leave my shop and go all the way to a place I've never heard of, just because I had a dream . . . Hey . . . Where are you going?'

'Home,' called the pedlar over his shoulder.

'What a strange fellow,' said the shopkeeper and went back to his shop, shaking his head. How was he to know that the pedlar lived in a place called Swaffham and that there was an orchard behind his house?

As soon as he got home, the pedlar went into the orchard and started to dig. Sure enough, he found a chest of buried treasure and his dream came true. So the pedlar was rich until the end of his days and all because of a dream. Or rather because of two dreams.

JULY 5

Ash Lodge –
Out in the Rain

It was a wet morning at Ash Lodge. Willie decided that he and his two Badger friends, Basil and Dewy, would have to stay indoors.

'I don't see why,' said Dewy. 'We could try out our new waterproofs.' Basil got down their new oilskin coats and sou'wester hats from on top of the wardrobe. 'It's a pity they didn't have a smaller size for Willie,' he said as they dressed

themselves. Willie agreed. As it was, the coat dragged on the floor and he could hardly see from under his hat. Willie had the feeling this was not going to be fun.

Basil and Dewy strode off into the woods and Willie shuffled along behind them. Unfortunately, with the noise of the rain and the size of his hat, Willie didn't hear or see Basil and Dewy turn right at a fork in the path. He was just thinking that the path they were following was rather steep when he trod on the bottom of his coat and went tumbling down a hill. He came to a stop with a bump against the foot of a tree.

'What do you suppose it is?' said a voice.

'Looks like a giant yellow mushroom,' said another. Two ducks were prodding him.

'It's a yellow mushroom with a hat on,' said the first duck.

'Don't make fun of me,' said Willie.

'It's a talking yellow mushroom with a hat on,' said the second duck.

Willie had had enough. He stood up, lifted his oilskin coat like a skirt and ran off. But he didn't get far before he ran straight into Basil and Dewy.

'Well, this *has* been a nice walk,' puffed Willie.

'All right, Willie,' said Dewy. 'Time to go home now.'

JULY 6

The Fable of
the Wolf and the Goat

A wolf saw a goat nibbling grass at the top of a cliff and thought what a good dinner she would make. The wolf wasn't as surefooted as the goat and could

find no way to the top of the cliff. If he was to have the goat for his dinner he would have to make her come to him.

He put on his craftiest smile, and called up to the goat, 'Madam Goat, why are you risking your life on that dangerous cliff where there is only dry grass for you to eat?

Take the advice of a friend. Come down here where the grass is fresh and green.'

The goat looked down at the wolf and tossed her head. 'Little you care whether the grass I eat is dry and brown, or fresh and green,' she said. 'I know perfectly well that all you want to do is to eat me. I shall stay here where I am safe.'

JULY 7
The King of Birds (Part 1)

Once, long ago, the King of Birds lived with his subjects in the hilly highlands of Burma. One day one of his subjects flew down to the flat lowlands. When he returned he called the other birds together.

'Today I have seen a marvellous thing,' he said. 'In the lowlands there are fields full of seeds just waiting to be eaten. It is foolish to spend so much time searching for food in the hills when it is waiting to be picked up in the fields.'

'Let's all fly to the lowlands,' twittered the birds in great excitement.

'Stay here in the highlands where you are safe,' said the King of Birds, who was king because he was wise. 'There will be men guarding the fields. You will be captured.'

But the birds were so excited they wouldn't listen to his wise words. 'We will fly in a flock,' they said. 'There is always safety in numbers.'

Nothing the King said would make them change their minds and off they flew. When they reached the rice fields, they swooped down with a deafening chorus of chirps and cheeps and began to eat as fast as they could. 'The King was wrong and we were right,' they said between mouthfuls. But the men who had planted the rice needed it for their families. They had prepared a trap. The birds had never seen a net before.

Suddenly there was a shout. Men and boys jumped from hiding places in the field and sprang the net. The birds were captured. They fluttered and they struggled but the net was strong and held them tightly.

'The King was right and we were wrong,' they said sadly.

JULY 8
The King of Birds (Part 2)

Against the advice of the King of Birds, his subjects had flown down to the lowlands and now they were caught in a net. Up in the highlands, the King was scanning the sky anxiously. His subjects had been gone a long time. Too long. Something must have happened. He decided to go to the lowlands himself.

'It's the King,' cried the birds when they saw him. 'It's the King. Oh, please help us.'

The King of Birds, who was king not only because he was wise, but because he was kind as well, said, 'I can only help you if you do exactly as I tell you.'

'We will . . . we will . . .' twittered the birds eagerly.

When the King of Birds was sure everyone was listening he said, 'When I give the signal you must all beat your wings at the same time and rise into the sky together.'

'We are ready . . . we are ready . . .' twittered the birds. Up flew the birds. As they rose into the sky the net that surrounded them on all sides rose into the air with them. They were still trapped.

'Fly! Fly! Fly! Follow me home to the highlands,' ordered the King of Birds as his subjects flew after him

JULY 9
The King of Birds (Part 3)

What a strange sight it was to see a net full of birds flying across the sky. They reached the highlands safely. But they were not free.

'Are we to stay in this net forever?' they asked one another.

'I will get help,' said the King of Birds. He called upon his friend the mouse. 'Please come at once,' he said.

'What can a tiny mouse do against such a big net?' asked the birds sadly when they saw the tiny scampering creature sniffing round the edge of the net. The mouse scampered away to fetch his relations. What one mouse can do in an hour, a dozen mice can do in a few minutes. They nibbled and gnawed at the strands of the net. One by one the strands snapped. Soon there was a hole large enough for even the largest bird to slip through. One by one they soared into the sky and spread their wings.

'The King was right,' they sang. 'The King was right.'

The net lay empty and forgotten on the ground. How good it was to be free. How lucky the birds were to have a king who was kind enough to forgive their foolishness and wise enough to find an answer to their problem.

JULY 10

Minnie the Mouse

Minnie Mouse went off to sea,
Her first time in a boat;
The sail was just a patchwork rag;
Such fun to be afloat!

All went well till the weather changed
And waves were tossed on high;
Up and down she rose and fell,
She thought that she would die.

Minnie lay down – she felt so ill,
Held on with hands and tail.
The night was dark, the gale was strong;
It ripped away the sail.

When morning came, the sea was calm.
'Hooray,' she cried and waved,
As far away against the sky –
An island! She was saved!

The tide then swept her up the beach;
She jumped out on dry land;
She met a friendly tortoise,
That walked along the sand.

'I need a shell like yours,' she said.
'Just turn my boat, please do.'
So, tortoise tipped it upside-down;
It made a fine house too.

Young Minnie loved her island home;
With friends and food in store;
She'd never go to sea again,
Not ever any more!

JULY 11

The Talking Tree

Bob Hedgehog likes to talk. He always has a lot to say. He talks about the flowers, the trees, the sky, the things he has done. He'll talk about anything to anyone.

One day Bob found a stone with a hole in it and wanted to tell someone about it. He went to see Little Hamster. 'Look what I've found,' said Bob.

'Not now, Bob. I'm busy digging,' said Little Hamster. 'Tell me later.'

Bob went to see Polly Pig. 'Just look at this, Polly,' started Bob.

'I'm doing my washing right now, Bob. Tell me some other time,' said Polly.

Bob set off to see Cheepy Chick. 'Hello, Cheepy,' said Bob. 'You'll never believe what I've found.'

'Can't stop now,' said Cheepy. 'I've got all my cleaning to do. Come back later.'

Everyone was too busy to listen to Bob. Then Bob saw a tree. The tree wasn't busy. The tree didn't say, 'Tell me later'. So Bob told the tree all about his stone.

Polly Pig and Little Hamster saw Bob talking to the tree. 'Let's play a trick on him,' said Polly.

They crept behind the tree. 'Where did you find the stone?' asked Little Hamster, trying to sound like a tree. Bob couldn't believe his ears; the tree was talking to him.

Bob ran to tell someone about the talking tree. He could only find Cheepy Chick. 'Come and see this talking tree,' he said, pulling a very cross Cheepy Chick back with him to the tree.

'Say something, tree,' said Bob. The tree didn't make a sound. 'Come on, tree. Speak.' The tree gave a giggle. Then it started laughing. Cheepy Chick looked behind it and pulled out Little Hamster and Polly Pig who couldn't stand up for laughing.

'We've been playing a trick on you, Bob,' they both cried. For the first time ever, Bob Hedgehog didn't have a thing to say.

JULY 12

The Elves and the Shoemaker (Part 1)

Once there was a shoemaker. He was a good worker, but times were hard and the day came when he was left with just enough leather to make one pair of shoes. He cut the pieces very carefully. One mistake and there wouldn't have been enough leather to make even one pair.

During the night, as he and his wife slept, something very mysterious happened. 'Wife? Come quickly!' he called when he went to start work next day. On the bench, where the pieces of shoe leather had been, was as fine a pair of finished shoes as they had ever seen.

'How could that have happened?' gasped his wife.

'We must have a friend,' said the shoemaker. 'And look how well they are made. I couldn't have made them better myself.'

He sold the shoes that very morning and for a very good price. Now he could buy enough leather to make two pairs of shoes. He cut the pieces and left them on his bench as he had done the previous night.

When he came down to breakfast the following morning there were four finished shoes on the bench. And so it continued, night after night after night. The more leather he was able to buy the more shoes he was able to cut. The more pieces he left on his bench, the more finished shoes he found in the morning. The more finished shoes he found, the more leather he was able to buy. It wasn't long before he began to grow rich for the shoes were so beautifully made everyone wanted to own a pair.

JULY 13

The Elves and the Shoemaker (Part 2)

A shoemaker found that if he left pieces of leather on his bench at night, by morning they were shoes. One evening, not long before Christmas, his wife said, 'I wish we knew who was making the shoes so that we could thank them.'

They decided that instead of going to bed that night they would stay up and keep watch. At midnight the door opened and two elves came into the shop. They sat crosslegged on the bench and worked hard until all the pieces of leather had been sewn into shoes. Then they left as quietly as they had arrived.

The shoemaker and his wife crept from their hiding place. 'Did you notice how ragged their clothes were?' said his wife. 'I will make them each a new suit.'

The shoemaker jumped to his feet and said, 'Did you notice that their feet were bare? I will make them both a pair of shoes.'

The shoemaker and his wife were so pleased with their idea that they set to work the very next day. By Christmas Eve they had finished. The shoemaker had made four tiny shoes. His wife had made two pairs of tiny green breeches, two green coats and two tiny shirts, two pairs of white stockings and two caps each trimmed with a feather.

That night they set out the new clothes. Then they hid and kept watch. When the elves came out and saw the two sets of clothes they shouted with delight. They danced from the shop dressed from tip to toe in their new clothes, as happy as any two elves could possibly be.

The shoemaker and his wife never saw the elves again. But their luck had changed and they were happy ever after.

JULY 14

Adventures of *The Tulip* – Up the Creek

'Let's take the dinghy and go exploring,' said Thomas one sunny morning. So the other two, Minty and Wilbur, moored their riverboat, *The Tulip*, packed themselves a picnic and all three set off rowing up a winding creek.

'It's so peaceful,' said Thomas, trailing his hand in the water as the other two took the oars. After a while they left the trees behind as the creek wound its way through grassy fields. Thomas lay back in the boat and closed his eyes. As Minty and Wilbur rowed on, the river bank grew steeper. Then a shadow came over the boat.

'Now the sun has gone in,' said Minty. He looked up to see how big the cloud was . . . and then gasped. It wasn't a cloud at all. It was an angry fox.

'Trespassers!' hissed the fox to someone behind him. Then four more foxes appeared beside the first one. Minty nudged Thomas awake. He yawned, glanced upwards and was soon very wide awake.

'I'll take the oars,' said Thomas, turning the boat. Minty and Wilbur took the spare paddles and off they rowed back the way they came as fast as they could go. The foxes followed them along the bank until there was no footpath left. Only when they reached the mouth of the creek and got back to the river did Thomas slow down.

'Oh dear,' said Wilbur. 'That could explain it.' He pointed to a sign on the bank hidden by leaves. They could just make out: PRIVATE PROPERTY . . . KEEP OUT . . . TRESPASSERS BEWARE!

JULY 15

Sports Day in the Forest

Chuck the rabbit was very excited. Everyone in the forest was excited. They had planned a sports day and the Fairy Queen had accepted their invitation to come and open it. Everyone was busy planning the races: a relay race, an obstacle race, a six-legged race and many more.

'I'm doing the nut-and-spoon race,' said Chuck's friend, Albie.

'And I'm running in the hundred metres,' said Doolan. 'What are you doing, Chuck?' Chuck looked thoughtful; he wasn't very good at sport.

'I should like to meet the Queen,' he said.

Doolan laughed. 'So would everyone,' he said.

Chuck grinned slowly. 'I have an idea,' he said.

The following day Chuck shut himself up in his little house and wouldn't come out when his friends called. 'I wonder what he's doing,' sighed Albie.

The next morning Chuck opened the door to them. 'I've done it,' he said, waving a piece of paper in front of them. 'I've written a song for the Queen.' Albie and Doolan were astonished.

'How will she hear it?' asked Doolan.

'Leave it to me,' said Chuck and off he went to see Barney the Bear who was the Forest Choirmaster.

The Sports Day arrived. They all had a wonderful time and the Queen presented the awards to everyone who took part.

At teatime everybody gathered round the biggest tree and it was then that the Forest Choir filed on to the platform to sing. Barney introduced Chuck's song and Chuck conducted it himself. It was a great success and the Queen clapped and clapped. Chuck even went up to shake her hand. It was the proudest moment of his life. This is the chorus of Chuck's song:

> Three cheers for the Fairy Queen,
> Hip, hip, hip, hooray.
> We hope she's had a happy time
> With the Forest Folk today.

JULY 16

The Fable of the Fortune Teller

A fortune teller was standing in the market place telling fortunes. A great many of the townsfolk were jostling around him. All had money in their hands. All were eager to learn what the future had in store for them.

Suddenly a boy began to push his way through the crowd. 'Do not push, boy. You must wait your turn,' called the fortune teller. But the boy would not be stopped.

'I've come to tell you the news,' he said.

'What news is that?' asked the fortune teller.

'Your house has been broken into. Thieves have taken everything you have.'

'What! What did you say?' shouted the fortune teller turning bright red with anger.

'Thieves have broken into your house,' repeated the boy.

The fortune teller pushed his way through the crowd. He ran home shouting and waving his arms about as though he was ready to start a fight.

The crowd stared after him in amazement. 'It's strange, isn't it,' said one of them, 'that he who claims to know what the future holds for us, cannot see what it holds for himself.'

JULY 17

The Crocodile that Yawned (Part 1)

Casimir was becoming rather a lazy old crocodile. He enjoyed a swim in the river but best of all he liked to crawl on to the river bank and sunbathe. But Casimir never stayed awake for very long when he was out of the water. As soon as he had settled himself comfortably he would begin to yawn. Turning his big head this way and that, admiring the trees and flowers around him, Casimir would yawn and yawn.

It was very frightening for the birds who lived in the riverside bushes. They would shiver in fear at the sight of Casimir's open mouth. His huge teeth looked very fierce. The birds were terrified that one day the great crocodile would reach into the bushes, snap his jaws shut and eat a bird for lunch!

Whenever Casimir fell asleep every bird heaved a sigh of relief. But in an hour or so he would wake up and then, in no time at all, the lazy old crocodile would be yawning again and the birds would be trembling.

'I don't see why we should fly away because of the crocodile,' the braver birds argued. 'After all, these bushes are our homes.'

'But it's so frightening,' others would reply.

'He has such a huge mouth he could swallow a dozen of us at once!' cried a tiny hummingbird.

So Pedro, the green parakeet, decided that something must be done. 'I've got a plan,' he told the quivering birds.

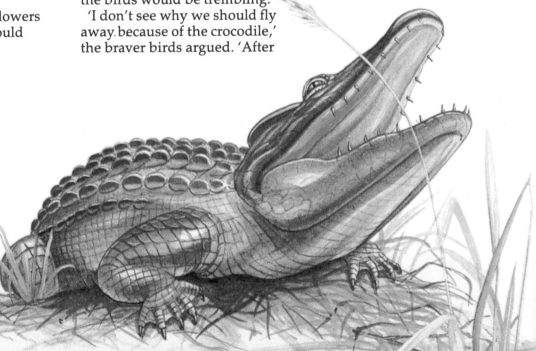

104

JULY 18

The Crocodile that Yawned (Part 2)

Pedro the parakeet had a plan to help the other birds who were afraid of the crocodile's big teeth when he yawned. 'There are two notices on the river bank, aren't there?' he said.

'That's right,' replied the kingfisher in surprise. 'One says NO LITTER and the other says NO SAILING.'

'Well,' said Pedro slowly, 'we'll make a third notice. It will say NO YAWNING.'

So, with Pedro's help, the birds prepared the notice and placed it next to the others on the river bank. Before long, Casimir returned from his swim, ready for a good sleep. At once he saw the new notice.

'Dear me!' he muttered. 'NO YAWNING. BY ORDER! Whatever shall I do? I love a good long yawn before I sleep.' Then he had a brainwave. 'I know,' he announced with pleasure. 'Instead of yawning I shall sing myself to sleep.' So Casimir opened his mouth wider than ever and sang in a dreadful, tuneless voice.

The birds were horrified. 'Oh Pedro,' cried the hummingbirds, 'the singing is even worse than the yawning. The crocodile's teeth look larger than ever and the noise is terrible! We'll have to fly away.'

'Please be patient just for a little longer,' Pedro begged them. Pedro worked hard again that night. Next day there was a fourth notice on the river bank: NO SINGING. BY ORDER!

When Casimir crawled out of the water he shook his head in amazement. 'Another notice,' he grumbled. 'NO SINGING! Dear me! Whatever can a poor old crocodile do?' Casimir lay quietly for a moment thinking things over. Then he noticed something strange. 'Why,' he muttered. 'The birds are all singing at the top of their voices.'

The birds started trembling as Casimir crawled from the edge of the river bank towards their bushes . . .

JULY 19

The Crocodile that Yawned (Part 3)

The birds had put notices up to stop Casimir the crocodile yawning and singing. But now he was coming over to the birds who were all singing. The birds were so scared that they couldn't fly away. They watched in horror as Casimir opened his mouth.

'Excuse me,' began the crocodile. 'So sorry to interrupt you, but I don't think you've seen the new notice. It's a dreadful nuisance, I'm afraid. It says we're not allowed to sing any more. There's one that says we're not allowed to yawn.'

Now it was the birds who had their mouths open! They were so surprised to hear this friendly warning from old Casimir they simply didn't know what to do. But Pedro was thinking quickly. The birds could all see and hear the crocodile close to. Now they would never be so afraid of him again. At this very moment they were peering down into the great toothy mouth as Casimir continued, 'I hope you don't mind my mentioning it,' and he turned to leave.

'It's very kind of you,' said Pedro. 'I wonder if we could change the notices.'

'I don't quite understand,' said Casimir, puzzled.

'Well,' Pedro continued, 'if we put EXCEPT FOR BIRDS on the singing notice and EXCEPT FOR CROCODILES on the yawning notice, everyone would be happy.'

'I say, that is a good idea.' Casimir laughed in delight. To their surprise, even the tiniest birds didn't find his huge mouth so terrifying any more.

'I've got a brush and paint if you'd like me to do it,' said Pedro. And that is exactly what he did.

'That's much better,' said Casimir, when Pedro had finished. Soon Casimir was yawning away, just as usual. And in the bushes beside him all the birds sang happily.

JULY 20

How the King's Tea was Spoilt

Peter had a pet white mouse called Cuthbert. Cuthbert lived in Peter's pocket. Peter worked as a kitchen boy in the royal kitchens. None of the cooks knew about Cuthbert and if they had known they would have been worried. Cooks are afraid of mice. When mice are running about, cooks just don't know what to do. They panic and everything goes to pieces.

Now the King liked to be served tea and cakes every afternoon. One particular afternoon, Peter was sitting hidden under the kitchen table chatting to Cuthbert. But Cuthbert had seen the legs of the cooks passing by and he decided to run up one of them. It was the Head Cook's leg that Cuthbert chose to run up.

'Eeek!' he screamed. 'It's a mouse!' He jumped in the air and landed on the table, face down in a chocolate cake. All the other cooks shouted and screamed, jumping on the table to get away from the mouse. They didn't care as they trod in the custard tarts, sent jellies flying, kicked over teacups. Anything just to get away from that mouse.

Meanwhile Peter found a small piece of cheese. Cuthbert sniffed and ran straight into Peter's hand.

'Well done, boy,' said the Head Cook, wiping chocolate cake from his face. 'Thank goodness you've caught it. Now take that animal away.'

That is why the King had toast and jam for tea instead of cakes one afternoon. And why, after that day, Peter decided to leave Cuthbert at home when he went to work.

JULY 21

Frisky has some Fun

Frisky Frog was sulking. He was the best swimmer of all the frogs. Every pond creature agreed. But just across the park, near to Frisky's pond, a new swimming pool had been built.

At first Frisky would smile at the swimmers and say, 'They're quite good in the water, but not nearly as good as I am!' Then Frisky noticed something strange. Sometimes the people would climb up a ladder, walk along a plank and jump into the water from a great height. They even turned somersaults on the way down!

'I can't do that,' Frisky grumbled to himself. 'And I *live* in the water. Those people live on the land.' So he tried jumping high into the air off his lilypad. But he fell into the water with a "plop", like a stone and felt rather silly!

Frisky went for a walk around the pond. At last he found a tree with good, strong branches leaning across the water. So up he climbed. When Frisky reached the very edge of the branch he peered down into the water. It looked so far away. His legs trembled, but Frisky was no coward. Drawing a deep breath, he dived into the pond. He shot into the water like an arrow.

'I'll try a little somersault this time,' he decided. It was splendid! Soon the other frogs noticed him and they all clapped and cheered. The younger ones began to dive into the pond from the rocks. But they were not brave enough to climb the trees like Frisky. So he is the only frog in the pond who can do a triple twisting somersault with no splash on entry.

JULY 22

Goldilocks and the Three Bears (Part 1)

Once there were three bears: Father Bear, Mother Bear and Baby Bear. One morning Mother Bear made the porridge for breakfast as usual. 'The porridge is very hot this morning,' she said.

'Let's go for a walk while it cools,' said Father Bear.

There was someone else walking in the wood that morning: a little girl with long golden hair. She was called Goldilocks. She could smell the porridge and she followed the smell until she came to the open window of the Bears' house. When she saw the three bowls of porridge on the table they made her feel so hungry she climbed straight in through the window.

'I think I'll try some of that,' she said. She tried the porridge in the large bowl first. 'Oh no,' she said, 'that's much too hot.' She tried the porridge in the middle size bowl. 'Oh no,' she said, 'that's much too sweet.' She tried the porridge in the small bowl. 'Mmm. That's just right,' she said and ate it all up.

When the small bowl was quite, quite empty she walked around the house opening cupboards, looking at this and looking at that, and trying everything she could see. She sat on Father Bear's big chair.

'Oh no,' she said, 'this is much too hard.' She sat on Mother Bear's middle size chair. 'Oh no,' she said, 'this is much too soft.' She sat on Baby Bear's chair. 'That's just right,' she said, and she made herself comfortable. But she wriggled about so much that one of the legs snapped in two and fell to the floor.

Goldilocks picked herself up and went into the Bears' bedroom. She tried Father Bear's big bed. 'Oh no,' she said, 'this is much too lumpy.' She tried Mother Bear's middle size bed. 'Oh no,' she said, 'this is much too squashy.' She tried Baby Bear's small bed. 'That's just right,' she said and she fell fast asleep.

JULY 23

Goldilocks and the Three Bears (Part 2)

When the three bears got home they could tell at once that someone had been inside their house.

'Who has been eating *my* porridge?' growled Father Bear.

'Who has been eating *my* porridge?' growled Mother Bear.

'And who has been eating *my* porridge and finished it all up?' squeaked Baby Bear.

'Who has been sitting on *my* chair?' growled Father Bear.

'Who has been sitting on *my* chair?' growled Mother Bear.

'And who has been sitting on *my* chair and broken it?' squeaked Baby Bear and he burst into tears.

'Who has been lying on *my* bed?' growled Father Bear.

'Who has been lying on *my* bed?' growled Mother Bear.

'Who has been lying on *my* bed and is still there?' squeaked Baby Bear. 'LOOK!'

Goldilocks opened her eyes and sat up. When she saw the three bears staring at her, she jumped off the bed and out through the window.

The bears didn't bother to chase after her. She looked so frightened they knew she had learned her lesson and would never go uninvited into someone else's house again.

Instead, Mother Bear made some more porridge for Baby Bear, Father Bear mended his chair and they all sat down and had breakfast.

JULY 24

Pip the Pup

Pip was only a puppy and there were lots of things he wasn't sure about. His tail was one of them. He wasn't sure if it belonged to him or if it just kept following him about. Pip gave a sharp bark to warn it. Then he heard someone bark back at him.

'Wuff, wuff, wuff,' he barked. 'Wuff, wuff, wuff,' he heard. There must be another dog. He set off to find him. First he met Harry the Horse in the field. 'Have you seen another dog?' asked Pip.

'You're the only dog round here, and you're not really a dog yet,' snorted Harry.

Pip dashed on but he didn't know where to go. Then he saw Mrs Penny Pig coming along the lane, followed by her eight piglets.

'Have you seen another dog round here, Mrs Pig?' asked Pip.

'Another dog?' Mrs Pig grunted. 'One is quite enough, dear. Come along, piglets.' And off they all trotted.

'Wuff.' Pip gave another bark. 'Wuff.' Yes, there it was again and not so far away. He chased off up the lane barking every now and then to tell the other dog he was coming. The other dog barked back each time.

'What's the meaning of all this noise?' said a sharp voice as Pip ran along. It was Mrs Owl up in the trees. 'Don't you know I go to sleep during the day?'

'Sorry, Mrs Owl,' said Pip. 'I was just saying hello to the dog that keeps barking back at me.'

'What dog?' asked Mrs Owl.

'Listen! Wuff, wuff, wuff!' he barked. 'Wuff, wuff, wuff,' came the answering call.

'You silly puppy,' said Mrs Owl. 'That's not another dog. It's your echo.'

'Oh dear,' said Pip, very disappointed.

'Pip! Pip! Where are you?' came a voice. Hooray! The children were home from school and Pip dashed away, everything else forgotten.

JULY 25

My Clown

As I was walking in the town
I met a white-faced, painted clown.
'Good day!' said he. 'Good day!' said I.
He tossed his hat and winked an eye.

'I hope you'll come to see the show.
You'll love the elephants, I know.
The horses prancing round the ring
Will make you clap and want to sing.

The two who walk the wire up top
Will make you gasp for fear they'll drop.
Just watch the girls who swing on bars
Or see the clowns, the circus stars.'

'I'm sorry, sir,' I had to say,
'I cannot come – I cannot pay,'
'You mustn't miss the fun,' he said.
'Look, here's a pass for you instead.'

That night I watched from my front row
The elephants begin the show.
The horses pranced around the ring
The music made me clap and sing.

I gasped to see the tightrope pair
And girls go flying in the air,
But best of all I loved the clowns
Who played their tricks and tumbled round.

I had such fun that circus night
And, leaving, saw a flash of white.
A voice cried out and waved goodbye,
He tossed his hat and winked an eye.

JULY 26

Something to Laugh About

Todd the mill horse liked going to market with his master, Mungo the miller, but he didn't enjoy the journey home. Often, after Mungo collected the money for his flour and was on his way home, masked men would throw him off the cart and steal all his money. Then the two of them would trail sadly home. Life was no fun any more.

All Mungo's friends, the farmers and millers living nearby, had been robbed at one time or another. They were all as poor and miserable as Mungo.

One day Mungo recognised the robbers in the market place and told his friends. Wanting to catch the robbers in the act, they thought of a plan. 'This is what you must do,' they told him. 'When you get paid for your flour, flash your money about.

Brag about what a good price you got for it. See that the robbers hear you. Leave the rest to us.'

When Mungo bragged about his money, the robbers pricked up their ears. On the way home, as expected, the robbers stopped him and ordered him down from the cart. They told him to hand over his money. But suddenly a man jumped out of every flour bag in the cart. The other farmers and millers had been hiding there. They soon rounded up all the robbers and tied each one in a flour bag.

The robbers were loaded on board the cart. 'Let's give them a rough ride,' laughed Mungo as he and Todd set off to the prison. Todd gave a horse-laugh. Now *that* was something to laugh about.

JULY 27

The New Ferryman

'Why do you wish to cross the river to the King's castle?' the ferryman asked Jack.

'I believe the King is looking for a new ferryman,' Jack replied.

The man nodded. 'That's true. I'm not really a ferryman. I'm just helping out.'

As Jack took his seat a fat man approached the ferry. 'Take me across the river,' he shouted. 'I'm going to the King to be his new ferryman.' Jack made room for the fat man to sit down. Then a woman carrying a baby ran towards them.

'Please take me across the river,' she cried. 'My baby is sick. I must take her to the King's doctor.' The ferryman asked the fat man if the woman could take his place but the fat man refused.

'She can take my place,' Jack said, leaping ashore. 'I'll wait for you to come back.' When the ferryman returned he asked if Jack was afraid the fat man

would reach the castle first.

'I'll run and overtake him,' Jack replied smiling.

They had almost crossed the river when the ferryman lost his balance and toppled into the river.

'Help! I can't swim,' he cried. Jack plunged into the swirling water and swam ashore with the ferryman. Wet through, they ran to the ferryman's cottage. The ferryman gave Jack some dry clothes and went into another room.

'I'll never overtake the fat man now,' Jack thought, changing into the dry clothes. Then the ferryman came into the room dressed as the King.

'You're the King!' Jack gasped in surprise.

'I did say I wasn't really a ferryman,' the King said laughing. 'I want you to be my new ferryman, Jack, because you are both kind and brave. The fat man has had a wasted journey and your first task will be to ferry him back across the river.'

109

JULY 28

Cheeky Mouse and the Green Cheese (Part 1)

One day Cheeky Mouse said to his four brothers and sisters, 'I'm tired of the same old cheese. The moon is made of green cheese, so let's go to the moon.'

'Yes, let's,' squeaked his brothers and sisters.

But Grandfather Mouse said:

'A cat I hear,
A dog I smell:
Please do not go
For all's not well.'

Cheeky Mouse only said, 'We can look after ourselves, Grandfather, and so they set off, singing:

'Modern Mice are we,
Brave and bold we be.
To the moon we'll fly.
Goodbye, old mouse, goodbye.'

'How will we fly to the moon?' asked one of Cheeky Mouse's brothers.

'We'll fly in the children's spaceship. It's ready in the garden.' And so it was.

JULY 29

Cheeky Mouse and the Green Cheese (Part 2)

Cheeky Mouse and his brothers and sisters were heading for the children's spaceship.

'To the moon, to the moon,
We'll be there before noon.
We'll eat green cheese,
As much as we please.'

So sang the mice, ignoring the warning of old Grandfather Mouse. Cheeky Mouse began to scramble into the spaceship. His brothers and sisters followed him. But what was that strange noise? And what was that strange smell?

A dog! And a cat! Asleep in the spaceship! The mice scrambled out, tumbling over each other. And the first mouse to get back to Grandfather Mouse was Cheeky Mouse.

'That was a quick trip to the moon,' said Grandfather Mouse.

'We don't like green cheese after all,' said Cheeky Mouse. 'Could we have some of your cheese, please. We're very hungry.'

Grandfather Mouse smiled to himself as he watched the mice nibbling happily at the cheese he gave them.

JULY 30

The Fable of the Crow and the Water Jug

A thirsty crow was looking for something to drink. She knew if she didn't find something soon she would die of thirst. Presently she spied some water in the bottom of a water jug. She could see it, but she couldn't reach it. Her beak was too short.

The crow knew that if she tipped the jug on to its side the water would run out and soak into the ground. It would be lost forever.

'Am I to die,' she thought, 'when I can see the very thing which will save me?' The crow was so desperate for a drink she had to find an answer to the problem somehow.

There were some small pebbles lying on the ground. She began picking them up, one by one, and dropping them into the water jug. As the heap of pebbles inside the water jug grew, so the level of the water rose. When it reached the rim of the water jug the thirsty crow was able to drink.

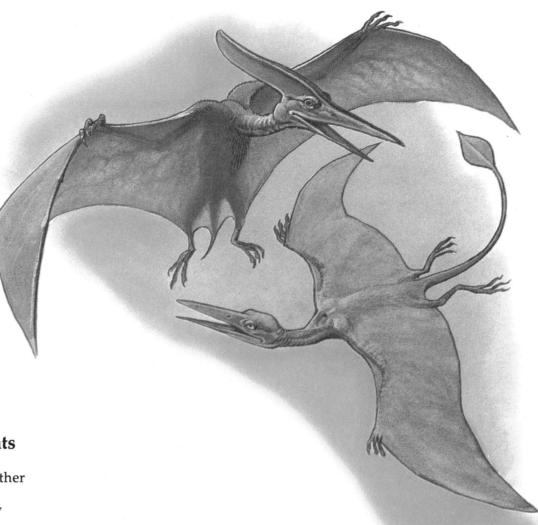

JULY 31

Michael's Flying Giants

Michael loved it when his father had time to tell him a story.

'Tell me a new kind of story this time,' he said, when he found his father half asleep in the garden. 'Something real . . .'

'I'll tell you about some flying giants that really lived,' his father said after a moment. 'Will that do?'

Before Michael could say anything his father quickly went on, 'These weren't fairy-tale giants. They actually lived millions and millions of years ago. They flew in the air like birds.'

'Were they like Sarah's two canaries?' Michael asked.

His father laughed. 'Wait here and I'll fetch a book and show you a picture of them,' he said. Michael waited impatiently until his father returned with a large book and began turning the pages.

'Well, they look like birds!' Michael said, when his father found the page he was looking for.

'They flew in the air like birds,' said his father, 'but they were really lizards with wings. Their leathery wings were enormous but their back legs were very small and weak. So they weren't much good on land.'

'What did they eat?' Michael asked. 'And what are they really called?'

'They fed on fish they caught in the sea,' said his father, smiling. 'And you won't remember their name but it's pterosaurs . . .'

'Like . . . like tyrannosaurs?' Michael burst out, very proud of himself. 'I once did a picture of one at school – as tall as a house and with a mouth like a door and full of horrible long teeth!'

'I wish I'd seen your picture!' his father laughed.

'It's hanging on the classroom wall,' Michael said. 'It was the best. Shall I do another picture of these flying giants? Maybe the teacher will hang that on the wall too!'

'If she doesn't, I will!' said his father, closing his eyes. Michael ran off to get paper and crayons for his flying giants.

AUGUST

AUGUST 1

Chuffa the Runaway Train (Part 1)

Chuffa was working underground in a coal mine. It was dark and dirty and dusty and Chuffa always needed cleaning. It was his job to carry the coal from the coalface to the pit shaft. Then at the end of the day he would carry all the miners to the shaft. They would climb out into the daylight to go home. But Chuffa never got out into the daylight; the mine was his home.

At the end of one day, Chuffa had been dusted down and all the men had left for home. But Chuffa wasn't alone. His two squirrel friends, Nutty and Husky, had come to see him. They would tell him stories about the trees and the fields and the river and the sunlight.

Chuffa thought how much he would like to see the sunlight again. 'We'll help you run away,' said the two squirrels. 'Let's go off and see the world. Now which is the starter lever?'

'Chuffa-chuff,' said Chuffa, as he chuffed out of the mine with the two squirrels in the cab. It was still light outside as they chuffed along the countryside. It was good to be outdoors again.

They didn't know where they were going. Soon it began to grow dark. Nutty was worried. 'We're going to get lost,' he said.

'Who cares?' said Husky. 'We're free.' Chuffa gave a whistle. He liked being free.

AUGUST 2

Chuffa the Runaway Train (Part 2)

Chuffa had been working in a coal mine. His two squirrel friends, Nutty and Husky, had helped him run away into the great outdoors. The two squirrels didn't know much about driving railway engines. They travelled on through the night. By the morning they found themselves on a very old track that had not been used for years.

The rain started to fall and the track became muddier and muddier. It slowed Chuffa down until at last he was up to his axles in sticky mud and he couldn't move.

'I guess we shouldn't have helped Chuffa run away,' said Nutty, as the rain turned the track into a lake that got deeper and deeper. Chuffa floated away from the track. Nutty and Husky found some pieces of wood that they could use as paddles and they started to paddle Chuffa towards dry land. Chuffa was beginning to wish he was back in his dry coal mine, when his wheels felt a track again.

Chuffa didn't know it but he and the squirrels had found their way on to a mountain railway track.

AUGUST 3

Chuffa the Runaway Train (Part 3)

Chuffa and his two squirrel friends, Nutty and Husky, had run away from a coal mine. Now they found themselves going up and up a snowy mountainside. They were on a mountain railway track. Every now and then Husky had to get out to clear the snow from the track. Chuffa's wheels had never been cold like this in the mine.

Finally they reached the very peak of the mountain. Then they started to go down the other side. They chuffed along quite gently at first, but then the mountain became steeper and they went faster. Then it became even steeper and they went much faster. Now Chuffa's wheels were whizzing round and he couldn't stop. Chuffa had really become a runaway train! Hardly daring to look down, Nutty spotted the most enormous electric train down in the valley below and it was heading across their track.

'We're going to crash,' cried Nutty, as they thundered downhill. The two trains were about to meet head on at the crossing, when Husky found Chuffa's brake and pulled on it with all his strength. Chuffa screeched to a halt just in time. The electric train went rushing by and didn't even notice them.

'I think it's time to go home now,' said Husky, as they all breathed a sigh of relief. Chuffa gave a whistle, to show he agreed. He'd had enough of running away; it might be dirty in the mine but it was safe and it was home.

AUGUST 4

Katy's Dream

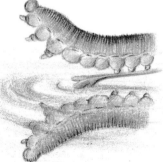

Katy Caterpillar felt lonely. No one wanted to be friendly with her. 'You're so plain and slow,' called out King Thistle, as she crawled along.

Katy crawled over to the garden pond to take a bath. Perhaps that would cheer her up. Just then she noticed an ugly, green object staring back at her from the water. 'Who are you?' she shrieked.

'What's the matter, Katy?' called Goldie Goldfish, popping her head out of the pond. 'Don't you know that's your reflection. It's just as if you were looking in a mirror.'

Poor Katy. Feeling very tired and sad, she curled up underneath a warm leaf and fell asleep. Katy had a marvellous dream. She dreamed she was the most beautiful creature in the garden.

Some time later the gardener was very busy one day. 'I must dig up all these thistles,' he muttered. 'They spoil the garden.'

King Thistle shook with fear. A big tear rolled from the corner of his thorny eye on to the ground where a pretty butterfly was dancing. 'I'm going to be cut down,' cried King Thistle sadly. 'How I wish I was beautiful like you.'

'Don't cry! I'll help you,' called the butterfly. She flew up on to his prickly crown.

'Well,' said the gardener. 'You look so beautiful perched on that thistle. Perhaps it's your favourite flower. I'd better leave it where it is after all.'

'You're so kind,' whispered King Thistle gratefully. 'What's your name?'

'It's Katy, of course,' came the reply. 'I fell asleep, and had the most wonderful dream. When I woke I had grown two beautiful wings, and I could fly high into the air.'

King Thistle hung his head in shame. He had been so unkind to Katy when she was a caterpillar. Katy smiled as she fluttered daintily around King Thistle's head. It was wonderful to think that sometimes dreams really did come true.

AUGUST 5

The Big Race (Part 1)

Percy Prickles was very proud of his turnip patch. He and his wife Rose loved to eat the turnips and to drink the turnip wine they made. Percy was watering his turnip patch one day when a stranger tapped him on the shoulder with his gold-topped cane.

'Excuse me, my boy,' he said. 'My name's Horace Hare. Fine turnip patch you have here.'

'Thank you, sir,' said Percy. 'Did you want to buy one of my turnips?'

'I was thinking more of a small wager, my boy,' said Horace. 'What do you say to betting your turnip patch against my fine gold-topped cane, on the result of a running race.'

'A race?' said Percy. 'But you're a hare, sir.'

'Oh, a very old hare,' said Horace slyly. 'I can hardly hobble over any distance.'

'All right,' said Percy. 'Shall we also bet my turnip wine against one of your gold coins?'

'Fine idea,' said Horace.

'Shall we say the first one to run up and down the turnip patch five times is the winner?' said Percy.

'Agreed,' said the hare.

They shook paws on the bet and Percy said, 'I'll just get ready for the race. With that he dashed into his house and told Rose what he planned to do.

AUGUST 6

The Big Race (Part 2)

'All right, my boy,' said Horace Hare, changed and ready for the race in his running shoes. 'Ready when you are, and when I win, your turnip patch and all your turnip wine will be mine.'

'Five times to the far end of the turnip patch and five times back,' said Percy. 'Ready, steady, go.'

The hare shot off like a streak of lightning. In ten seconds flat he had reached the end of the turnip patch but he couldn't believe his eyes when he saw Percy had got there before him. Horace turned and whizzed off back to the other end. Somehow Percy had managed to get to that end before him as well.

Horace turned and sprinted extra fast to the other end, but Percy was standing there waiting for him.

Horace rushed back and forth but each time Percy was there before him. Hardly able to walk up the last stretch, Horace struggled halfway along the turnip patch and sure enough Percy was waiting at the top, hardly out of breath at all.

'I give up. You win.' shouted Horace, as he fell in a heap.

'I'll take the gold coin,' said Percy, walking up to Horace. 'But you can keep your gold-topped cane. I think you need it more than me.'

Horace hobbled away on his cane, picking up his clothes as he went. Percy walked to the other end of the turnip patch and there stood his wife, Rose, dressed in the same clothes and looking exactly like Percy. Of course, the hare had thought it *was* Percy at both ends of the turnip patch.

'Well done, Rose,' said Percy. 'The hare gave up, so I win. Shall we have a glass of turnip wine to celebrate?'

AUGUST 7

The Fable of the Man and the Satyr

There was once a man who shared a house with a satyr. A satyr is half man and half goat. All went well between them until one cold day in the middle of winter. The man's hands were cold and he was blowing on them.

'Why are you doing that?' asked the satyr.

'To warm them, of course,' said the man. 'I do it all the time.'

That same evening they had porridge for supper. The porridge was very hot and the man was afraid he would burn his tongue. He lifted the bowl to his lips and blew on the porridge.

'Why are you doing that?' asked the satyr.

'To cool the porridge, of course,' said the man, surprised that the satyr should have to ask. The satyr got up from his chair.

'Where are you going?' asked the man.

'I am leaving,' said the satyr.

'Leaving? But why?' asked the man in surprise.

'Because I cannot remain friends with a man who can blow hot and cold with the same breath,' said the satyr, and he hurried out of the door.

AUGUST 8

Sam's Scorpion

One day at his school in Nigeria, Sam's teacher said, 'I am giving a small prize for the best model of a bird or animal.'

Sam was very excited. This was better than sums. He loved carving old pieces of wood that he found in the river.

That evening after school, Sam took the family's goats to feed by the river. He paddled in the water looking for a good piece of wood to carve. The only wood to float past was an old tree root. It was thick at one end and curved at the other. Sam sighed. Perhaps he would find a better piece tomorrow. He rounded up the goats and started home.

Suddenly a scorpion scuttled across the path. Sam stopped. The scorpion arched its tail over its back before disappearing into the scrub.

'That's what I'll make!' exclaimed Sam. 'A scorpion!'

He hurried home and began to carve. The curve of the tree root became the curve of the scorpion's tail. Gradually the thick end began to look like pincers, body and legs. It was a fierce-looking scorpion.

On the day of the competition the models were laid out on a long table.

'Choosing the winner is very difficult,' said the teacher.

Then someone shouted: 'Look out! There's a scorpion!'

A scorpion was darting in and out of the models. It came face to face with Sam's model. It stopped and curved its pointed tail over its back. 'It thinks it has met another scorpion,' said teacher. Everyone laughed. The real scorpion dropped off the table and scuttled away.

'If your model can fool a real scorpion, Sam,' said teacher, 'you must be the winner.' Everyone agreed and Sam received his prize.

AUGUST 9

Sing-Lo and the Dragon (Part 1)

Long ago in a small village in China, there was great excitement. A messenger from the great Emperor in Peking had called all the people into the village square because he had something very important to tell them.

'The Emperor wishes it to be known that the Royal Dragon has escaped. There will be a big reward to anyone who can find him and an even bigger reward for anyone who is able to capture and return the Dragon to the Royal Palace.'

At the end of the village, there lived an old woman with her grandson, Sing-Lo. She was old and did not go out into the village very often. Sing-Lo stopped on his way home from school so that he could listen to the Emperor's messenger and tell his grandmother.

Sing-Lo hurried home to practise flying his kite before supper, as there was going to be a prize given at school at the end of the week for the boy who could fly his kite the highest.

Soon he set off up the hill overlooking his home, singing merrily. The evening was very warm and Sing-Lo sat down for a short rest. There were many caves nearby but Sing-Lo had never been inside them. A strange feeling came over him. He could sense he was not alone; someone was watching him. Turning round, he could see two very large eyes looking at him from the darkness of one of the caves.

AUGUST 10

Sing-Lo and the Dragon (Part 2)

Sing-Lo was up in the mountains about to fly his kite when he saw two eyes. He nearly jumped out of his skin. Could this be the Dragon, he wondered. 'Who's there?' he whispered.

A gentle snort came from inside the cave and a deep voice said, 'Don't be afraid. I am Kwang Fu the Dragon, and I've escaped from the Emperor's palace. I'm tired of breathing fire all day and scaring everyone. I really want to be a friendly dragon but no one will come anywhere near me.'

'Oh!' cried Sing-Lo, feeling much happier. 'May I be your friend? I don't know anything about dragons but I'm willing to learn.'

'Well dragons do like oranges, you know,' said the Dragon.

Each evening that week Sing-Lo went up the hillside to the cave with as many oranges as he could carry. He thought it best to say nothing to anyone about the Dragon as Kwang Fu was determined to stay in the cave; but it would only be a matter of time before the Emperor's soldiers found him and took him back to the palace.

Finally Sing-Lo decided he would go and see the Emperor's chief minister. He explained about Kwang Fu without telling him where the Dragon was hiding.

'So, Kwang Fu is lonely,' said the minister. 'Tell him we shall bring another dragon to the palace to keep him company.'

Sing-Lo rushed off to the mountains to tell Kwang Fu. Kwang Fu finally agreed to meet the new dragon.

The next night Kwang Fu slipped into the palace grounds and soon made friends with the other dragon. 'I'll stay,' said Kwang Fu to the Emperor, 'as long as my friend, Sing-Lo, brings me my oranges.'

So Sing-Lo became official orange bringer to the imperial Dragon and when he grew up he became Chief Keeper of Dragons at the palace.

116

AUGUST 11

Chicken Licken

One morning, when Chicken Licken was sitting under an oak tree, an acorn fell upon his head.

'Oh dear,' said Chicken Licken, 'the sky is falling. I must run and tell the King.' On the way to the palace he met his friend, Henny Penny.

'Where are you going?' asked Henny Penny.

'To tell the King the sky is falling,' said Chicken Licken.

'Then I'll come with you,' clucked Henny Penny.

Cocky Locky was scratching for grain. 'Where are you both going in such a hurry?' he asked.

'To tell the King the sky is falling,' said Chicken Licken.

'Then I'll come with you,' crowed Cocky Locky.

'Where are you all going?' asked Ducky Lucky, when she met them.

'To tell the King the sky is falling,' said Chicken Licken, without stopping.

'Then I'll come with you,' quacked Ducky Lucky.

'Where are you all going?' called Drakey Lakey from the pond.

'To tell the King the sky is falling,' said Chicken Licken.

'Then I'll come with you,' said Drakey Lakey.

Goosey Loosey was listening. 'I'll come with you,' she hissed.

'And I'll come too . . . too . . . too,' gobbled Turkey Lurkey who didn't like to be out of anything.

Foxy Loxy was lurking behind a bush. 'Where are you all going in such a hurry?' he asked slyly.

'To tell the King the sky is falling,' said Chicken Licken.

'Then you had better follow me,' said Foxy Loxy. He led them all, Chicken Licken, Henny Penny, Cocky Locky, Ducky Lucky, Drakey Lakey, Goosey Loosey and Turkey Lurkey, through the bushes to his den. That sly old fox had them all for his dinner and the King never did find out that a piece of sky had fallen on Chicken Licken's head.

AUGUST 12

Ash Lodge – Treasure

Willie was walking through the woods near Ash Lodge one day when he heard rustling in the undergrowth. He looked more closely and saw a flurry of leaves and twigs. In the centre of it was Jake Squirrel.

'What are you doing, Jake?' asked Willie.

'I'm looking for something,' said Jake.

'What have you lost?' asked Willie.

'I've lost my treasure. I dropped it when I was up there . . . and now it's down here.'

'Treasure!' cried Willie, and he dived into the leaves throwing them in the air. He had been searching for two or three minutes when he realised he didn't know what he was searching for. He looked up at the squirrel who was standing, hands on hips, tapping one foot rather impatiently.

'Er . . . what does your treasure look like?' asked Willie.

'Brown and round and fat,' said Jake.

'Oh . . .' said Willie. 'Don't you mean sparkly and shiny and golden?'

'No,' said Jake. 'But if you're going to help, you look over there and I'll look down here.'

They set to work and soon there was a great cry from Jake: 'Hooray! I've found it!'

'Let me see, let me see,' said Willie eagerly. 'Why it's only an old nut.'

'It's my best nut,' said Jake proudly.

'But you said *treasure*,' moaned Willie.

'It's *treasure* to me,' said Jake.

Willie stomped off grumpily. Then when he got home he had a thought. He went to his bedroom and got out his box of special things from under his bed.

'I suppose my treasures are only treasures to me,' he said, going through each one. 'I wouldn't want to lose any of mine either.'

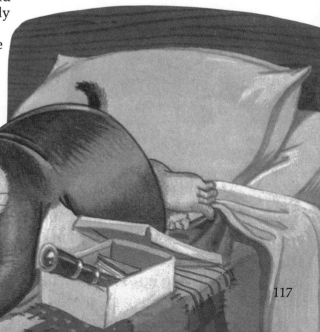

AUGUST 13

Jonathan John has a Lazy Day (Part 1)

'You're lucky, wife,' said Jonathan John to his wife, Gertrude, one day. 'I work in the fields and you just stay at home all day and play with the baby.'

'But I churn the butter, look after the animals, cook and clean,' protested his wife.

'You don't call that work!' said Jonathan. 'Work is weeding and hoeing and raking.'

'All right,' said his wife. 'You stay at home tomorrow and I'll go out into the fields.' Jonathan was quick to agree. Now Gertrude would find out what work really was.

Next morning Gertrude left Jonathan his instructions and set off for the fields. Jonathan decided to have a snooze first. Then he churned the butter for a while but it made his arm ache and it made him thirsty. He went down to the cellar for a drink of ale. But then he heard a pattering sound upstairs. He left the jug to finish filling from the barrel and ran up into the kitchen. The pig had got out of the sty and knocked over the butter churn. There was sticky butter everywhere.

Jonathan chased the pig out and started to clear up the pool of butter. Then the baby started crying. By the time he'd fed the baby he remembered his jug of ale. 'Oh no!' he cried, running down to the cellar. There was beer flowing everywhere.

'Well at least I shall have a lazy afternoon,' said Jonathan to himself as he started clearing up the cellar.

AUGUST 14

Jonathan John has a Lazy Day (Part 2)

Jonathan John was having a lazy day. He had changed places with his wife: she had gone out to the fields and he was looking after the house. The morning had not gone too well for Jonathan. He finished clearing up the mess he had made in the cellar and was mopping up the butter in the kitchen when he remembered the cow.

'I'd forgotten all about her,' said Jonathan. 'No time to take her to pasture now.' Then Jonathan had a brilliant idea. He decided to take the cow on to the roof and let her graze there. 'There's plenty of grass for you, and if I slip this rope round you, down the chimney and tie it round my waist I can be sure you don't stray.'

Jonathan was very pleased with himself as he sat back in his chair having a read. He had put the porridge pot on the fire. Now he could have a rest. He was surprised how tired he felt. It wasn't long before he was fast asleep.

Jonathan woke very suddenly and couldn't understand why he was dangling in mid air over the porridge pot halfway up the chimney.

The answer was simple. The cow wasn't used to grazing in such a small space. She had wandered too close to the edge of the roof and had fallen off. As she and Jonathan were tied together, when she went down, Jonathan went up and now they both hung in the air, one outside the house and the other inside.

That's how they stayed, Jonathan and the cow, until finally Gertrude came home. She saw the dangling cow and quickly cut the rope. The cow gave a grateful moo as it dropped to the ground. There was a cry and a splash from inside the house. Gertrude went indoors to find Jonathan sitting in the porridge pot. When she had cut the rope, Jonathan had fallen down.

'Tomorrow,' said Jonathan climbing out, 'I'm going to the fields and you can stay at home.'

AUGUST 15

Who Killed Cock Robin?

Who killed Cock Robin?
I, said the Sparrow,
With my bow and arrow,
I killed Cock Robin.

Who saw him die?
I, said the Fly,
With my little eye,
I saw him die.

Who caught his blood?
I, said the Fish,
With my little dish,
I caught his blood.

Who'll make the shroud?
I, said the Beetle,
With my thread and needle,
I'll make the shroud.

Who'll dig his grave?
I, said the Owl,
With my pick and shovel,
I'll dig his grave.

Who'll be the parson?
I, said the Rook,
With my little book,
I'll be the parson.

Who'll be the clerk?
I, said the Lark,
If it's not in the dark,
I'll be the clerk.

Who'll carry the link?
I, said the Linnet,
I'll fetch it in a minute,
I'll carry the link.

Who'll be chief mourner?
I, said the Dove,
I mourn for my love,
I'll be chief mourner.

Who'll carry the coffin?
I, said the Kite,
If it's not through the night,
I'll carry the coffin.

Who'll bear the pall?
We, said the Wren,
Both the cock and hen,
We'll bear the pall.

Who'll sing a psalm?
I, said the Thrush,
As she sat on a bush,
I'll sing a psalm.

Who'll toll the bell?
I, said the Bull,
Because I can pull,
I'll toll the bell.

And the birds of the air
Fell a-sighing and a-sobbing,
When they heard the bell toll
For poor Cock Robin.

AUGUST 16

Fluffy and the Green Rabbit

Fluffy the white rabbit was sitting in her hutch when a tiny green rabbit rattled at the door.

'I'm hungry. Have you any milk?' the green rabbit asked.

'I haven't any milk. Would you like a carrot?' said Fluffy.

'I can't eat carrots,' the green rabbit said. 'I come from the planet Lottabottle where rabbits live on milk.'

Fluffy left her hutch and led the green rabbit into the barn. 'There's a bucket of milk in here,' she said.

The green rabbit had to stand on Fluffy's back to reach the top of the large bucket. He leaned over the edge to drink the milk, lost his balance and fell in. Fluffy couldn't pull him out on her own so she left him swimming in the milk and ran for help. She found the dog asleep in his kennel and shook him awake.

'There's a green rabbit drowning in a bucket of milk,' she cried.

The dog didn't believe her. 'Green rabbit! Who ever heard of a green rabbit?' he yawned and went back to sleep.

Fluffy found the horse eating the hay in his stable. 'Help me save the green rabbit!' she cried.

'Green rabbit!' laughed the horse. 'Who ever heard of a green rabbit?' He carried on eating.

Fluffy was desperate. Nobody believed her and she didn't know how to save the green rabbit. Then she saw him running towards her. 'However did you escape from the bucket of milk?' she asked.

'I swam round and round until the milk turned into a large pat of butter,' the green rabbit replied, 'and when it was firm to stand on I climbed out of the bucket.'

Fluffy found that hard to believe. But then, as she said to the dog and the horse when the green rabbit had gone back home, she wasn't sure what to believe. After all she hadn't met a green rabbit from the planet Lottabottle before.

AUGUST 17

Beauty and the Beast (Part 1)

Once there was a rich merchant who had three daughters. Two were ugly and always cross. The third was beautiful and always kind. When the merchant lost his money and the family was forced to move from their grand house to a little cottage, the two ugly sisters sat about all day and did nothing but grumble and complain. Beauty, as the youngest was called, looked after her father and her sisters. She cleaned the house, cooked the food, made the beds and washed the dishes. She didn't complain at all.

One day the merchant came home with some good news. 'I have been offered work in a distant town,' he said. 'When I return I would like to bring you all a gift. What shall it be?'

'A silk dress,' said the two elder girls at once. Beauty knew that her father hadn't enough money to buy gifts. 'I would like a rose,' she said, for she knew that a rose would cost nothing.

The merchant completed his business some weeks later and began the journey home. On the way a storm blew up and somehow he lost his way. He climbed a tall tree in order to spy out the land and saw a distant castle. 'Perhaps there will be someone there who can direct me,' he thought and he made his way towards it.

The castle door stood wide open. There was no one about. There were candles flickering in the candlesticks and logs blazing in the fire-place. There was food upon the table, so he sat down and ate. There was a bed prepared, so he lay down and slept.

In the morning he found fresh clean clothes, and breakfast upon the table. When he had eaten he went into the garden and picked a rose to take to Beauty.

AUGUST 18

Beauty and the Beast (Part 2)

A merchant had spent the night in a strange, deserted castle. The next morning he picked a rose from the garden for his daughter Beauty. Suddenly there was an angry roar. He turned and came face to face with a creature which had the body of a man and the head of a beast. It was very angry.

'I have made you welcome in my home,' the beast roared, 'and now you steal from my garden. Prepare to die.'

The merchant begged for his life. He explained that he had picked the rose for his dearest daughter. At last the beast said the merchant could go if he promised to send in his place the first living thing he saw when he returned home. The merchant's dog was always the first to greet him when he had been away, so he gladly agreed and the beast let him go.

The merchant's joy at being home turned instantly to sorrow. His dog was inside the cottage lying asleep by the fire and it was Beauty who ran to greet him. She asked him why he looked so sad.

'I must say goodbye to you all,' said the merchant. He couldn't send Beauty to the beast. He would return himself. But Beauty made him tell her what had happened, and in spite of his protests, she said she would go to the castle.

AUGUST 19

Beauty and the Beast (Part 3)

Beauty agreed to stay with the beast in an attempt to save her father's life. She shuddered when she saw the ugly beast.

'Do not be afraid,' said the beast. 'I will not harm you.' Although the beast was ugly, he was kind and did everything he could to make Beauty happy.

One day he said, 'Do you think me ugly?'

'Well . . . er . . . yes,' said Beauty.

'Will you marry me?'

'Oh no . . .' said Beauty. 'I cannot marry you.'

Time passed and one night Beauty dreamed that her father was ill.

'Go home to him,' said the beast. 'But please return when he is well again.'

Beauty's father soon recovered when he saw that Beauty was well and happy.

The days and the weeks went by and Beauty almost forgot about the beast. Then one night she dreamed that the beast was dead. She woke from her dream crying. She dressed quickly and returned to the castle.

At first she thought the beast had gone, and then she saw him lying by a fountain. She splashed water gently on his face to revive him.

'Dear beast . . .' she said. 'What does it matter that you are so ugly? Of course I will marry you.' Then a wonderful thing happened. The ugly beast turned into a handsome prince.

'I was bewitched,' said the Prince, 'by a spell that could only be broken when someone loved me in spite of my ugliness.'

'And that is how the merchant gained a prince as a son-in-law and Beauty became a princess.

AUGUST 20

Adventures of *The Tulip* – Lost and Found

The riverboat, *The Tulip*, with its crew of Thomas, Minty and Wilbur, was floating downstream one sunny morning when Minty spotted a friend of theirs on the bank. It was Fergus Frog and he was sitting beside his bicycle, crying.

'What's wrong, Fergus?' called Minty.

'I've lost my bicycle bell in the river and I've dived for it and dived for it and I can't find it and I'm tired and I've got cramp and I've lost it for ever.' Fergus collapsed in tears.

'Don't worry, Fergus,' cried Wilbur, 'I'll get it for you.' With that, Wilbur dived into the river and started searching among the lily stems. Suddenly he felt something nudge him. There was a shoal of fish beside him.

'You're in our way,' said the fish-in-charge. 'It's our playtime now.'

Wilbur swam straight to the surface. 'Trouble I'm afraid,' he shouted to Thomas who had gone ashore. 'The fish are at play. They'll soon have churned up all the mud and I'll never find the bell.'

'Oh no!' cried Fergus desperately. 'Go back down. Go back down.' Wilbur dived down again. 'Can't you do something?' Fergus pleaded with Thomas.

Thomas called loudly across the water, 'Come on fish. It's storytime.'

'Storytime?' Fergus nearly exploded. 'I meant do something sensible.' But Thomas soon had all the fish listening quietly to his story about pirates and sunken treasure.

Suddenly Wilbur burst through the water. 'Got it,' he cried, holding the bicycle bell in his hand.

'Shush,' said Fergus rudely.

'Can't you see we're listening to a story?' But when the story was over, Fergus was very pleased to have his bell back.

AUGUST 21

The Fable of the Peacock and the Crane

Once there was a peacock who was very vain. He was always boasting about his beautiful feathers. Whenever it rained he would strut about looking for a puddle. When he found one he would stand and look at his own reflection until the puddle dried up.

'Just look at my tail,' he would say. 'Just look at the colours in my feathers. Just look at me! I must be the most beautiful bird in the world.' He would open out his tail and stand as proudly as a king, waiting for someone to come along and admire him.

One day a crane walked by. The peacock looked down his beak at the crane's grey feathers.

'You are extremely plain and very dull,' he said rudely. 'Can't you do something to brighten yourself up?'

'I can't deny that your feathers are more beautiful than mine,' said the crane as he spread his wings. 'But I notice you do not fly. For all their beauty, your feathers cannot lift you from the ground, while mine, though plain, can carry me into the sky.'

AUGUST 22

The Proud Mouse and the Kind Mouse

Once there was a mouse who was in love with a very beautiful lady mouse. 'Will you marry me?' he asked her one day.

The lady mouse answered proudly:

'If you wish to marry me,
You must bring me jewels
    from across the sea.
Come back here in a year and
    a day,
Then you can marry me and
    take me away.'

So the mouse sailed away across the sea but his boat was caught in a dreadful storm. He was washed ashore more dead than alive and taken to hospital. There he was cared for by a nurse mouse.

As he lay in his hospital bed he thought to himself, 'The lady mouse I risked my life for is very beautiful but she is very proud. The nurse mouse who is looking after me is not very beautiful but she is very kind.' So when he was well again the mouse asked the nurse mouse to marry him.

When the beautiful lady mouse saw the picture of the wedding in the *Mouse News* she was very angry. Her anger made her ugly and no other mice wanted to marry her.

The nurse mouse was never angry and she was so kind that her husband said to her:

'O dear nurse mouse
My love is true:
For there's no better mouse
In the world than you.'

And they both lived happily ever after.

AUGUST 23

Big Bold Dan the Pirate

Danny had no one to play with but he didn't care. In fact, he liked being on his own, because then he could play his favourite game – pretending.

Today he was pretending that he was a big bold pirate. He found some old clothes and a big hat. He had sailed the Seven Seas in search of adventure and now he was looking for somewhere to hide his treasure.

'Land ahoy!' he shouted, as he steered his ship towards a desert island that stood in the middle of the sparkling blue sea.

'Danny!' called his mother from the kitchen, 'Will you give the rabbits their food, please?'

'Sorry,' replied Danny in a deep gruff voice. 'I'm Big Bold Dan the Pirate. I'm too busy bringing my ship into the bay.'

Big Bold Dan the Pirate went scrunching round the desert island until he came to the foot of a sandy hill. Some tall palms were growing there beside an old dead tree.

'Aha!' growled Big Bold Dan. 'Just the very place for my treasure.' He picked up an old shovel.

'Danny!' called his mother. 'Will you take this shopping in to Mrs Jones next door for me?'

'Sorry,' grunted Danny. 'I'm Big Bold Dan the Pirate and I'm busy digging a hole to bury my treasure in.'

Soon it was time for lunch. Danny ran in to the house. 'Big Bold Dan has been working so hard he's really hungry. Will you cook him some sausages, please?'

'Sorry,' called his mother from the kitchen. 'I'm the Fairy Queen today and I don't cook sausages for big bold pirates unless they're my special friends.'

'How do they become your special friends?' Dan asked the Fairy Queen.

'By doing jobs their mums ask them to do,' said the Fairy Queen firmly.

'Oh,' said Big Bold Dan. He picked up the food dishes and took them out to the rabbits. He collected the shopping basket and took it to Mrs Jones. Then he came back into the kitchen.

'Are you still the Fairy Queen?' he asked his mother.

'Yes,' she smiled, 'and I'm busy cooking some sausages for a special friend of mine. Shall we eat them together on his pirate ship?'

'Mmm. Yes please,' said Big Bold Dan.

AUGUST 24

The Three Huntsmen

Slim, Tubby and Mr Jolly told marvellous stories of their hunting adventures, though really they had never hunted in their lives! One night, whilst enjoying themselves round the Mayor's dining table, a loud banging interrupted them. In burst a clown.

'Sirs!' he gasped. 'I need some men who can hunt. A lion's escaped from the circus.'

'You're in luck,' said the Mayor. 'We've three fine huntsmen here. Come, Mr Jolly, what a chance for you!'

Slim, Tubby and Mr Jolly fiddled with their hats, straightened their ties and fumbled with their guns, getting them mixed up with their umbrellas.

At last the Mayor waved them off. All three hoped the lion was miles away, but he wasn't. There, at the bottom of the garden, the great animal lay licking his paw.

'Leave the guns here,' whispered Mr Jolly. 'Mustn't scare him.'

'Well, old chap,' Tubby began. 'What are you doing? Running off, eh?'

'Have you got a bad toe?' asked Slim. 'Show your uncle then,' and they edged nearer. Moonlight shone on a piece of glass stuck between the pads of the lion's foot.

'Now,' said Slim, 'Tubby will hold your hand and I'll have that glass out in no time . . . There . . . What a brave boy! Give it a nice lick and Mr Jolly will bandage it.'

While Mr Jolly found the bandage, Slim and Tubby knotted all their ties together to make a lead. They looped it round the lion's head. Then they took the lion on a silk lead back to the circus. People watched amazed as they entered the Big Top. The three hunstmen were famous at last!

AUGUST 25

Cheese and Bees

'Away and lock the doors,' the people of the village would shout. 'The tinkers are coming.'

These were not the tinkers who mend pots and pans. These tinkers stole clothes from washing lines, broke fences and put other people's possessions in their pockets. When they were in the village nothing was safe, unless it was locked up or hidden.

'Something has to be done about this,' said Old John. 'We must consult the wizard.' So Old John and the village elders went to visit the wizard.

'I know why you have come,' said the wizard before they could utter a word. 'Turn round and go home. Next time the tinkers come to the village, close your windows and lock your doors and leave the rest to me.'

A few days later the tinkers arrived. Windows were closed and doors locked in the twinkling of an eye.

'Ha ha ha,' laughed the tinker chief. 'Someone was in such a hurry he forgot his cheese.' Standing right where the tinkers couldn't fail to see it, on a three-legged stool to raise it from the ground, was a round, ripe cheese.

'The cheese is mine,' said the wizard hobbling from his house, pretending to be afraid.

'Oh no it isn't . . . not any more,' said the tinker chief.

'Just let me take one slice,' said the wizard, quickly sinking his knife into its creamy skin.

'Away from there!' shouted the tinker in a temper. He pushed the wizard roughly to one side. But from the hole the wizard had made, rose a thousand humming, buzzing, angry bees.

'Ow . . . ow . . . ow!' screeched the tinkers as they took to their heels and ran, with the bees following close behind. The bees may be chasing the tinkers to this day because neither the bees nor the tinkers were ever seen again.

AUGUST 26

Roll Over

There were 10 in the bed
And the little one said,
'Roll over, roll over!'
So they all rolled over
And one fell out.

There were 9 in the bed
And the little one said,
'Roll over, roll over!'
So they all rolled over
And one fell out.

There were 8 in the bed
And the little one said,
'Roll over, roll over!'
So they all rolled over
And one fell out.

There were 7 in the bed
And the little one said,
'Roll over, roll over!'
So they all rolled over
And one fell out.

There were 6 in the bed
And the little one said,
'Roll over, roll over!'
So they all rolled over
And one fell out.

There were 5 in the bed
And the little one said,
'Roll over, roll over!'
So they all rolled over
And one fell out.

There were 4 in the bed
And the little one said,
'Roll over, roll over!'
So they all rolled over
And one fell out.

There were 3 in the bed
And the little one said,
'Roll over, roll over!'
So they all rolled over
And one fell out.

There were 2 in the bed
And the little one said,
'Roll over, roll over!'
So they all rolled over
And one fell out.

There was 1 in the bed
And the little one said,
'Roll over, roll over!'
So she rolled over
And she fell out.

There were none in the bed
And no one said,
'Roll over, roll over!'

'We are all down here!'

AUGUST 27

The Fable of the Piping Fisherman

Once there was a fisherman who could play on a pipe. One day, he took it with him when he went down to the seashore.

'If I can make the fish come to me, I will not have to throw out my nets and then have the hard work pulling them in again,' he said. He took out his pipe and began to play the liveliest tune he knew. 'This will make the fish jump from the sea in their thousands,' he thought.

The fisherman blew on his pipe until he had no breath left, but not one fish jumped from the sea on to the sand at his feet. He was very disappointed. He would have to go back to fishing the hard way.

He put his pipe into his pocket and then threw his net out to the sea. When he hauled it back to the shore it was full of fish.

When the fisherman saw the fish leaping and dancing in the net, he cried out crossly, 'Why is it that when I piped not one of you would dance, but now I have stopped piping, you are all dancing?'

The Emperor's New Clothes (Part 1)

Once there was an emperor who was always changing his clothes. He had a different outfit for every hour of the day. Whenever his ministers wanted him for something special, they always went to the royal clothes closet first. He was more likely to be there deciding what to change into next, than passing laws in his Council Chamber, or balancing the budget in his Counting House.

One day two men arrived in town. They knew how fond the Emperor was of new clothes and they had hatched a plan. They spread the news that they could weave the most beautiful cloth anyone had ever seen and what's more it was magic. The cloth was invisible to anyone who was stupid or unworthy of the position he held.

'I must have an outfit made from that marvellous new cloth everyone is talking about,' said the Emperor. So he sent for the weavers. They agreed to weave some of the cloth for him and went away from the palace carrying a large sum of money.

They set up their loom. There was the steady clack, clack and whirr of a busy loom for days. The Emperor was very anxious to see how the new cloth was coming along but he was just a bit afraid.

'What would I do if I couldn't see the cloth?' he thought. Although he was sure that he was worthy of being Emperor, he sent his faithful old Prime Minister to look at the cloth.

AUGUST 29

The Emperor's New Clothes (Part 2)

Two cunning men pretended they could weave the most beautiful cloth. They said the cloth was invisible to stupid or unworthy people. The Emperor ordered them to weave him some of their cloth and sent his Prime Minister to inspect it.

The weavers led the Prime Minister to their loom. He could not see a single thread.

'Oh dear,' he thought. 'If the Emperor finds out I can't see the cloth I will lose my job. I must pretend I can see it.'

'It's the most beautiful piece of cloth in the world,' he told the Emperor on his return to the palace. The Emperor decided he would go and see it for himself. He gathered his favourite councillors around him and went to the weavers.

'Show us your beautiful new cloth,' he said.

'Can you not see it? It's there on the loom,' said the weavers.

'So it is . . . so it is . . . ' said the Emperor, his voice full of shame, because he could not see the cloth either. But then neither could anyone else, though everyone thought everyone else could see it. There were so many cries of delight at the beauty of the new cloth, it was quite astonishing.

'Make me a suit of clothes from the cloth and I will wear it in the procession tomorrow,' said the Emperor.

At eight o'clock next morning the suit was ready. Or so the men told the Emperor. The Emperor bathed. He powdered his hair. He put on his shoes and stockings. Then he let the weavers dress him in the new suit of clothes.

AUGUST 30

The Emperor's New Clothes (Part 3)

The Emperor had ordered a new suit of clothes for the great procession. Unfortunately, the men who made the suit had tricked him by saying the cloth could not be seen by stupid people. Not wishing to appear stupid, the Emperor and all his councillors admired the suit even though there was no suit there.

'It's a perfect fit,' said the men who made the suit.

'It's a perfect fit,' said all the councillors.

'It's a perfect fit,' said the Emperor, although he could see nothing but his own pink skin.

When the Emperor was ready, or thought he was, the procession began through the streets of the town. Everyone knew about the wonderful cloth. Everyone knew that only those worthy enough could see it and that to everyone else it was invisible.

'Look at the Emperor's new suit! Isn't it beautiful . . .?' sighed the people in the crowd as the Emperor walked proudly by.

Then a little voice rang out above the others. It was a boy. He hadn't heard the stories about the wonderful cloth.

'The Emperor has no clothes on!' he shouted.

Someone began to laugh. 'The boy's right! The Emperor has no clothes on!' The cry was caught up by the people in the crowd.

'The Emperor has no clothes on!'

The poor Emperor was shivering with cold so he knew the crowd must be right, but he walked proudly through the streets and back to the palace with his head held high and his skin blushing a bright red.

He sent guards to fetch the men who had dared to trick him but they had vanished and were never seen again. From that day on the Emperor spent less time on his clothes and more time on the affairs of state.

AUGUST 31

The Last Load Home

John, the farmer's son, was leading Dobey home and giving an old stranger a ride on the last load. He had been helping for over a week. He called himself Skip; and John liked him.

'How about coming to our party tonight, Skip?' John asked. 'Plenty to eat and drink and pretty girls to dance with. What d'you say?'

'I'd enjoy that,' Skip answered. 'Thank you.'

That evening, Skip, clean and tidy, sat in the barn trying out tunes on his pipe when John walked in.

'Hello, Skip!' he called. 'I didn't know you were a musician! My players haven't turned up. If they don't come soon would you help at all?'

'Of course,' Skip agreed, 'if you find me a fiddle. I didn't think to bring mine.'

John laughed. 'You shall have one. You're full of surprises.'

That night dancing feet glided and twinkled to Skip's music. Everyone clapped and shouted for more.

During supper the three players arrived; their horse had gone lame. 'Now Skip,' said John, 'you'll have time to dance yourself – good at it too, eh?'

'Not bad,' Skip replied. 'Quite famous with the clogs.'

'Right!' said John. A space was cleared for Skip. In a few

seconds Skip was clack-clacking faster and faster. Then, circling the barn floor, he cried: 'Follow me!' Young men grabbed a partner, all laughing so much they could hardly keep up. Out of the yard and up the hill went Skip with his pipe. From the top he turned and waved, but when the others reached it, the road before them lay empty.

Standing there in silence, they heard the notes of his pipe growing fainter and fainter. Skip had disappeared and no one saw him again.

SEPTEMBER

SEPTEMBER 1

Kalunda of the Silver Sky (Part 1)

Kalunda of the Silver Sky was a fine baby, born just as the moon was rising, one night in December. His parents, both Indians living on a settlement in North America, had longed for a boy. Kalunda's father was a tall, dark man. His mother also had the dark skin of her tribe. They expected a dark-skinned child.

But the women who were present at his birth were amazed. 'The child has no hair!' they cried in horror. For the strong, black Indian hair usually started to grow even on the newest baby. The skin too was normally dark and tough.

'He looks like a girl,' whispered the women. 'His skin is soft and fair and not one strand of hair!'

As Kalunda grew, his mother prayed and prayed that the Gods would let his skin darken, that his hair would turn black. Her prayers were not answered. By the time Kalunda was three years old, his hair was long and silver like moonshine. His skin was soft and fresh like silk.

Because he was different, Kalunda was feared by all the Indians in his tribe. Even his own mother was ashamed of the strange, silver child who slept beside her. Before the boy reached five years of age she no longer cared for him. He wandered alone in the village, lonely and often hungry. What would become of the child?

SEPTEMBER 2

Kalunda of the Silver Sky (Part 2)

Kalunda was an Indian boy who was born fair instead of dark-skinned. Beyond his village, in her own tent, lived an ancient Indian woman called Anra. No one knew her age but the Indians respected her for her wisdom. Yet, because of her great age, she too was different and the tribespeople were afraid of her.

Kalunda found a friend in wise old Anra. She looked after the child and soon realised that it was not only his hair and his skin that were unusual. The child had strange powers. Anra's land had become dry but the boy gently tended the shoots until they sprang again into green life. He had a special understanding of all natural things. Animals and birds loved and trusted him at once. Even the wolves, which sometimes destroyed Indian crops, were tame with the boy and walked by his side.

So the two lived happily together and on long moonlit nights the silver-haired youngster would sit beside the wrinkled old woman. 'Tell me more about the days of long ago,' Kalunda would beg. And so he learned all about his great Indian tribe.

Now, the Indians in the settlement were wary of this strange pair. One year, when, without any reason the crops failed badly, gossip began among the tribesmen. 'It is the fault of Anra and Kalunda who live on the edge of our land,' said one. 'They mean evil for our tribe.'

That night, as Kalunda sat listening to Anra's stories, the child saw three tall braves. They were approaching the tent, bows and arrows raised, wearing warpaint and feathers. Anra took the boy's hand tightly in her own, as they waited.

SEPTEMBER 3

Kalunda of the Silver Sky (Part 3)

Kalunda and Anra, two American Indians, were blamed by the tribe for the crops failing. Anra greeted the warriors who came in her usual way: 'Peace to you,' she called out, untroubled by their warpaint.

'We come because of the famine,' the first brave shouted angrily.

'Tell us of your troubles,' Anra said kindly. The warriors felt uncertain now. Could the wise old woman and the pale shy boy be evil? Unwillingly, the braves sat down, crosslegged, facing Anra and Kalunda. They told how all their crops were dying. 'And often wolves attack the settlement,' they added. 'Listen! You can hear them now.'

'We shall come to help,' Anra said. Rising up, she and Kalunda returned to the settlement. Sure enough, wolves were on the prowl. Watchful and afraid, the braves heard young Kalunda call out and quieten the howling animals.

Next day, the astonished Indians watched as Kalunda and Anra moved through the fields. Almost at once the crops improved. By the end of the week new shoots were appearing. The threat of famine was over.

The Indian Chief called Anra and Kalunda to his tent. 'Forgive us,' he said humbly. 'We feared you because you are different. But you have proved yourselves our friends. Come! Live with us again in the settlement.'

Anra answered for them: 'Thank you. We are grateful. But our lives are happy. We will stay in our home. Our help is yours whenever it is needed.' Quietly, while the other Indians peeped through the flaps of their tents, the two began their journey home.

And so, years after Anra'a death, the man Kalunda, with his fair skin and silver hair, protected the settlement in which he never lived.

SEPTEMBER 4

Toot-toot Goes Swimming

Toot-toot, the little steam engine who had escaped from his rails, tootled out of the town to look for somewhere to get a wash. He was very muddy after working on the farm. Toot-toot sniffed the air. It was rather salty. Then he found his wheels sinking in soft sand. He tootled along a bit further and there was nothing but blue water in front of him.

Toot-toot rolled forward to the edge of the sea and felt it with one front wheel. Ooooh! It was cold. But there were children bathing in it, so he went deeper. He liked it; it was so cool and he would soon be clean. He didn't go too deep; he didn't want to get his whistle wet. The children splashed Toot-toot and played ball with him. Toot-toot would catch the ball on his funnel and blow it out again.

Then the ball went out quite a long way. Toot-toot followed it and went deeper and deeper until all that showed above the water was his funnel. At that moment the beach guard, who had been sleeping, woke up. He scanned the horizon with his binoculars and spotted Toot-toot's funnel. He rushed to the end of the pier.

'No submarines allowed on my beach!' he shouted. Toot-toot came out on to the sand, spluttering and blowing seaweed out of his whistle. The guard was so surprised to see the little engine tootling up the beach that he forgot to shout at him for leaving wheel tracks in the sand.

'Goodbye, goodbye,' said the children, waving to Toot-toot. The little engine gave them a toot on his whistle, just for fun.

SEPTEMBER 5

Blackberry Jam (Part 1)

There was once an old woman who liked blackberries. She didn't eat them. She made them into jam; jar upon jar of blackberry jam. Her cupboard was full of them. She could never use all the jam she made, but she used to store it like a miser stores gold.

As soon as the wild fruit was ripe, out she would go and pick every berry in sight. The creatures of the forest liked blackberries too but she pushed them out of the way as she picked the bushes bare.

On her way home with her heavy baskets of fruit the old woman came upon a bear.

'Can I have some of your berries?' asked the bear.
'Pick your own,' said the old woman.
'But you've picked them all,' said the bear.
'Then you should get up earlier,' said the old woman.
'There are enough berries for us all to share,' said the bear.
'If I want to pick all the berries, I shall,' said the old woman and marched past the bear with her nose in the air.

The bear decided to call all the creatures together to teach the old woman a lesson.

SEPTEMBER 6

Blackberry Jam (Part 2)

'We will give the old woman one more chance to share the blackberries she picks,' said the bear, 'then this is what we'll do . . .'

The next day the bear called at the old woman's house.

'If we can't have any blackberries, can we have a jar of your blackberry jam?' asked the bear.

'Certainly not,' she replied and slammed the door.

That night the animals crept into her house and took away every scrap of food she had stored up,

but they left all her blackberry jam.

Next morning the old woman realised she had nothing to eat until next market day, which was a whole week away. Nothing, that is, except blackberry jam.

She had blackberry jam for breakfast, blackberry jam for lunch, blackberry jam for tea and when she was hungry before bed she had to open another jar of blackberry jam.

After a week of blackberry jam the old woman decided she never wanted to see another blackberry ever again. From then on everyone picked their fair share of blackberries and the old woman was pleased to let them.

SEPTEMBER 7

Humpty Dumpty

Humpty Dumpty fell from the wall;
He'd really no business there at all.
He cut his hand,
He tore his trews
And scuffed the toes of his newest shoes.

He slithered down on to grassy ground
Then brushed himself off and looked around;
All the King's horses
And all the King's men
Couldn't put him back on the wall again.

So they marched him off to the King's High Court;
Humpty trembled at the very thought.
The King looked up,
Eyes open wide,
He laughed and laughed till he almost cried.

'Pray, what on earth do you call yourself?
Your place is on the dairy shelf.
Aren't you an egg,
And a cracked one too?
What you need, my friend, is a spot of glue.'

At the name of Humpty Dumpty, the King
Laughed again: 'You're a very strange thing;
A mascot, eh?
To cheer my men!
Clean him up and I'll see him again.'

Humpty was dressed in uniform fine
And there he marched at the head of the line.
When he was tired,
They held him up
And bore him along in the King's egg-cup.

His fame spread wide from land to land,
He'd a special tune and a special band.
And eggstra care
They had to take,
For never, oh never, must Humpty break!

SEPTEMBER 8

Spike Rings Fairyland

Spike the elf was on his way out of Bluebell Wood when he came upon a telephone. There it lay at the foot of an old tree. Spike stopped and looked at it carefully.

'This is a funny place to find a telephone,' he said to himself. 'No wonder it looks so lost.' Then Spike had a bright idea. For a long time he had been thinking about his friends in Fairyland. 'I know,' he said. 'I'll give then a call! I've got so much to tell them. I'll speak to them all.'

Now there is a very special code number to Fairyland and Spike had to sit down and think for a moment. Then he remembered what it was. He dialled the number. He heard it ring twice and then it was answered. 'Hello. This is Fairyland. Queen of the Fairies speaking,' said the voice.

Queen of the Fairies! Spike couldn't believe it. He was on the phone to the Queen of the Fairies.

'Hello?' said the voice sharply. 'Is anyone there? State your business.' Spike was so surprised he didn't know what to say. Everything he had planned was driven out of his mind.

'Who's at the other end of this telephone?' said the voice getting very impatient. 'Because you're going to be in big trouble.'

Spike gulped. 'Sorry. Wrong number,' he said quickly and put the phone down. 'Maybe it wasn't such a good idea to ring Fairyland today,' thought Spike. 'I'll try again tomorrow.'

Spike was rather relieved the next day to find the telephone had disappeared. But he proudly told all his friends in Bluebell Wood about the time he'd had a conversation with the Queen of the Fairies.

SEPTEMBER 9

Ash Lodge – A Fair Exchange

Willie the Mole lives with his two Badger friends, Basil and Dewy, at Ash Lodge. One day when Willie was out, Basil discovered the bottom had fallen out of his bucket. Willie hadn't meant to do it. He'd been using it to stand on to reach something and his foot just went through it. He hid the bucket under a pile of leaves and hoped no one would notice.

Just as Basil was wondering where the bottom of the bucket was, Tinker Weasel came round the corner of the house with pots and pans dangling from his belt.

'Just the fellow I want to see,' said Basil. 'Have you got a new bucket there?' Indeed he had, and in a few moments Basil had exchanged his old bucket and two slices of Dewy's currant cake for one of Tinker Weasel's new buckets.

Willie, on his way home, bumped into Tinker Weasel in the lane. 'I'm saved,' he gasped. He grabbed the bucket Tinker was carrying and gave him his telescope in return. Tinker had no chance to explain it was a broken bucket and Willie didn't notice as he ran happily home and went to the shed to hang it up.

There Willie saw the new bucket. 'What's that doing up there?' he asked.

'Why shouldn't it be up there?' said Basil. 'What's that behind your back, Willie?'

'Oh, this. I thought it was time we had a new bucket,' said Willie.

'That won't carry much,' said Dewy, putting his hand through the bottom.

Willie gasped. 'I've been cheated.' Just then Tinker Weasel appeared.

'I think there must be some mistake,' he said, handing the telescope to Willie.

Basil gave the bucket back to the confused Weasel. 'We might have known you'd be at the bottom of this, Willie,' he said with a smile.

SEPTEMBER 10

Jorinda and Joringel (Part 1)

Once upon a time there was a witch who lived in a castle in the middle of a dark wood. At sunset she changed herself into an owl and flew about the wood, ready to cast a spell on anyone who dared to get too close to her castle.

One day a boy and girl were walking in the wood. They were planning their wedding and went deeper into the wood than they intended.

Just as the sun was setting, Joringel said, 'We should turn for home . . . we are getting too close to the witch's castle.' But it was already too late, for as he spoke an owl flew from the trees and circled round them.

'Whoo! Whoo! Whoo!' it cried. The witch's spell had been cast. Joringel could not move and Jorinda had been turned into a little brown bird.

The owl flew into the middle of a bush. There was a rustle and a moment later the old witch herself appeared. She caught the brown bird in a wicker cage and hurried away with it towards the castle. And though Joringel could see everything as it happened, he could do nothing to help Jorinda. He was rooted to the spot. And there he stayed, as still as a stone statue, until the old witch returned and removed the spell.

'Where is Jorinda? What have you done with her? Please bring her back to me,' he begged. But the old witch was deaf to all his pleas.

'Go home . . .' she said. 'Stop wasting my time.'

SEPTEMBER 11

Jorinda and Joringel (Part 2)

A witch had turned Jorinda into a bird and taken her in a cage to her castle. Joringel tried again and again to get into the castle, but whenever he got near the walls she cast her spell afresh and he could not move. He despaired of ever seeing Jorinda again.

Then one night when he had fallen into a fitful sleep he had a strange dream. He dreamed that he had found a large pearl in the centre of a beautiful red flower. In his dream he picked the flower and found that everything he touched with it was released from the witch's spell.

When Joringel woke he decided to search until he found the flower. He searched through the woods and the meadows for eight whole days and then on the ninth day he found a flower just like the one in his dream. But instead of a pearl nestling inside its velvety red petals, there was a bright and glistening dewdrop. Joringel picked it carefully so that he did not disturb the dewdrop, then cradled it gently in his hands and hurried towards the castle.

SEPTEMBER 12

Jorinda and Joringel (Part 3)

Joringel had found a flower that he hoped would break the witch's spell over Jorinda.

He reached the castle door without being stopped. He had never been so close to the castle before. He touched the door with the flower. It flew open. As he walked through the castle the witch danced round him, screeching and shouting and casting all the spells she could think of. But nothing worked. The flower's magic was stronger than hers.

Presently Joringel came to a room where seven hundred wicker cages hung from hooks in the ceiling. Sitting in each cage was a sad brown bird. Out of seven hundred, how could he tell which was Jorinda? Then Joringel saw the witch sneaking away with one of the cages. He knew at once that that was Jorinda. He snatched the cage from the witch and opened the door. The instant the velvety red petals of the flower brushed against the bird's wing it turned back into Jorinda.

'I knew you would come,' she whispered. Now Joringel set about freeing all the other little brown birds from the witch's spell. Soon there were seven hundred empty cages swinging from the ceiling.

From that day onwards the witch lost her power to cast spells and it was safe to walk anywhere in the wood, by day or by night.

SEPTEMBER 13

Charlie the Chimpanzee

Thomas and his father spent the whole afternoon in the field at the back of their house raking up the hay into heaps to dry.

'I'll try to get tickets for the circus tomorrow as a reward for all your hard work,' said Thomas's father as they went indoors.

Early next morning, while Thomas was still in bed, Charlie, the chimpanzee from the circus, ran into the field. He bumped into one of the heaps of hay and it collapsed around him covering him in hay from top to tail. Charlie was frightened and ran round the field in circles.

When Thomas woke up he looked out of his window and was amazed to see a small haystack running round the field. Thomas ran downstairs and opened the kitchen door to have a better look. The haystack ran straight through the open door into the kitchen.

Now it was Thomas's turn to be frightened. He ran upstairs screaming. 'Help! A haystack has come to life and it's in the kitchen.'

When Thomas's father came downstairs, Charlie had shaken all the hay off him and was leaping around the room.

'It's a chimpanzee,' Thomas's father laughed. 'It must belong to the circus.' He telephoned the circus and in no time at all the circus owner arrived to collect Charlie. He was so pleased to find Charlie safe and sound he gave Thomas and his father a ticket each to see the circus that afternoon.

Thomas thought the circus was great fun, especially the chimpanzees' tea party. Charlie ended up with custard pies and cream cakes all over him. 'He's good at that,' said Thomas. 'This morning he was a running haystack; now he's a walking ice-cream!'

SEPTEMBER 14

The Fable of the Mouse and the Bull

A mouse bit a bull on the nose, and was chased for his daring. The mouse was very nimble and far too quick for the bull who, though very strong, was more than a little clumsy. The mouse ran into a hole at the bottom of a wall and then turned and looked at the bull. The mouse knew he was safe, and could afford to be cheeky. The bull was very angry. A little mouse was not going to get the better of him.

The bull charged at the wall. The bull was strong, but so was the wall. The bull charged until his head was sore but he did nothing to the wall at all. He finally sank to his knees with exhaustion. It was the chance the mouse had been waiting for. He darted from the hole and bit the bull again.

The bull rose to his feet with an angry roar, but he wasn't quick enough. The mouse darted back into the hole. The bull bellowed and he stamped his feet until the ground shook. There was nothing else he could do.

Presently a shrill little voice called to him from the safety of the wall: 'It's not always best to be big and strong.'

SEPTEMBER 15

Diffy Duck (Part 1)

Mrs Duck was very happy. She was listening to the little creaks and cracks that meant her eggs were breaking open and soon there would be a family of baby ducklings. One of the eggs kept rolling away and that one didn't make any sound at all.

'Now why?' Mrs Duck asked herself, staring hard at it.

CREAK! CRACK! POP! went all the other eggs and out popped the fluffy yellow ducklings.

'Beautiful! sighed Mrs Duck happily. She glared at the egg that was left unopened.

SNAP! Without any warning at all the last egg burst open and the duckling inside it shot up into the air. Mrs Duck watched open-beaked as the youngest duckling soared into space.

But the little fellow soon came down to earth again because, of course, he couldn't fly, and he landed upside down next to his brothers and sisters.

Mrs Duck eyed her son fondly. 'I thought you would be different,' she said.

'DIFFERENT!' gurgled the little duckling. 'Call me DIFFY!' The very first thing Diffy wanted to do was to leave home.

'You can't!' snapped Mrs Duck. 'You've only just got here.'

'I have a spirit of adventure,' explained Diffy.

'Save it until you're grown up,' shrieked Mrs Duck. She had to shriek because little Diffy was already on his way.

SEPTEMBER 16

Diffy Duck (Part 2)

Diffy Duck was different. He was born with a spirit of adventure, and he decided to travel the world with it.

The first place Diffy came to was not as adventurous as he thought it might be. He thought that after all that walking he must have reached foreign parts, but he hadn't. He had only got as far as the farm-house.

The farmer's wife was cleaning the kitchen. She didn't like the job and she was doing it as quickly as she could. She was rather short-sighted and when Diffy perched on the handle of a wooden spoon for a rest, she thought he was a feather-duster.

Diffy had to cling hard to that wooden spoon because the farmer's wife shot him up to dust the pictures. Then she pushed him sideways to dust the clock and then down to dust inside a vase.

Diffy could have been named 'Dusty' before she had finished with him. He raced away from the wooden spoon as soon as she put it down. He meant to make for the door, but with all that dust in his eyes he went the wrong way and ended up against the wall.

Just then her son, Fred, came in from school. Fred didn't see Diffy sitting on the floor trying to brush the dust out of his eyes. Fred took off his hat as soon as he came in and tossed it across the room. He missed the hook and the hat fell straight on top of Diffy.

Diffy thought the roof had fallen on top of him and was running to try and shake it off. Fred looked at his hat scuttling across the floor and screamed.

With the scream ringing in his ears, Diffy left his spirit of adventure behind him in the farm-house. He knew that his beak was pointing towards his duck-pond home because he could hear his mother telling his brothers and sisters what to do as she took them for their first swim. Diffy decided to join them and go back later for his spirit of adventure. But he was so pleased to be swimming with his mother and brothers and sisters he never did bother to look for it again.

SEPTEMBER 17

The King's Galleons

King Grabalot, he stamped in rage
And sent for Admiral Armitage:
'Get to your ships! Go, search the sea,
And bring my daughter back to me!

She's run off with that Lancelot!
And do you know what they have got?
Great bags of treasure from my caves,
Get moving man – go, ride the waves!'

His ten fine galleons, tall and grand,
Were cheered to the sound of a big brass band.
They sailed in glory from the port
And missed the weathermen's gale report.

Meanwhile, the princess sailed a raft
With her dear Lance – and how they laughed.
They found a lovely island home
And settled down – it was their own;

That night the storm blew fierce and strong;
Poor Armitage, his fleet now gone,
Cried: 'Ships are smashed! Sails in tatters!
Save yourselves! Life's all that matters!'

The weary sailors kept afloat
By hanging on to bits of boat;
They'd swallowed water – quite a lot;
Who pulled them in? . . . Yes, Lancelot.

The King told Lance he'd changed his mind.
'You've saved my men so I'll be kind.
My treasure's yours and there it stays,
But . . . I'll come to you for holidays.'

SEPTEMBER 18

Chuffa's Moon Trip (Part 1)

Chuffa the engine is cheerful, chunky and
charming. He is also dozy, dreamy and drowsy.
Today he is dozing in the silvery moonlight and
on his funnel is Sebastian the seagull, who is one
of Chuffa's best friends. Chuffa dreams of flying
like a bird – like Sebastian. He gives a big sigh,
'Ch-uff,' and dozes off to sleep.

Suddenly he hears Sebastian calling. Not just one

Sebastian, but six Sebastians! They're lifting
Chuffa up into the air. All six of them. How strong
they are! Chuffa is flying like a bird in the sky. He
looks down and sees the whole world silvery in
the moonlight, while they soar up into the air.

Chuffa is not the least bit afraid even when they
have left the Earth far, far behind and are up in
Cloudland where the angels live.

But even six strong Sebastians can't go on lifting
a Chuffa engine without getting rather tired. They
may drop him . . .

SEPTEMBER 19

Chuffa's Moon Trip (Part 2)

Chuffa the engine has been lifted high in the sky by six Sebastian seagulls. But now they're getting tired. They're about to drop Chuffa . . . when two little angels come to the rescue.

'You need to get airborne,' says one angel. 'We'll each lend you a wing. We'll only need one each if we join arms and fly together.'

So that is what they do. Each takes off one wing. Then the angels fix the wings on to Chuffa's cabin. He carefully flaps one and then the other. Then both at once. And yes! He can fly. Chuffa, the first engine in space! And now for the Moon. Chuffa-chuff, flap-flap. Up and up.

So the angels guide him to the great, round, dusty surface of the Moon. Chuffa feels himself being pulled down and down until he lands in a moon crater. But it isn't a hard bump at all. It is as soft and gentle as when you land on your bed. Chuffa feels as light as a feather.

'Now, what shall we do next?' asks one angel.

'Well, how about a trip to the Great Station-in-the-Sky?' says the other. 'That's where all the good trains go when they are very old. Just give a blast on your whistle.'

One blast is enough to launch Chuffa into Outer Space and away beyond until they come to a land of beautiful-coloured clouds. First a fine blue cloud where all the engines live when they come to the end of the line. There they live happily without a timetable or anything to worry them. They promise Chuffa that one day he can come and live there too!

SEPTEMBER 20

Chuffa's Moon Trip (Part 3)

Chuffa the engine is on a trip in space with two angel friends. The angels take him to a pink cloud where he sees the cutest little engine and he decides to land on the cloud and make friends.

'Don't do it,' cry the angels. 'It won't hold you up. You're too heavy for it.' But Chuffa won't listen. WHOOOSSH! Right through that rosy, pink cloud Chuffa goes. Down and down and down.

As he falls, the feathers of the wings that keep him up, float away. Soon there isn't a single feather left on either wing and there is nothing to keep him up. Poor Chuffa!

But as in a dream, when you fall you never hurt yourself, so it is that Chuffa lands back on his rails without so much as a bump. There he is, back on Earth with the Moon shining overhead and old Sebastian fast asleep on his funnel. And there on the cabin roof is a single feather. It might be one of Sebastian's feathers or it might be an angel's feather. Who can tell?

SEPTEMBER 21

The Fable of Hercules and the Wagoner

A man was driving his horse and cart along a muddy lane when the wheels of the cart sank deep into the mud. The cart was stuck. No amount of pulling on the part of the horse would move it.

The man held his head in despair. 'What am I to do?' he wailed. 'Why doesn't someone come and help me? Why doesn't the mighty Hercules who is stronger than any man on Earth come to help me?'

Hercules heard his name being called and came to see what was wanted of him.

'Stop wailing and put your own shoulder to the wheel,' said Hercules. 'If you show you are willing to help yourself, I will gladly share your burden. How can you expect others to help you if you do not help yourself?'

SEPTEMBER 22

The Witch and the Windmill

Thomas the miller was busy in the mill. He loved to hear its sails blowing round, turning the great grinding-stones, crushing the wheat into flour.

A loud bang came on his door. It was the witch, Bossy Boots! 'Here,' she said, dumping her small sack of grain in front of him. 'This won't take long. I'll call this evening.' Then she was off on her broomstick.

The miller was grinding Farmer Brown's grain so he filled a bag from some flour he had already. When the witch called later she never even thanked him.

The next week Bossy Boots brought a sack of plants fresh from the hedges. 'Grind these herbs!' she ordered. 'By tomorrow!'

'But, madam,' cried Thomas, 'they'll spoil the next lot of flour!'

'Rubbish!' yelled the witch. 'I need them – for spells!'

Thomas worked late. He dried the herbs in his wife's bread oven and then chopped them. Bossy kept bringing more herbs.

Thomas was so tired and worried he didn't hear her knocking. Suddenly, from his top platform, he saw her riding her broomstick round the sails.

'Silly old woman!' he shouted. 'You'll hurt yourself!' Screaming with laughter, she darted between the sails. Before Thomas could stop the windmill her broom brushed one of the sails.

Snap! . . . Pieces of broomstick scattered everywhere! The witch's petticoats filled out like a parachute. But she didn't float down; she rose higher!

'Oh, my goodness!' cried Thomas. 'What can I do?'

'Nothing, my dear,' said his wife. 'We can't throw her a rope. But she'll settle somewhere.'

Far away on an island the witch landed on a thistle. There was no kind miller, no broomstick and Bossy Boots couldn't swim. So there she stayed.

SEPTEMBER 23

A Pot of Gold (Part 1)

Patrick lived with his mother and a cow and some hens in a tiny cottage in the middle of Ireland. They were poor but they were happy.

Every morning, as she blew on the peat fire to make it hot enough to cook their breakfast porridge, Patrick's mother would call, 'Wake up and get up, you lazy boy! You will never catch a leprechaun with your eyes closed.'

Leprechauns are fairy shoemakers. They live in holes in the ground and between the roots of trees. They are said to be very rich and wherever there is a leprechaun there is sure to be a pot of gold hidden somewhere close by.

There were leprechauns living near the cottage where Patrick lived with his mother. The wind had only to stop blowing for an instant and Patrick's keen ears could hear the sound of their tiny hammers hammering against leather.

'If you happen to see a leprechaun,' said Patrick's mother, at least once every day, 'do not take your eyes off him for a moment. If you do he will disappear and then you will never find his pot of gold.'

One day, when Patrick was returning home, he heard the sound of tapping. He looked down and there, in the long grass at his feet, was a leprechaun. He was so busy hammering away at a pair of hobnailed boots he didn't notice Patrick.

SEPTEMBER 24

A Pot of Gold (Part 2)

Patrick had discovered a leprechaun. 'Got you!' he cried as he caught the leprechaun in his hand.

'Let me go! Let me go!' shouted the leprechaun, struggling to get free.

'Tell me where your gold is hidden first!'

'G . . . g . . . gold . . ?' The leprechaun turned very pale. 'Quick! Look behind you! There's a cow in the corn!' cried the leprechaun. Just in time, Patrick remembered not to look.

'Ha . . . ha . . . you don't catch me that way. I won't take my eyes off you. Now where is your pot of gold?'

'I haven't got a pot of gold!' cried the leprechaun. 'Quick! Look behind you! Your house is burning!' Patrick almost did look that time.

'It's no good trying to trick me,' said Patrick. 'I'm not letting you go until you tell me where your gold is hidden.'

'All right, all right. I'll show you where it is,' said the leprechaun, and he led Patrick to a field of thistles.

'It's under that thistle,' said the leprechaun, pointing to an extra-prickly one. 'You'll need a spade to dig it up. You had better go home and get one.'

'I'll put my garter round it to mark it first,' said Patrick, and taking off one of the garters that

held up his woollen socks, he placed it over the prickly thistle.

'Now I'll go home and get the spade,' he said, 'and to make sure you don't play any tricks on me I'll put you in my pocket.' But by putting the leprechaun in his pocket, Patrick had taken his eyes off him.

By the time Patrick returned to the thistle patch with his spade, *every* thistle had a garter round it. Which one should he choose? Patrick felt in his pocket for the leprechaun. But he had worked his magic and disappeared long ago, and Patrick's pockets were empty once again.

SEPTEMBER 25

Harmony Wood

There was great excitement in Harmony Wood. It was the day of the Concert. Grasshopper had made a flute from a long blade of grass, while Spider had woven a thick web into the shape of a triangle. It made a gentle twanging sound when he gave it a tap with his foot. Rabbit was very proud of the

drum he had made by drying leaves in the sun and then stretching them over a hollow tree trunk. His strong hind legs were just right for beating a good rhythm. Even Fox had joined in the fun by gathering all the left-over bits and pieces and making a most unusual guitar.

Owl peered sadly from his hole in the tree. Because he usually slept all day he hadn't had the time to make or learn to play anything.

'On your instruments, get set, PLAY,' called Hare, who was in a hurry to get the Concert over with so he could start on the food. Oh dear! They'd never played their instruments together before. It didn't sound right at all.

'Stop!' screeched Owl. 'That sounds awful.' He flew down on to a large branch so everyone could see. Then, by pointing and waving his wings, he instructed everyone when to start playing their instruments. Owl began to feel quite proud. 'That's better,' he said.

Snail wrote some musical notes in snail-trail on a large leaf, and Blackbird held it up high for everyone to read. All around birds sang sweet notes, while butterflies danced daintily to the music.

Soon they all felt very hungry, and so sat down to a huge meal of nectar-leaf sandwiches, pollen-cakes and blackberry pie. What a wonderful day in Harmony Wood!

SEPTEMBER 26

The Golden Goose (Part 1)

Once there was a man who had three sons. One day the eldest went to the forest to chop wood. At midday, as he was eating his lunch, an old man appeared from nowhere and asked for a small bite to eat.

'Go away,' said the eldest son. 'I share my lunch with no one.' He didn't know that the old man had magic powers and he thought it was just bad luck when his axe slipped as he worked that afternoon and he cut his thumb.

The following day the middle son went to the forest. At midday the old man appeared again.

'Go away,' said the boy. 'I share my lunch with no one.' He too thought it was just bad luck when a log fell on his toe and bruised it so badly that he limped all the way home.

On the third day it was the turn of the third and youngest son to go to the forest to chop wood. At midday, as the youngest son sat eating his lunch, the old man appeared yet again, and once more asked for a small bite to eat.

'Come and sit beside me,' said the boy. 'We'll share the food.' When the old man had finished lunch he pointed to an old and rotting tree stump.

'Cut that down,' he said, 'and you will find a reward for having a kind heart.' With that, he disappeared as mysteriously as he had arrived.

SEPTEMBER 27

The Golden Goose (Part 2)

A boy had been told to cut down an old tree to find a reward for his kindness. He chopped it down as the old man had suggested. Lying unharmed at the stump was a goose with golden feathers. It let the boy stroke its head and nestled quietly in his arms when he picked it up.

'I can't leave you here,' said the boy. 'Someone is sure to kill you for your golden feathers. I think I had better take you with me.'

On his way home the boy stopped at an inn. The landlord of the inn had three daughters. One of them looked enviously at the goose's golden feathers and made up her mind to have one.

While the boy wasn't looking, she tried to pluck a feather from the goose's back, but as she tried to pull it she found her hand would not move. She tried to let go of the feather and found that she couldn't.

'Oh . . . oh . . .' she cried, 'my hand is stuck. Sister, pull me away.' Her sister came to help her, but as soon as she touched her sister's dress she found that she was stuck too. The same thing happened to the third sister when she tried to pull the second sister free.

The boy set off again with the golden goose tucked safely under his arm. He pretended not to notice the three sisters trailing behind him. Then a disapproving clergyman tried to pull the girls away and was caught himself. So were the clergyman's young assistant and three diggers who joined the chain for fun and couldn't get free.

SEPTEMBER 28

The Golden Goose (Part 3)

A boy had found a golden goose. Now a great chain of people stretched behind him as he travelled across country. They were all stuck to one another by the goose's magic. Whenever anyone touched the chain they couldn't get free. The boy at the front thought it was great fun as the chain got longer and longer.

They happened to pass through a land where a very sad princess was living. When she saw all these people tagging along behind a boy with a goose under his arm, all of them tripping and bumping one another, she couldn't help smiling. Then her smile became a laugh.

'Who has made my daughter laugh?' called the King. The boy let go of the goose and walked up to the King. 'You shall marry my daughter, if you wish,' said the King. 'No one has ever made her laugh before.'

'Thank you, sir,' said the boy.

He and the Princess laughed together as the human chain disappeared over the hills, all stuck to one another behind the goose flying on at the front. The boy and the Princess lived happily ever after and the human chain may be going and growing to this day.

SEPTEMBER 29

Sixes and Sevens

Once there was a little house surrounded by seven pine trees. Behind the house were seven bumpy mountains. In the house with the seven pine trees under the seven bumpy mountains lived six dwarfs. Yes, six dwarfs.

Now in each of the seven bumpy mountains there was a mine. The dwarfs had one each. There was a diamond mine, a gold mine, a tin mine, a salt mine, a copper mine, a silver mine and a coal mine. Seven mines and only six dwarfs. No one worked in the coal mine.

One evening the dwarfs were walking home through the forest when they met a huge brown bear. 'Hi, neighbours,' said the bear. 'I'm going to move into that empty old mine of yours next week for my winter sleep.'

'But what about our work?' protested the dwarfs.

'That's all right,' said the bear. 'You can go on working in the other mines. Just so long as you don't make any noise. I can turn very nasty if I'm woken up. Like a bear with a sore head.'

The bear lumbered off. 'What shall we do?' said the dwarfs. 'We can't work without making a noise and bears sleep all winter.'

'I know,' said the wisest dwarf. 'We'll advertise for another dwarf. The bear won't want to move in if someone's working there.' They wrote out their advertisement for the newspaper. 'Urgent. Dwarf wanted. Must like coal. Good with bears. Apply to the six dwarfs at the little house with the seven pine trees under the seven bumpy mountains.'

A lonely dwarf, living in a hut seven miles away, saw the advertisement and set off immediately. The six dwarfs liked him at once. They told him about the bear and the mine. 'Oh, the bear can sleep in my old hut. It's very quiet there. And I've always wanted to work in a coal mine!'

So the bear slept soundly in the hut all winter and in the house with the seven pine trees under the seven bumpy mountains lived the seven dwarfs.

SEPTEMBER 30

Twirly and the Thieves

Twirly, the little yellow helicopter, was flying home one day listening to his radio when the music stopped. A voice said: 'Attention please! This is a police announcement. There has been a bank robbery and the thieves escaped in a red car, number BAD 123. The car was last seen heading north. Anyone seeing the car should report it to the police at once. Thank you.'

Twirly kept his eyes on the road, checking the number of every red car he saw. Finally he spotted one moving very fast out of the city. Twirly swooped lower to check the number: BAD 123. This was the one! Twirly called the police on his radio. 'Twirly calling. I can see the car BAD 123. It's speeding along the north highway out of the city. Please send help.'

Twirly followed the car. How could he stop it? Then he remembered the hook and line he carried in his hold. He whirred along behind the car and let down the hook. It was just like fishing, as he tried to hook the back of the car. Yes, the hook had caught hold. The men in the car looked very surprised to see themselves dangling in mid air.

'Help! Let us down!' they shouted.

'I'll let you down,' said Twirly and he dropped the car with a bump in front of a waiting police car.

'Well done, Twirly,' said the policeman. 'We could do with you in the police force.'

'Call me any time you need me,' said Twirly and off he flew, giving a little twirl as he went.

OCTOBER

OCTOBER 1

The Little Nuisance

Mrs Bellini had to watch her little boy, Tony, every minute. He was into everything! . . . Just every-thing! He loved to pull at the tablecloth and watch the dishes crash down. He dragged things out of cupboards. He turned on the water taps and left them on. He would even hide things like keys and hats, and once Mrs Bellini found some tomatoes under a cushion, squashed flat . . . What a mess!

'What a little nuisance you are!' moaned Mrs Bellini. But little Tony was too small to understand and he hadn't learned to talk yet.

When it was Mr Bellini's birthday, Mrs Bellini decided to have a party for him. Granny came to look after Tony while Mrs Bellini prepared the 'goodies' and hung up the decorations. At the end of the day, she went into the bedroom to change into her party dress and put on her pearl necklace. But she was in for a shock. There were muddy footprints all over the carpet, the dresser drawers were pulled out and her necklace was gone!

'My necklace has been stolen!' she cried. 'I must phone the police!' In the living room, she found little Tony reaching for the goldfish bowl. 'Stop him!' she cried. 'Or he'll have it over!' Then her mouth fell open in surprise. For there was her pearl necklace under the goldfish bowl!

'Tony must have put it there!' laughed Gran.

Mrs Bellini grinned. 'If Tony hadn't hidden the necklace, that robber would have taken it.' She took Tony up in her arms. 'You're a precious little nuisance sometimes,' she added. Then, the "precious little nuisance" reached up and pulled down all the party decorations.

'Oh dear!' said Gran. 'Here we go again.'

OCTOBER 2

Toot-toot Has a Fright

Toot-toot was a little steam engine who had escaped from his rails. He was just thinking about the fine time he had had at the seaside as he tootled along the road when, what a fright, he nearly bumped head on into a car coming the other way. Worse still, he recognised the men in the car! They were the ones from the goods yard who were going to scrap him.

They recognised Toot-toot at once. 'Quick, catch him!' they shouted. What could Toot-toot do? Then he had an idea. He went round and round them in circles making lots of black smoke.

'Which way did he go?' shouted one of the men.

'I don't know,' said the other. 'I can't see a thing in all this smoke.'

The men were still arguing about which way to go as Toot-toot slipped quietly away down a side street. He kept very quiet until the men had given up and gone home.

Nobody was going to scrap him. Not while he had a puff left in his boiler. There was still so much to see and do, he thought to himself, as he tootled merrily down the street. His boiler rattled, his wheels wobbled and he had barnacles stuck to his buffers, but he didn't care. And to prove it, he gave a toot on his whistle, just for fun.

OCTOBER 3

The Sultan Gives a Party

The Sultan who ruled the Far Eastern Lands spoke to his people. 'My daughter, Princess Ishmel, has been ill. The doctor has cured her and says that she now needs to laugh and enjoy herself. Tonight, you are all invited to a party. Anyone who can dance, tell a story or perform magic will be most welcome. Please come!'

Hundreds came. Sparkling lights and brilliant colours filled the palace. Princess Ishmel looked beautiful. Acrobats, story-tellers and magicians made her laugh and clap her hands.

Later, when the princess felt rather tired, Ramie stepped before the throne. How handsome he was! How splendid and full of life! Just looking at him, Ishmel no longer felt tired.

'Great Sultan of the East,' he said, bowing. 'Your Highness, Princess Ishmel, I am Ramie, the snake-charmer. Will you allow

me to show you my snakes and my skills?' The Sultan was about to refuse.

'Please, father,' begged Ishmel, smiling at Ramie. So a space was cleared and Ramie's baskets were brought in. After removing the lids, Ramie sat in the middle playing his pipe. No one moved.

Then a snake's head arose, swaying to the music. Another and another! From every basket they came, slithering across to Ramie, winding round his neck, his arms and ankles. Ramie stood up, bowing and smiling to the Sultan and Princess Ishmel.

Stroking each snake, he placed them in their own baskets and piped soft, slow music. One by one the snakes went back to sleep.

A burst of clapping showed how much they'd all enjoyed the performance. Ramie had charmed not only the snakes but everyone there – especially Princess Ishmel. The next party could be a royal wedding.

OCTOBER 4

The Fable of Jupiter and the Tortoise

In the days before the tortoise carried his shell with him, Jupiter invited all the animals to a feast. Everyone attended except the tortoise.

'The tortoise must have a very good reason for not coming,' said Jupiter. 'I'm sure he would have come if he had been able.'

When Jupiter next met the tortoise he asked why he hadn't

been at the feast. 'We all missed you,' he said, looking concerned. 'Were you ill? Did you suffer some misfortune?'

'I've been perfectly well' said the tortoise. 'The truth is I didn't feel like going out. I prefer being at home.'

Jupiter looked at him sternly. 'In that case,' he said, 'you had better carry your home with you wherever you go.' As an order from Jupiter was one that must be obeyed, the tortoise has carried his house with him ever since.

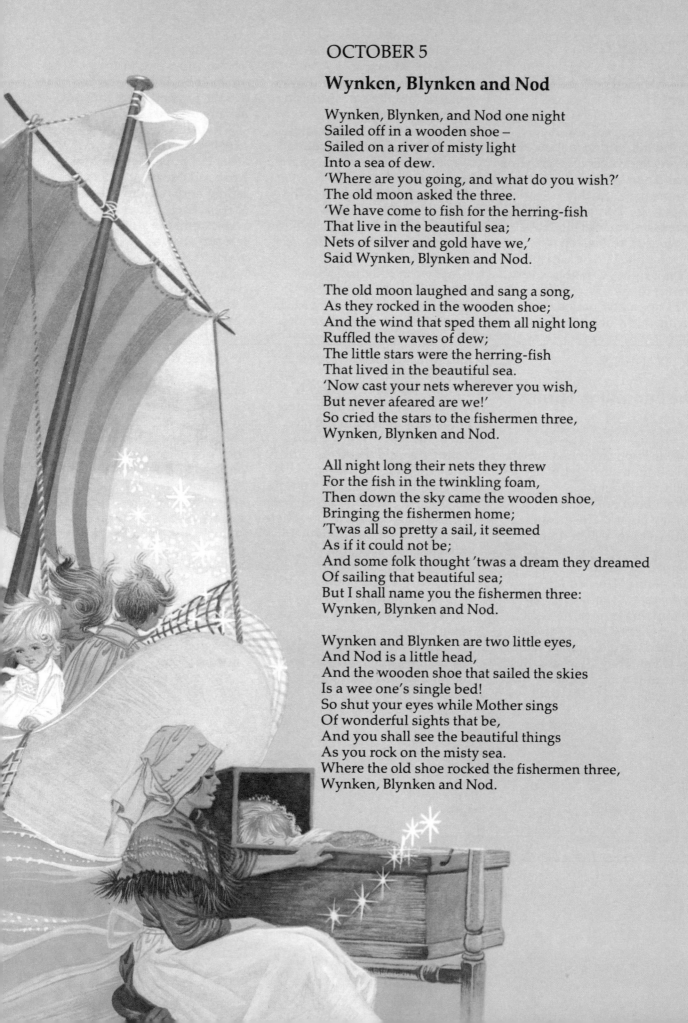

Wynken, Blynken and Nod

Wynken, Blynken, and Nod one night
Sailed off in a wooden shoe –
Sailed on a river of misty light
Into a sea of dew.
'Where are you going, and what do you wish?'
The old moon asked the three.
'We have come to fish for the herring-fish
That live in the beautiful sea;
Nets of silver and gold have we,'
Said Wynken, Blynken and Nod.

The old moon laughed and sang a song,
As they rocked in the wooden shoe;
And the wind that sped them all night long
Ruffled the waves of dew;
The little stars were the herring-fish
That lived in the beautiful sea.
'Now cast your nets wherever you wish,
But never afeared are we!'
So cried the stars to the fishermen three,
Wynken, Blynken and Nod.

All night long their nets they threw
For the fish in the twinkling foam,
Then down the sky came the wooden shoe,
Bringing the fishermen home;
'Twas all so pretty a sail, it seemed
As if it could not be;
And some folk thought 'twas a dream they dreamed
Of sailing that beautiful sea;
But I shall name you the fishermen three:
Wynken, Blynken and Nod.

Wynken and Blynken are two little eyes,
And Nod is a little head,
And the wooden shoe that sailed the skies
Is a wee one's single bed!
So shut your eyes while Mother sings
Of wonderful sights that be,
And you shall see the beautiful things
As you rock on the misty sea.
Where the old shoe rocked the fishermen three,
Wynken, Blynken and Nod.

OCTOBER 6

The Enormous Turnip (Part 1)

Old Mr Poppascoff walked around his garden looking at his flowers and vegetables growing there. Then he saw the turnip!

'Come here, quickly,' he called to his wife. 'I only planted this yesterday. You can almost see it growing as you watch it,'

'I don't like it,' she whispered. 'It's not right . . . it seems very strange to me.'

Mr Poppascoff patted the turnip. 'Now don't grow any more today . . . I'll come and see you in the morning.'

Early the next morning they woke to find the sun streaming in through the bedroom window. It was a lovely pale green. Mr Poppascoff padded over to the window in his bare feet.

'Oh dear!' he muttered. 'Oh, my goodness me!' His wife came to see what he was looking at. She had to stand on tiptoe, as the floor was very cold.

'That wretched turnip!' she cried. 'I knew there was something wrong as soon as I saw it.' They went down into the garden to have a look at it. The turnip was enormous. They fell over backwards just trying to see the top and there they sat, staring up at it.

'Whatever shall we do?' wailed Mrs Poppascoff.

'Eat it, I hope,' said her husband. He went to fetch a ladder and a saw to cut off its leaves. Then he tied one end of a rope round the stumps that were left and one end round his waist.

'Now, my dear,' he said, 'you push the turnip from that side. I will pull from this . . . we'll soon have it over.'

OCTOBER 7

The Enormous Turnip (Part 2)

Old Mr Poppascoff had grown an enormous turnip but he couldn't uproot it.

'We'll both pull,' said his wife. So they pulled. The turnip wouldn't move. Children coming home from school stopped to watch.

'Hi, Johnny!' called Mr Poppascoff. 'Come and help us pull up this turnip.'

'Right,' cried Johnny and he grabbed the old woman round her waist. They all pulled. But the turnip wouldn't move.

Johnny called to Sally, his sister, so she came to help.

'Pull!' cried Mr Poppascoff. 'And again!' They dug in their heels, they got red in the face, but try as hard as they could, nothing would move the turnip.

'Call the dog,' Johnny said. So Mr Poppascoff whistled for Bess the dog. She helped to pull. But the turnip wouldn't move. Then Tabitha the cat came and held on to the dog's tail. But the turnip wouldn't move.

Suddenly, a little mouse raced across the garden. Down went Tabitha's paw, right across the mouse's tail.

'Come and help pull,' said the cat. So the little mouse twisted his tail round the cat's tail and he started to pull. Once . . . twice . . . they pulled. Then all at once, the turnip shot out from the ground. Everyone fell over in a heap!

Mr Poppascoff invited them all to supper. 'Bring your friends,' he cried. 'Bring everyone . . . You'll love my wife's turnip soup.'

After supper, when they had all gone, Bess and Tabitha lay snoozing on the mat, the little mouse was curled up in his hole and Mr Poppascoff and his wife sat watching the fire.

'It was a good party,' said the old man.

'Very good,' his wife agreed. 'But I don't want to see another turnip as long as I live!'

'No,' said the old man. 'Neither do I.'

OCTOBER 8

Ash Lodge –
A Misty Morning

Willie the Mole lives with Basil and Dewy at Ash Lodge. One misty morning Willie had to go out to post a letter.

'Don't be long now,' called Basil after him. 'The mist is getting thicker.'

'I suppose you think I'll get lost. Don't worry. I can look after myself,' called Willie and off he marched. But Willie started to dawdle. He stopped to look at some interesting-looking leaves and then he turned over some flat stones to see what was underneath. By the time he had found a comfortable log and sat down to read over the letter he was going to post, the mist was very thick indeed.

He got up and bumped straight into the mail box. 'Well that was easy,' he said, posting the letter. 'Now back home.'

As Willie set off back home in the mist he didn't recognise anything. The trees seemed to jump out at him at the last minute. As he bumped from tree to tree he lost which way he was going and stumbled and staggered on, getting more and more frightened.

Finally Willie found a very smooth tree and he decided to hold on to it and call for help. 'Basil! Dewy!' he called.

'All right,' said a voice right next to him. 'There's no need to shout.' It was Basil. Willie was saved. 'Why are you grabbing hold of our pillar like that?' asked Basil, appearing out of the mist. Willie looked harder and there behind Basil was his own front door. By chance, Willie had stumbled all the way home.

'Oh, no particular reason,' said Willie casually. 'I was just hanging on for you to come to the door. That's all.'

OCTOBER 9

The Prince
Who Couldn't Lie

'A prince should be charming,' the Queen told her son. 'How will you ever find a wife when you always say what you think?'

The Prince sighed. 'But I can't seem to control my tongue, mother. The truth always comes out.'

The Queen said, 'I hear that Princess Megan is looking for a husband. But you must flatter her to win her. You must say things like, "Your eyes are as blue as sapphires; your lips are like rose petals; your hair is like golden sunshine".'

'Very well,' said the Prince, and off he rode.

Riding through the forest to the castle where the Princess lived, he kept repeating, 'Your eyes are as blue as sapphires; your lips are like rose petals; your hair is like golden sunshine.'

But when he saw the Princess he forgot everything! She wasn't beautiful but there was something about her that captured his heart. And he loved her there and then. He knew he could not lie now.

'Princess,' he said. 'Will you marry me? You're not beautiful, your eyes are too large, your nose is all freckled and your lips are too full.'

Everyone gasped. 'He has insulted the Princess!' They rushed to attack him.

'Let him finish!' cried the Princess.

The Prince went on, 'But there's a softness in your eyes . . . a smile lurks on your lips . . . and I love your freckled nose.'

'Yes! I'll marry you,' smiled the Princess. 'Flattery doesn't fool me. I've been waiting a long time for an honest prince to come along.'

'My mother will be surprised,' laughed the Prince.

OCTOBER 10

Rocky's Magic Spell

'Oh no!' said Rocky Rook, peering down from his tree. 'It's that witch's cat again! Why doesn't he go away; he makes me feel nervous!'

Inky padded and sniffed around until Winnie the Witch called him, 'Come on Inky, time to be brushed!'

But as she walked off, something dropped from Winnie's pocket. Rocky swooped down for a closer look. It was her Book of Spells! He took it up to his tree and studied it. 'Wonderful!' he cried. 'Here's a spell to make cats disappear!' He flew off to the wood chanting the spell over and over. 'A bucket of berries, some twigs and some stones; a dockleaf, a toadstool and ten chewed-up bones!'

Soon he found everything and mixed them all up together. The mixture bubbled and smoked and then . . . BANG! It exploded.

Bits flew everywhere. Shocked and frightened, Rocky flew back to his tree.

He was shaking all over but, then he realised, so was the tree! He peered down, 'Oh no!' he groaned. 'Look what I've done!' Inky had grown ten times bigger and was scratching his chin on the tree. Rocky and his nest swayed and rocked and then crashed to the ground.

Winnie couldn't believe her eyes when she saw Inky. Rocky rescued the Book of Spells from his smashed nest and went over to Winnie. 'I'm sorry,' he gulped. 'I borrowed your book. I tried to make Inky disappear because he frightens me.'

'Frightens you?' echoed Winnie. 'Why, Inky's very gentle. Just a bit large at the moment. But you've lost your nest. Here, I've got a wonderful idea.' She found a ladder and gave Inky a good brush. Then she scooped up the huge ball of black fur that had come out with the brushing. With a few magic words the ball of fur became a big fluffy nest!

Rocky was so happy and Winnie was right: Inky *was* gentle. He soon shrank back to normal size and Rocky became his good friend. The black fur nest was soft and warm and Rocky thought his magic spell had turned out rather well, after all!

OCTOBER 11

Help for Ben

Ben the carthorse was very tired. It had been a long day for him pulling the plough up and down the big field. His legs ached and his hooves felt as heavy as lumps of stone.

'Poor old Ben!' said the farmer. 'I think the work's getting a bit much for you. I suppose I'll have to think about getting a tractor, though I don't like the idea much. Nasty, noisy, smelly things.'

This worried Ben. 'What would happen to me if the farmer got a tractor?' he thought. 'Out in the meadow all day counting daisies, if I'm lucky; minced to make cat food, if I'm not.'

The next day Ben decided to try

harder but his old legs just wouldn't go any faster. 'It's no good,' he thought to himself, 'I'm on the way out.'

The farmer was worried too. He didn't want to stop using Ben. He loved to see the great horse at work with his strong shoulders pulling the plough.

Just then an old friend, who had a farm nearby, came to call. He had problems too. He had just retired and left his farm for his son to run. The son was going to modernise the farm and get new machinery. 'So I don't know what will happen to poor old Bess, my carthorse. She's worked hard for me all these

years, and I can't bear to see her put down,' he said.

'I know what you mean,' said the first farmer. 'My Ben is getting slower and slower and I don't think I can keep him much longer.'

'I've had a marvellous idea,' said the second farmer. 'Why don't you have Bess? I'll give her to you, and you can harness her to the plough with Ben. Two carthorses will pull that plough with no problem!'

So now Ben and Bess work happily together.

OCTOBER 12

Lin Goes Fishing

Lin and his mother were very hungry. The harvest had been poor and now there was nothing for them to eat.

'I will go fishing,' said Lin.

'Maybe I can catch something for supper . . .'

'. . . or the Emperor's jewels,' said his mother. 'I heard at the market that the Emperor lost his jewels in the Great River as he travelled north.'

'I'll catch a bag of rubies for you,' laughed Lin.

'A fish for tonight's supper would be better, I think,' replied his mother.

Lin went down to the Great River, to where Master Tung kept his boat. 'Will you lend me your boat, Master Tung?' asked Lin. 'We have nothing for supper and the fish are bigger where the water runs deep.'

'Of course,' said Master Tung. 'Maybe you'll catch the Emperor's jewels.'

Slowly Lin paddled the boat out to the middle of the Great River. He dropped anchor, threw his line over the side and lay back in the sun dreaming of bags of rubies.

Suddenly he felt a sharp tug on the line. He started to pull it in. Perhaps it was a bag of rubies. But as the line shortened, Lin could see it was an enormous fish.

He paddled back to the shore, thanked Master Tung and hurried home, with the great fish slung over his shoulder.

'This is better than the Emperor's jewels,' said Lin's mother, cutting the fish open.

Suddenly she dropped the knife with a gasp. Inside the fish lay a jade ring, carved with dragons and set with three huge pearls. 'It's the Emperor's famous Dragon Ring. Surely there will be a great reward for finding this.'

There was indeed. The Emperor gave Lin enough silver to buy his own boat; so he and his mother never went hungry again.

OCTOBER 13

Simple Simon

Simple Simon met a pieman,
Going to the fair:
Says Simple Simon to the pieman,
Let me taste your ware.

Says the pieman to Simple Simon,
Show me first your penny;
Says Simple Simon to the pieman,
Indeed I have not any.

Simple Simon went a-fishing,
For to catch a whale;
All the water he had got
Was in his mother's pail.

Simple Simon went to look
If plums grew on a thistle;
He pricked his fingers very much,
Which made poor Simon whistle.

He went for water in a sieve
But soon it all fell through;
And now poor Simple Simon
Bids you all adieu.

149

OCTOBER 14

Never Talk to Strangers

Little Chick was having fun sliding down a patch of ice, when a voice whispered through a hole in the fence, 'Hello, Little Chick, How would you like to slide down a big slide?'

Little Chick looked through the hole in the fence and saw Fox. 'My mother told me not to talk to strangers,' he said.

Fox laughed. 'Quite right! But I'm not a stranger. Your mother knows me. I've just had a word with her. She says you can come with me.'

'That's all right then,' said Little Chick innocently. 'But where is your big slide?'

'Up the hill,' grinned Fox. 'It's a wonderful slide, very steep and very slippery. Only a brave chick would dare to slide down it.'

'That's me!' cried Little Chick. 'I'll show everyone how brave I am.'

'Crawl through that hole in the fence,' said Fox, 'I'll run ahead. You follow.' And he ran off.

'Don't go!' said the farmer's dog who had overheard their conversation. 'That fox wants to eat you!'

Little Chick took no notice. He just followed Fox up the hill. But there was no slide at the top.

Only Fox waiting to eat him!

Fox was about to swallow Little Chick when there was a shout. It was the farmer with his dog barking at his side. The dog had woken the farmer. Now Little Chick was saved, as Fox ran off.

'Next time,' said the dog to Little Chick, 'you should remember your mother's advice.'

OCTOBER 15

Samantha Pig

Once upon a time there was a big, fat, jolly pig called Samantha. She had a cute little tail with a proper curl in it. Farm life suited her as long as she had her mud bath every morning. She would roll in the squelchy brown mud and then lie in it, sunning herself and grunting with pleasure.

But one morning her bath wasn't there! The lovely brown squelchy mud had been hidden by stones and planks of wood. Samantha let out a squeal of rage and decided to run away. So off she went.

She kept on trotting up the lane until she saw a little cottage and in front of it some soft squelchy mud. She rolled in it backwards and forwards and then lay perfectly still, her snout twitching. It was one of the best baths she had ever enjoyed.

As she lay there, a fat old woman came out of the cottage and stared in amazement at the pig enjoying herself. The old lady laughed. Samantha was pleased. She liked to see people happy, especially if she was happy too!

'Well, you are a pink beauty!' said the old woman at last. 'I expect you're from the farm. I'll let them know you're here, though I'd dearly like you for myself.'

The farmer collected Samantha a little later and she was soon happily back in her sty. It was then that she decided, if she couldn't find her mud bath there one morning, she knew exactly where she would go to find a good bath and a good friend.

OCTOBER 16

The Frog Prince (Part 1)

A beautiful princess was playing with her golden ball one day when she dropped it. The ball rolled to the edge of a deep, clear pool and fell, with hardly a splash, to the bottom. She could see it lying on the white stones but she could not reach it, and soon her tears began to fall.

'Why are you crying?' asked a voice close by. The only creature the Princess could see was a green frog. She was so astonished to hear a frog speak that she answered immediately.

'My golden ball is lying at the bottom of the pool,' she said sadly.

'If I bring it back to you,' said the frog, 'will you let me sit upon your chair, share your food when you eat, and lie upon your bed when I'm tired?'

'Anything, anything at all,' promised the Princess. 'If only you will bring my ball to me.' But when the frog had dived to the bottom of the deep clear pool and given her back the golden ball, the ungrateful Princess snatched it from him and ran laughing across the palace lawns. She did not give the frog, or the promise she had made, another thought.

OCTOBER 17

The Frog Prince (Part 2)

In return for a promise a frog had rescued the Princess's golden ball. Next morning, when she was skipping along the palace corridor, she met the green frog, and she knew at once that he had come to claim his promise. She ran and hid behind her father.

The King took her gently by the shoulders. 'You look very pale,' he said. 'Has something frightened you?'

The Princess told the King how the frog had returned her lost ball and of her promise to him. 'Please make him go away, father,' she pleaded.

But the King said sternly, 'A promise is a promise and must be kept. Invite the frog to our table.' The Princess did as she was told and the King and his five daughters sat down to breakfast. The frog hopped to the Princess's side.

'May I sit upon your chair?' he asked. The Princess lifted him on to the polished wooden arm.

'May I share your food?' asked the frog. The Princess lifted him to the side of her plate.

When the frog had eaten he said, 'I am tired, may I lie upon your bed?' The Princess carried the frog to her bedroom, but she was so afraid that the frog would hop on to the pillow, that she put him on a chair in the corner.

'I will tell your father you have not kept your promise,' warned the frog. The Princess burst into tears. She picked up the frog and threw him across the room to her bed. Suddenly the green frog turned into a handsome young prince. He had been bewitched and because the Princess had shared her chair, her food and her bed with him, she had broken the spell.

The Prince and the Princess were married and lived happily ever after in a land where promises were always kept.

OCTOBER 18

The Fable of the Wolf and the Horse

A wolf was on his travels when he came to a field of oats. The oats were ripe and just ready for eating. Wolves do not eat oats so the wolf passed on his way without giving them a second glance.

Presently he met a horse. 'That is a fine field of oats, you must agree,' he said. 'I saw you coming and I know horses like eating oats, so out of the kindness of my heart, I have left the whole field for you. My pleasure will be in hearing your strong teeth crunch their way through the ripe grain.'

The horse was not fooled for a moment. 'If wolves enjoyed eating oats,' he said, 'you would not deny your stomach a treat just to hear me eating them. There is no virtue in giving me something you do not want yourself.'

OCTOBER 19

The Lonely Unicorn Finds a Friend

The Unicorn was lonely. 'Will you be my friend?' he asked the Stag.

The Stag answered, 'I belong to the world of today. You belong to the world of once-upon-a-time, so I cannot be your friend.'

So the Unicorn asked the Fox, 'Will you be my friend?'

The Fox answered, 'I belong to the real world. You belong to the fairy-tale world, so I cannot be your friend.'

Then the Unicorn asked the Rabbit, 'Will you be my friend?'

The Rabbit answered, 'I belong to the world of here and now. You belong to the world of long ago. So how can I be your friend?'

So the lonely Unicorn ran and ran until he came to the seashore. There he saw a mermaid weeping bitterly.

The Mermaid said sadly to him, 'The Pony on the beach says I am only make-believe, so I cannot be his friend. The Donkey says I am only pretend, so I cannot be his friend. And the Dog says I belong in the world of fables, so he will not be my friend.'

'But I will be your friend,' cried the Unicorn joyfully. 'I am like you. We are both fairy-tale creatures, and we both belong to the world of dreams.'

So the two friends travelled together down the sun's path and the moon's path over the sea. They raced the wind through the woods. When they were tired they listened to music from the horns of Elfland. And they were happy ever after.

OCTOBER 20

The Secret Cave (Part 1)

The little train puffed into the station and out tumbled all the excited children, ready for their day by the sea. Bobby was the last to step on to the platform and he wandered along to look at the engine. He loved trains and when the guard and the driver left for a drink he mounted the footplate. With a 'toot-toot!' the little train chuffed away – just for fun!

Bobby was all alone but he was a driver at last. He looked out of the window. The engine had switched on to an old disused set of rails. The little engine knew things weren't quite right and slowed down as it came to another tunnel. There, earth, boulders and rocks had spread right across the track. Bobby was disappointed; it was impossible to go on.

He got down and found there was room for him to squeeze through into the tunnel. It was very dark in there, except for a small round patch of light in the far distance, where the tunnel ended. He didn't get to the end, for about halfway, a large cave opened into the hillside. Hanging on the walls were lots of tiny, shining lamps. Low work-benches were under each light and small tools were laid out in neat rows. Pebbles were in piles; some dull, others smooth and shiny.

Then he saw them: six little men, heads down, scraping the sand. They were thin, quite old, with white hair and beards, but quick and active. Each had an apron tied round his middle. Suddenly they all stopped and came towards the cave.

'This must be their workshop,' thought Bobby and he hid in the darkest corner.

OCTOBER 21

The Secret Cave (Part 2)

Bobby had discovered a cave with six little men working in it. They worked at their benches without saying a word, while Bobby hid.

They were hammering and polishing what looked like tiny shells. Soon one of the men had finished a necklace. He turned to where Bobby was hiding and held it out to him. Bobby came out with a shy smile, thanked the little man and slipped the necklace in his pocket.

Now all the little men gathered round smiling and beckoned Bobby to follow them down a narrow passage. Down and down they went until, at the bottom of many steps, they came to a room with glass walls. Behind the glass was sea-water with rocks, plants and fish swimming around.

'We're under the sea,' cried Bobby in amazement. The little men just smiled. Suddenly there was a clanking sound and a ship's anchor appeared behind the glass. 'That will break the glass,' said Bobby in alarm. 'Quick! We must get out of here.'

Bobby pushed the little men ahead of him up the steps, just in time as the anchor smashed through the glass and the room began to fill with water. The men were horrified to see that their room under the sea was lost, but they were thankful they had been saved.

Bobby heard the engine tooting. Hurriedly he said goodbye to the little men and jumped into the engine as it went chuffing back to the station.

When they arrived at the station Bobby went back into the carriage he came in. Then all the other children came trailing on to the train, chatting about their day at the seaside.

'You missed all the fun, Bobby,' they cried. Bobby just smiled and felt the shell necklace in his pocket.

OCTOBER 22

Fit for a King (Part 1)

'Wife . . . ' said Samuel Duggett one fine Spring morning. 'I'm going to the market today to sell the white mare.'

'Then be sure to get a good price for her,' said his wife. 'She's a beautiful horse, fit for a king to ride upon.'

The way to the market led through the wood. Sam Duggett sat high on the mare's back and felt like a king himself as he jogged along through the dappled sunlight. Deep in the wood, where the brambles were most tangled and the shadows the deepest, he was greeted by an old man with a long white beard.

'Will you stop a moment? I have something to ask you.'

'Whoa there, my beauty!' called Sam to the white mare. She stopped with a soft whinny before he had time to tighten his grip on the bridle. 'Hello, old man. Is there something I can do for you?' asked Sam.

The old man's voice was quiet but surprisingly strong in one who looked so frail and old. 'You have a beautiful mare,' he said, fondling the mare's muzzle. 'If she is for sale, I will buy her.'

Sam took one look at the old man's robe with the worn elbows and he laughed. 'She *is* for sale, but not to the likes of you, I'm afraid. I'm taking her to market for some fine gentleman to buy. She will fetch a very good price; of that I am sure.' With that, he bid the old man goodbye and galloped off.

OCTOBER 23

Fit for a King (Part 2)

Sam was on his way to sell his fine mare at the market when he had met an old man. The old man had offered to buy the mare but Sam could see he couldn't afford it. The old man watched Sam and his horse gallop away and he smiled as though there was a secret which only he knew.

The market was crowded and business was good that fresh Spring morning. There were many gentlemen about. Several were looking for a fine horse to buy. Everyone admired Sam Duggett's white mare. He rubbed his hands and thought of the gold he would be taking home to his wife. But the day came and the day went. The market filled and the market emptied.

'What . . . not sold the mare yet?' asked a man who had sold every one of his pigs.

'I don't understand it,' said Sam. 'You can see for yourself what a beauty she is. I've nearly sold her a dozen times . . . but nearly isn't good enough.'

Sam took the mare's bridle in his hand and began the journey home. To his surprise, as he was passing through the wood he met the old man again.

'I see you still have your white mare,' said the old man. 'Come with me, if you please.' After a few minutes they came to the foot of a sandstone cliff. As far as Sam could see there was no path up it, over it, or round it. The old man struck the cliff with his fist.

Before Sam could laugh and say, 'You'll never move a cliff that way, old man,' two enormous gates appeared and flew open with a thunderous noise. The old man beckoned Sam forward. Now,

feeling very frightened indeed, Sam followed him into the cave which lay behind the gates.

OCTOBER 24

Fit for a King (Part 3)

Sam had been unable to sell his mare at the market and on his way home he met the old man again. The old man led him into a cave. An unbelievable sight met his eyes. King Arthur of the Round Table and his Knights lay sleeping in the darkness.

'King Arthur and his Knights will sleep for a long time yet,' said the old man, who, it seemed to Sam, had suddenly grown very tall and straight. 'But the day will come when England will have need of her ancient Kings, and then King Arthur and his Knights will wake and ride on white horses. They need one more white horse . . . a horse fit for a king to ride upon. Now, will you sell me your white horse?'

Sam Duggett didn't say a word. He handed the mare's bridle to Merlin, for the old man was indeed the wizard who had lived at the Court of King Arthur and who now kept watch over him as he slept. Sam took the purse of gold which Merlin gave him . . . and ran.

No one believed Sam's story, of course. The sandstone cliff was in the wood but no amount of banging and thumping ever made the gates reappear. In time, Sam himself found it hard to believe what had happened. But there was one thing of which everyone was certain: the white mare had vanished without trace.

OCTOBER 25

The Invitation

Hal Hamster was happy. The sun was shining and he was out walking nowhere in particular – one of the best places to go.

'Lovely morning,' he called out, as he passed Pete Porcupine who was standing in his garden.

'Not really,' said Pete wearily picking at his prickles. 'What's another year, anyway? At my age you try to forget about birthdays,' and he disappeared into his house.

'Oh dear,' thought Hal. 'I didn't know. I must think of something to cheer poor Pete up. I know! We'll have a party. I'll go and see Cassie Rabbit. She's got the biggest house around here. I'm sure she'll have the party there.'

Cassie and her friend Marvin Mole thought it was a great idea. 'I'll make a big fruit cake with lots of icing,' said Marvin, 'and write "Happy Birthday Pete" on it.'

'Ooh, great,' said Cassie. 'I'll get out the party hats and decorations to make the room look cheerful.'

'What can I do?' said Hal, feeling a bit left out.

'Could you make Pete a nice big invitation card?' said Cassie. 'You're the artistic one.'

'Oh yes,' said Hal happily. 'I'll go and do it now.'

On his way home, Hal collected three leaves: one with a wiggly edge, one with a spiky edge, and one with a smooth edge. Then he got out his paints and a piece of card. He mixed a bright poppy red with the paints and painted the wiggly-edged leaf red. Then he pressed the leaf on to the card and lifted it off, leaving a red leaf shape. He did the same with the other two leaves, using blue

and yellow paint. Then he wrote on the back of the card: "Dear Pete, please come to a birthday party at Cassie's today at 3 o'clock." He put it in an envelope and hurried off to Pete's house.

Pete was delighted to go to the party, and he was so pleased with his party hat, his cake, and especially his invitation card that he said it was the best birthday party he had ever had.

OCTOBER 26

Little Red Riding Hood (Part 1)

Little Red Riding Hood's mother was packing a basket with eggs and butter and home-made bread.

'Who's that for?' asked Little Red Riding Hood.

'For Grandma,' said her mother. 'She hasn't been feeling well.' Grandma lived alone in a cottage in the middle of the wood.

'I'll take it to her,' said Little Red Riding Hood. She put on her red cape with the red hood and picked up the basket.

'Make sure you go straight to the cottage,' said her mother, 'and don't talk to any strangers.'

Little Red Riding Hood meant to go straight to the cottage but there were so many wild flowers growing in the wood she decided to stop and pick some for Grandma.

'Good morning,' said a voice at her elbow. It was a wolf. 'Where are you taking these goodies?' the wolf asked, peeping inside the basket.

'I'm taking them to my Grandma,' said Little Red Riding Hood, quite forgetting what her mother had said about talking to strangers.

'Where does she live?' asked the wolf.

'In the cottage in the middle of the wood,' said Little Red Riding Hood.

'Be sure to pick her a nice big bunch of flowers,' said the wolf, and he hurried away. The wolf went straight to Grandma's cottage. He knocked at the door.

'Who's there?' called Grandma.

'Little Red Riding Hood,' replied the wolf, copying Little Red Riding Hood's voice.

'Then lift up the latch and come in,' called Grandma. But she screamed when she saw the wolf's face peering round the door. He was licking his lips. She jumped out of bed and into the cupboard and locked herself in.

The wolf picked up her frilly bedcap, which had fallen on the floor, and put it on his own head. He pulled the covers up round his neck, then sat and waited for Little Red Riding Hood to come.

OCTOBER 27

Little Red Riding Hood (Part 2)

Little Red Riding Hood was on her way to visit her grandmother but a wolf had got there first and was pretending he was her Grandma. Soon there was a knock at the door.

'Who's there?' called the wolf in a voice that sounded like Grandma's.

'Little Red Riding Hood,' came the reply.

'Then lift up the latch and come in,' called the sly old wolf.

Little Red Riding Hood went in. 'Are you feeling better, Grandma?' she asked.

'Yes dear, I am,' said the wolf. 'Let me see what you have in the basket.' As the wolf leant forward the frilly bedcap slipped and one of his ears popped out.

'What big ears you have,' said Little Red Riding Hood.

'All the better to hear you with,' said the wolf.

'What big eyes you have,' said Little Red Riding Hood, beginning to feel frightened.

'All the better to see you with,' said the wolf with a big grin.

'What big teeth you have,' said Little Red Riding Hood, now feeling very frightened indeed.

'All the better to eat you with,' said the wolf. He threw back the covers and jumped out of bed.

'Help! Help!' screamed Little Red Riding Hood, as the wolf chased her out of the cottage and into the wood. A woodcutter heard her screams and came to the rescue. As soon as the wolf saw the woodcutter's axe he ran away as fast as he could.

Little Red Riding Hood told the woodcutter what had happened. 'Where is your Grandma now?' asked the woodcutter.

'I don't know,' sobbed Little Red Riding Hood. 'Perhaps the wolf has eaten her.' But when they got back to the cottage they heard the sound of knocking coming from inside the cupboard and a voice asking if it was safe to come out.

'It's me, Grandma!' called Little Red Riding Hood. Grandma unlocked the cupboard door. 'What a lucky escape we have both had,' said Little Red Riding Hood, and she gave Grandma a special hug.

OCTOBER 28

The Wanderer

Mother Rabbit was worried. She counted her children again. 'There's one missing.' she told Father Rabbit. 'Where is Ronnie?'

'He's in the cabbage patch,' the baby rabbits cried.

'The little rascal!' said Father Rabbit. 'I told him not to wander off.'

'Oh dear!' sighed Mother Rabbit. 'I don't like him wandering off when Wild Weasel is about. Wild Weasel just loves to eat little rabbits.'

'We don't want Wild Weasel to eat Ronnie!' cried the baby rabbits.

'I'll soon find him,' said Father Rabbit. And he went straight to the cabbage patch.

The first thing he saw was Wild Weasel lurking behind a cabbage plant. And he didn't look fierce at all. He just looked puzzled and jittery. For nearby was a large funny-looking tortoise who was making sudden jumps at him. What was this strange creature? The tortoise made one more jump at him and that was enough for Wild Weasel!

He was scared out of his wits and rushed home.

Then the funny-looking tortoise made a sudden jump at Father Rabbit. Father Rabbit laughed. The tortoise had long ears and a twitchy nose.

'Why! It's Ronnie! Come out of that tortoise shell!'

'I fooled Wild Weasel, didn't I?' chuckled Ronnie.

'You certainly did, you rascal! You brave little rascal,' said Father Rabbit. 'But don't do it again! He might not be fooled next time!'

So Ronnie left the tortoise shell and he decided right then, not to wander off again.

OCTOBER 29

The Fable of the Lark and the Farmer

A lark had made her nest in a field of corn. One day, just before the baby larks were ready to leave the nest, the farmer came to look at the corn.

'It's ripening well,' he said. 'I think it's time to have a word with my neighbours and ask them to help with the harvest.'

The little larks were very afraid. 'Quick, mother . . . we must move house.'

'A man who talks about going to his neighbours for help is in no great hurry,' said the mother lark. 'We have plenty of time yet.'

A few days later the farmer came back to the field. The corn was so ripe it was beginning to fall to the ground.

'I must hire men immediately and set them to work,' said the farmer, '. . . or I will lose all my corn.'

'Come, my children,' said the mother lark. 'The farmer is relying on himself now and not on the good will of his neighbours. It is time for us to move.'

Gordon the Ghost

'Whoooooooooo!' The deep, hollow voice of Gordon the Ghost echoed through the halls of Spooks Castle. It sent chills up and down the spines of all the people who had paid their money to hear him.

One day, Gordon the Ghost told the duke he would have to leave the castle if things didn't improve. 'Whoooooooooo! It's so cooooooooold in these halls!' he moaned. 'Why should I float about with only a sheet to cover me?'

'Don't go!' said the duke. 'The people only pay to hear you. And I need the money to keep the castle repaired. What do you want me to do?'

'Give me some money,' said Gordon. 'I'm going shopping.'

Nobody could see Gordon because he was a ghost. So the salesman in the shop gave a start when a deep, hollow voice said, 'I'm looking for some warm underwear!'

The saleman's eyes nearly popped out when a set of long underwear seemed to dance in front of him. (Gordon had picked them up.) Then, to his astonishment, the underwear did the strangest thing. It filled out and stood up. (Gordon had put them on.) 'I'll take these,' said Gordon. Some money appeared on the counter and the underwear floated away. There were shouts and screams when the headless set of underwear soared over the crowds and headed for the castle.

When the duke saw him, he hung a new sign on the castle door. It read: 'You've *heard* the Headless Ghost . . . Now come and *see* him!' So Gordon the Ghost made a lot of money for the duke and he went on scaring people. Now that he was warm he liked his job again and the crowds just loved him.

Bad Haggetty

Bad Haggetty, the wicked witch,
Came roaring down the lane.
She yelled, 'A thief has got my broom.
I want it back again!'

'Tonight's the night for Hallowe'en.
I need my stick,' she said.
'Or I can't fly across the sky;
I'll have to stay in bed.'

She chased the dogs and cats and mice,
She broke the babies' toys.
She frightened all the little girls
And thumped the little boys.

The cows all started mooing,
Sheep scattered through the hay.
The farmyard cocks went flying,
The hens refused to lay.

Then at a cottage window
Appeared a little child,
With rosy cheeks and curly hair
And face so meek and mild.

'Dear witch, I've got your broomstick here.
I'll give it back,' said she.
'If you will only grant one wish,
One magic wish for me.'

Bad Haggetty looked down at her.
The child smiled back with charm.
'I'll grant your wish but make it quick,
You can't do me much harm.'

'I wish, old witch,' the girl cried out,
'You'd turn into a cat!'
A bang, a crash, a great big flash,
Meeow! . . . and that was that.

NOVEMBER

NOVEMBER 1

Chuffa Goes to the Circus (Part 1)

One day Chuffa was hired to take the circus to a far-away town called Maryville. Very early in the morning Chuffa's trucks were loaded with tents and costumes and ropes and poles and elephants and tigers. It was a heavy load but Chuffa didn't mind as he rattled along. 'Chuffa-chuff, chuffa-chuff.'

When they arrived at Maryville, the clowns led the circus through the town. Poor Chuffa had to sit in the station. He couldn't join in the fun. All he could do was listen to the band playing and the crowds clapping and cheering.

Next it was time to set up the circus tents. Chuffa helped to bring up all the heavy things. He watched as the Big Top was heaved into place. He looked on as the side-shows were set up. He wished he could join in.

That night the circus owner opened the box office. How the people rolled up. Chuffa thought that everyone in Maryville must have bought a ticket. The money-bag was soon bulging. But Chuffa wasn't the only one to notice that fat money-bag.

NOVEMBER 2

Chuffa Goes to the Circus (Part 2)

Chuffa had taken the circus to Maryville and now everyone was enjoying the show except him. He was left outside wishing he was inside and all he could see was the tent . . . and someone creeping out of it! Someone was making his way to the box office. He was picking up the money-bag with all the night's takings in it. He was creeping away thinking no one had seen him.

Quietly Chuffa built up steam and chuffed his way along the track until he was behind the thief. Then Chuffa gave a terrific blast on his whistle. The thief leapt in the air with surprise. Chuffa kept whistling: 'Wooo-wooo. Wooo-wooo.'

Everyone was furious as they spilled out of the circus tent. 'That crazy train has stopped the show,' complained the owner. Then he saw the thief with his money-bag. 'After that man!' he shouted.

The thief was soon surrounded by clowns and acrobats and trapeze artists and animals. The thief was put in an empty cage and the circus owner locked his money-bag safely away.

Then the circus owner made a speech which ended, ' . . . and so Chuffa has saved the circus. As a special reward we shall put on a show for him out here in the open.' That is how, at last, Chuffa came to see the circus.

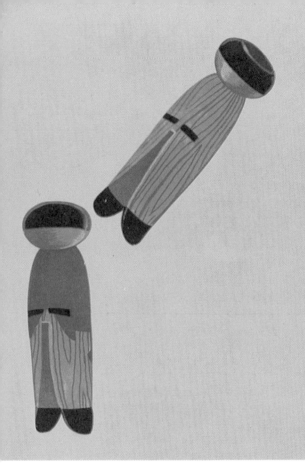

NOVEMBER 3

Soldiers

Four wooden pegs,
Smooth and brown,
On the table,
Lying down.

Black for boots,
And black for hats,
Red for tunics,
Front and back.
Dark blue legs,
With stripes of white,
Spots of gold,
For buttons bright.

Four soldiers made
From wooden pegs,
March up and down
On painted legs.

NOVEMBER 4

Adventures of *The Tulip* – The Aqueduct

'We'll cross the aqueduct today,' said Thomas to Wilbur and Minty. The three friends had been enjoying a fine time aboard their riverboat, *The Tulip*.

'What's an aqueduct?' asked Minty.

'That is,' said Thomas, pointing to a bridge with seven arches which crossed the valley.

'How will we get *Tulip* up there?' asked Minty.

'The river goes across the top,' explained Thomas.

The Tulip had got about halfway across the aqueduct with Minty holding his hands over his eyes so as not to look at the valley below them, when there was a cloud-burst. The rain pelted down on the wheel-house roof and then *The Tulip*'s engine spluttered and stopped.

'The water's got into it,' said Thomas. 'I'm afraid we're stuck.'

'But look,' cried Minty, 'the level of the river's rising with this rain. We'll all be washed over the edge!'

'Ahoy there!' came a voice from the footpath beside them. It was Fergus Frog in his oilskins, his bicycle underneath him. 'That's a silly place to stop. You'd better get out of there before it floods,' said Fergus cheerfully.

'We're stuck and can't get the engine started,' explained Thomas. Without a word, Fergus hopped aboard his

bicycle and rode away.

Ten minutes later they heard another shout: 'Ahoy there. Throw me a line.' It was Fergus and standing next to him was a big old cart-horse with a friendly face. Fergus tied the rope to the horse's collar and the horse plodded along the footpath pulling *The Tulip* to safety.

'Thank you, Fergus,' they all cried.

'Don't thank me. Thank Horace here,' smiled the frog.

NOVEMBER 5

The Pied Piper of Hamelin (Part 1)

The town of Hamelin was plagued by rats. They chased the cats and ate the grain. They frightened the babies and carried off apples. There were so many of them that it was impossible to walk in the streets without falling over them. The people of Hamelin tried everything to rid the town of rats but they all failed.

The Mayor and his council were so desperate they promised a huge reward to anyone who could find a solution to the problem. The whole town was in despair. Then a stranger arrived dressed in a coat of many colours.

'I have been told there is a reward for the man who rids this town of rats,' he said.

'Anything . . . anything . . . if only you will help us,' said the Mayor. The stranger walked to the middle of the town square and took a small pipe from his pocket.

'What is he going to do?' whispered the townsfolk. The stranger put the pipe to his lips and began to blow. As he blew a tune the rats began to creep from their holes to listen to him. As they gathered about his feet he began to walk through the town. Up streets and down streets he went and as he passed each door, the rats left what they were doing and scampered after him. When he reached the town gate every rat in Hamelin was behind him. The piper strode on across the meadow towards the river.

'What is he going to do now?' asked the townsfolk. When he reached the riverbank, the piper stepped straight into the water. It came to his knees. The tune he was piping grew sweeter and the rats followed straight after him . . . and were all drowned.

NOVEMBER 6

The Pied Piper of Hamelin (Part 2)

The piper had rid Hamelin of a plague of rats. But the townspeople were an ungrateful lot. As soon as the last rat was gone they hurried back to their dinners and their games. No one even offered the piper a thank-you.

The piper went to the Mayor and asked for his reward. The Mayor faced him with a scowl. Now the rats were gone he saw no reason to part with the money.

'Reward?' he said. 'What reward? There is no reward. Leave the town at once! You're not wanted here!'

The piper did not say another word but as he walked through the streets of Hamelin to the town gate, he began to blow another, prettier tune on his pipe. This time it wasn't the rats which ran from the houses. It was the children.

Every child in the town wanted to dance to the piper's tune and they followed him through the gate and across the meadow. But this time, instead of going to the river, he turned towards the bare mountains.

One small girl was lame. She couldn't keep up with the dancing, skipping procession of laughing children. She was the only one who saw what happened.

'The side of the mountain opened,' she told everyone, 'and all the children followed the piper inside. I tried to find the door so that I could follow too but it had disappeared.'

The townsfolk were in despair. They searched the mountainside for days, but they never saw their children again. They had disappeared, as surely as the rats had disappeared, and they had only themselves to blame.

NOVEMBER 7

Two Strange Birds

Uncle Bernard was coming. Jerry and Sally planned to play a joke on him as he was always tricking them. They put a nest of twigs up in a tree with two toy birds in it.

'When it's getting dark,' said Jerry to his sister, 'tell Uncle Bernard that there are two baby birds in the garden and they're not in the bird book. But for goodness sake don't laugh.'

All went well. Uncle Bernard was really puzzled until he noticed how still the birds were.

'Well,' he said seriously, 'I just don't know! I'll come down early tomorrow and study them in the daylight.'

Smothering their giggles, they thanked him and went upstairs. 'We've tricked him this time!' laughed Jerry.

Next morning at breakfast, Sally said, 'Have you been to see the birds yet, Uncle?'

'I certainly have,' he answered. 'I see there are a couple of strange eggs in with them too.'

Jerry and Sally couldn't resist going out to the nest to look. Sure enough, either side of the birds was a shiny egg.

'They're chocolate eggs,' laughed Sally.

'There's one for each of you to eat later,' said Uncle Bernard, with a smile.

'Mmm,' said Jerry, 'that's the sort of trick we like.'

NOVEMBER 8

The Jar Man

'Granny, tell us a story about when you were a little girl in England,' said David.

'Yes, we love your stories,' said Sasha.

Granny smiled as she settled herself comfortably in the armchair. 'Did I ever tell you about the jam jar man? I used to love Saturday mornings because it was the day Mr Frogget came round with his barrow. He collected empty jars and would always give something away in return. Sometimes sweets and sometimes balloons.

'One particular Saturday I saw that he was giving away paper windmills. They were all pretty colours and spinning in the wind. "Have you any empty jars?" I asked my mother. "No," she answered. "You had the last one last week." I *was* disappointed. "Anyway," said my mother, "I want you to see if Mrs Wood wants anything." Mrs Wood was an old lady living next door. She couldn't walk very well.

'"I'm so glad you've come," she said as I went in. "Look, I've dropped my box of pins all over the floor and I can't get down and pick them up."

'I was soon on my knees and had them all back in the box in no time. "Thank you," she said. "Now, what can I do for you?" "You haven't got an empty jar, have you?" I asked. "Why an empty jar?" said Mrs Wood. I explained about the windmill but I wondered if Mr Frogget had already gone. "Here you are," said Mrs Wood, handing me a jam jar.

'Thanking her as I went, I was careful not to run with the glass jar and I was pleased to see Mr Frogget at the end of the road. I chose a gold windmill and watched it spin round as I ran home.'

'Ooh,' breathed David. 'I wish Mr Frogget would come here.'

'So do I,' said Sasha. 'So do I.'

NOVEMBER 9

The Fable of the Stag at the Pool

A stag went to a pool to drink. When he had quenched his thirst, he stood and gazed at his own reflection.

'I really do have a very fine pair of antlers,' he said proudly. 'They are quite magnificent. What a pity my legs do not match them. They are far too weak and thin. If only I could do something to improve them.'

A lion saw the stag at the pool and gave chase. The ground was open and free from trees and gradually the stag drew ahead. He turned into the forest where there were plenty of safe hiding places. But before he could find a suitable place to hide, the magnificent antlers of which he was so proud, caught in an overhanging branch and held him fast.

'Woe is me,' he cried, as the lion came upon him. 'But for the antlers of which I was so proud, the legs which I despised might have saved me.'

NOVEMBER 10

The Meddler

There was a village once where everything was always going wrong. Bottoms dropped out of buckets of water, fences were always falling down, vegetables were always rotten inside, new laid eggs were bad and the people were always miserable.

Things had been like this as long as anyone could remember, ever since someone from the village had made an old witch get out of the wrong side of her bed. Since that day the old witch, who lived in a nearby cave, had meddled in the village's affairs. Now cats were too scared to meow and birds were too scared to sing for fear of the old witch's spells.

At last, three elders from the village went to see the Abbot of a distant monastery for advice. 'I think our brother here can help,' said the Abbot, pointing to a thin, weak-looking monk.

When the elders returned with the monk the other villagers sighed miserably. 'What can someone like him do when a strong man like the blacksmith runs away from the witch like a scared rabbit?' they all said.

But the monk was braver than he looked. The villagers followed him, at a safe distance, up to the mouth of the witch's cave. The monk went straight in. The witch came cackling from her hiding place. But as soon as she saw the monk in his brown robes she shrieked and tried to run away.

He calmly sprinkled water on her and the villagers who were brave enough to look saw the witch turned to stone.

'Good has triumphed over evil,' said the monk to the villagers. 'You can all live happily now.'

NOVEMBER 11

The Lion Man of Africa (Part 1)

Long ago in Africa there was a tribe of people called the Ukulu. Strangers to tribal villages were not normally welcome for the people were suspicious of anything unusual. But the Ukulus were one of the friendliest tribes in the whole of Africa. They had dark skins, tight curly hair and large friendly smiles.

Now, one night, an old man arrived at the Ukulu village. He did not look like anyone the Ukulu people had ever seen before, but they greeted him warmly. His skin was dark like theirs. He spoke their language. But his hair was long, wavy and a beautiful shade of gold. It was exactly like a lion's mane. As he had travelled far, he was given a tent to rest in and food to eat.

After several days the children of the tribe had a name for the visitor. They called him "The Lion Man", because of his hair. He smiled at them. 'You speak wisely, my children,' he said.

When the time came for the old man to leave the village, the people gathered to wave him goodbye. Turning to face them he made a promise: 'Because

you have received me kindly I leave a blessing on the Ukulu village. The lion shall always protect you.' Saying this, he raised his hand and walked away into the jungle.

'Can this be true?' asked the elders. In the distance the villagers could hear the roar of lions and they were afraid. But they wondered about the Lion Man's promise.

NOVEMBER 12

The Lion Man of Africa (Part 2)

Time passed and, strangely, the Ukulu village was never attacked by lions. To everyone's amazement, they were not troubled by tigers or bison or other beasts either. Sometimes they heard fierce animal battles deep in the forests. At last the menfolk, venturing out in a party, discovered that a pride of lions, living close to the village, was protecting them from danger. The Lion Man's promise was coming true.

Soon it became the custom to throw food out for the lions whenever there was a festival in the village and they would gather eagerly to enjoy it. In this way the Ukulu shared their celebrations with the lions who protected them.

Now, like all youngsters, the Ukulu children loved to play games. But one day a little girl cried out, 'A lion! A lion!' He was crouched very close to the children, watching their games. The girl ran to her brothers who calmed her and made the young children sit down.

The lion began to move from tree to tree, sometimes peeping out at the children, sometimes hiding. Then he found a large branch and threw it high in the air catching it between his paws. He did this time and time again, until the children, forgetting their fears, laughed and clapped. The lion's great tail thumped on the ground in pleasure.

'He is only a young lion,' said the oldest boy. 'He wants to join in our games.'

'He's very brave to come so close on his own,' said another boy. 'Let's call him Hero.' So they did. Hero became a friend of the Ukulu children, joining in their games of chase and run. But not one grown-up knew about this.

NOVEMBER 13

The Lion Man of Africa (Part 3)

Whenever Hero returned to the lion pack his
mother noticed him behaving strangely. He
seemed so lively and full of fun.

'Do not go too close to the village,' his mother
warned him. 'We must protect the Ukulu and
never trouble them.'

'I will never cause them trouble, mother,' Hero
promised.

Soon it was time for a festival in the village. As
the youngest lion, not yet full-grown, Hero would
not be going to enjoy the celebration food. Alone
in the jungle it seemed a long dark night to the lion
cub.

The Ukulu people knew how to enjoy a festival.
There was singing, dancing and loud drums. But
alone, among the greenery, Hero sensed danger.
A party of buffalo, knowing that the lions were
watching the celebrations, stalked through the
undergrowth getting nearer and nearer to the
village.

Hero knew at once that the village must be
protected. He lay in wait and sprang on the
leading buffalo. Hero fought for his life and finally
killed the huge animal. Frightened by the attack,
the rest of the buffaloes stood back for a moment.
Now Hero raised the alarm with a mighty roar.

All the lions thundered back into the jungle. The
buffaloes were soon chased away and Hero was
left standing unharmed. How proud his mother
was, and then how surprised, for the village
children rushed up to stroke her son.

'You've saved us all, Hero,' they cried. 'You've
protected the Ukulu people just as the Lion Man
said.'

NOVEMBER 14

Ash Lodge – The Missing Middle

Willie the Mole, who lives with his two Badger
friends, Dewy and Basil, at Ash Lodge, was
helping tidy the store cupboard one day.

'Mind that bag of flour, Willie, the bo . . .' Dewy
was too late. The bottom of the bag fell through
and there was flour everywhere.

Basil took charge while Dewy and Willie sneezed
and sneezed. 'Willie, you take the rug outside and
get it clean while Dewy and I clean up in here.'

Willie pulled the brightly coloured rug on to the
grass and began to whack it with the beater. The
more he whacked, the more he coughed and
sneezed and soon he had to go for a drink.

When he went out again he was horrified to see
the middle of the rug was threadbare. 'You didn't
have to beat it that hard,' said Basil.

'I didn't,' protested Willie. Basil wasn't sure
whether to believe him or not but then there was a
polite cough behind him.

'Er . . . does this belong to you?'
asked a very embarrassed dormouse
struggling under a bundle
of loose woollen pieces. 'The children were trying
to help keep us snug in the winter,' she explained.
'So they helped themselves to some of your rug. If
you'd like to come with me, there's more at home.'

Willie, Dewy and Basil followed the dormouse to
her home and saw all the dormice children curled
up asleep under their woollen bed.

'Don't wake them,' said Basil.

'But what about your rug?' said the dormouse.

'We'll mend it with something,' said Willie. And
that's why one of the rugs at Ash Lodge has a
brown middle and rainbow coloured borders.

NOVEMBER 15

Katy Goes Hop-About

Katy, the little kangaroo, told her mother, 'I'm grown up now. I'm going to escape from this zoo and see the world.' When the zoo-keeper wasn't looking, she made her escape.

'How wonderful the world is,' thought Katy, as she hopped through the park. When she stopped to eat some leaves, two children spotted her.

'Look!' they shouted. 'It's a little kangaroo!' They chased after her. Katy was frightened. There was no friendly mother's pouch to jump into now. But she found the next best thing: an empty flower basket hanging from a donkey's saddle. Katy jumped in and hid. When the children ran past her she hopped out again to see more of the world.

She came to the shopping centre. The hustle and bustle and all the traffic noises made her nervous. A lady passed by pulling a shopping trolley. Katy jumped into it. But when the lady saw Katy's leg sticking out of the trolley she fainted. What a commotion! Katy hopped away.

Suddenly she saw an enormous green thing coming towards her. It was only a bus but Katy didn't know that. Frightened, she jumped into the first pouch she saw. And that was a saddle-bag on a policeman's motorbike. The policeman grinned as he drove her back to the zoo and placed her in her mother's pouch.

Katy looked up into her mother's happy face. 'I guess I'm not so grown-up after all,' she sighed. 'Yours is the best pouch of all.'

NOVEMBER 16

The Fable of the Swan and the Crow

A crow saw a swan swimming in a pond and was filled with envy.

'I wish I had white feathers like the swan,' he sighed. His feathers were black as coal but they were not good enough for him. He wanted white feathers.

He watched the swan carefully, trying to understand why they were different.

'The swan spends most of his time on the water,' said the crow. 'That must be why his feathers are so white. I will live like a swan myself, then perhaps I will have white feathers too.'

The crow left the place where he had lived all his life, where he could find the kind of food he liked, and went to live beside a river. He learnt to swim in the flowing water. He bathed in the riverside pools and washed his feathers many times every day. It didn't matter how often he washed, his feathers stayed as black as they had always been. He began to grow thin, for although the food he found in the river suited the swans, it didn't suit him. He decided the life of a swan was not for him and he went back to being a crow.

NOVEMBER 17

The Gingerbread Man (Part 1)

Once upon a time there was a little old man and a little old woman who lived on a farm. The little old woman liked cooking and one day, when the little old man was asleep in his rocking-chair, she had an idea.

'I'll make a little gingerbread man,' she said. She set to work at once. She gave him a head and arms and legs. She gave him two currant eyes and a candy-peel mouth and then she put him into the oven.

Soon it was time to take the gingerbread man out of the oven, but before she could lift the baking tray from the shelf, the gingerbread man had jumped out of the oven by himself. The old woman screamed and the old man woke up suddenly as the little gingerbread man ran towards the door.

'Stop! Stop!' cried the little old man and the little old woman as they ran after the gingerbread man.

'Run, run, as fast as you can. You can't catch me, I'm the gingerbread man,' laughed the gingerbread man, leaving them far behind.

On his way across a grassy field he met a cow. 'Stop! Stop!' mooed the cow. 'You look good enough to eat to me.'

The gingerbread man laughed. 'I have run away from a little old man and a little old woman and I will run away from you too,' he said. And he did.

As he ran through a farmyard he was chased by a dog. 'Stop! Stop!' barked the dog. 'You look good enough to eat to me.'

The gingerbread man laughed. 'I have run away from a little old man, a little old woman and a cow and I will run away from you too.' And he did.

In the leafy lane he met a horse. 'Stop! Stop!' neighed the horse. 'You look good enough to eat to me.'

The gingerbread man laughed. 'I have run away from a little old man, a little old woman, a cow and a dog and I will run away from you too.' And he did.

NOVEMBER 18

The Gingerbread Man (Part 2)

The gingerbread man was just thinking how clever he was when he met a fox. The fox looked at the gingerbread man and licked his lips hungrily.

The gingerbread man said, 'You won't catch me. I have run away from a little old man, a little old woman, a dog, a cow and a horse and I will run away from you too.'

'There is no need to run away from me,' said the sly old fox.

'I don't want to catch you. Let's just walk along together.' And so they did.

Presently they came to a river. 'What shall I do?' asked the gingerbread man. 'I cannot swim.'

'That's no problem,' said the fox. 'I can swim. If you sit on my tail I will take you across to the other side.'

So the little gingerbread man sat on the fox's tail. When they reached the middle of the river, the fox said: 'The water is getting deep. You had better move up on to my nose or you will get wet.' The gingerbread

man didn't want to get wet so he walked along the fox's back until he came to his nose.

'I can see where we're going now,' he laughed. 'This is fun.' But as soon as they reached the far bank, the fox threw back his head, tossing the gingerbread man in the air. As the gingerbread man fell, the fox caught him in his mouth and gobbled him up. And that was the end of the gingerbread man.

NOVEMBER 19

The Dancing Shoes (Part 1)

Midge was a naughty elf. He was sitting in Mr Merryweather's shoe store one day when one of the King's officers came in. The officer gave Mr Merryweather a large letter.

'Hooray,' shouted the shoemaker. 'The King has asked me to make him a pair of shoes. I shall start right away.' Midge left the store and had mischief on his mind.

That night Midge returned to the shoe store carrying a tin. He found a window open and crawled through. Once inside, he spotted a pair of fine red shoes on the counter. He took some nails out of his tin and started banging them into the new shoes. The label on the tin read *Nails for Dancing Shoes.*

The King was delighted with his new red shoes which were delivered the next day. He decided to wear them that night at a special banquet where several important people would be present.

When everyone was sitting down and about to be served, the King felt his feet twitching. He tried not to take any notice. The twitching got worse and he had to get up and dance. All the important guests looked on as the King jigged round the room, his coat-tails flying.

The King smiled at first, hoping he would soon stop but after twenty minutes he shouted desperately, 'Help! Get these shoes off me!' The palace guards rushed to get the shoes off.

Everyone was very surprised at these goings-on; everyone, that is, except a little elf at the window who was looking in at the banquet.

NOVEMBER 20

The Dancing Shoes (Part 2)

The King was very angry at looking so foolish at the banquet. He ordered that the shoes be burnt. The guard thought the shoes too good to burn and so next day he left them outside the palace gates.

The elf looked on as an old lady came by. She saw the fine shoes; hers were old and worn. She tried the shoes on. They fitted nicely. She gave a little skip and set off towards the market place. Soon she found herself hopping, jumping and finally dancing through the streets.

'Help!' she cried, as she kicked her heels in the air round the square. A doctor was walking in the square. The old lady grabbed hold of him. 'Please take the shoes off,' she cried.

The doctor took off her shoes and held a bottle of smelling salts under her nose to help her recover. Then he looked carefully at the shoes. He knew a bit about magic. He placed the shoes on the ground. 'Go and find the one who started this,' he said.

The shoes gave a skip and danced to a spot behind a wall where Midge lay curled up like a ball, shaking with laughter. The shoes slipped themselves on his feet and danced Midge back to the doctor.

'Now let's see how well *you* dance,' said the doctor as Midge danced away down the street and out of the town.

NOVEMBER 21

The Goose and the Ring (Part 1)

I'm Barney, the wild goose. This is the story of my first long flight from Siberia. My brothers and sisters and I were born in Siberia; we were part of a huge flock that spent the summer there. The sun shone nearly all the time and there were lots of insects to eat. Days passed, and the weather began to get colder. The leader of the flock told us that when the wind changed we must all be ready to go. We were flying to a warmer land for the winter. I was nervous because I'd never flown so far before, but everyone had to go.

The first part of the journey was fun. We flew over forests and fields, villages and cities, but then the weather changed. There was thunder and lightning, the wind was blowing in gusts and I just couldn't keep up with the others. I was tired, cold and hungry. I had to rest.

Luckily, I noticed a gleam of water below me and landed on a small lake. I had just finished eating and was about to follow the others when I was terrified by loud barking behind me. Dogs! I splashed along the water trying to take off but the next minute I found myself caught in a net.

NOVEMBER 22

The Goose and the Ring (Part 2)

My name is Barney, the wild goose. On my journey from Siberia I stopped to eat and found myself trapped in a net. Struggling was useless, so I relaxed, and then I was gently taken from the net by a pair of firm hands. The next thing I knew a wide plastic ring was fastened around my leg and before I could panic about what might happen next, I was set free! Quickly, I set off in the direction I knew the rest of the flock had taken. I was very puzzled by my strange adventure.

I didn't have far to go and I soon landed beside my mother on the enormous lake where the flock spent the winter. I told her what had happened to me and she didn't seem very surprised.

She told me lots of geese had these rings put on their legs. The rings had numbers that people could read through binoculars. This meant that they could find out where the geese were and what happened to us through our lives. Knowing these things they could make sure that our lakes were left undisturbed for us. I'm pleased that my ring helps like that.

NOVEMBER 23

Where Are You Going To?

Where are you going to, my pretty maid?
I'm going a-milking, sir, she said,
Sir, she said, sir, she said,
I'm going a-milking, sir, she said.

May I go with you, my pretty maid?
You're kindly welcome, sir, she said,
Sir, she said, sir, she said,
You're kindly welcome, sir, she said.

Say, will you marry me, my pretty maid?
Yes, if you please, kind sir, she said,
Sir, she said, sir, she said,
Yes, if you please, kind sir, she said.

What is your father, my pretty maid?
My father's a farmer, sir, she said,
Sir, she said, sir, she said,
My father's a farmer, sir, she said.

What is your fortune, my pretty maid?
My face is my fortune, sir, she said,
Sir, she said, sir, she said,
My face is my fortune, sir, she said.

Then I can't marry you, my pretty maid,
Nobody asked you, sir, she said,
Sir, she said, sir, she said,
Nobody asked you, sir, she said.

NOVEMBER 24

Snow White and the Seven Dwarfs (Part 1)

Once there was a princess whose skin was as white as snow, whose cheeks were as red as roses, and whose hair was as black as ebony. Her name was Snow White. She had a stepmother who was beautiful and very vain. Every day she would look into her magic mirror and ask:

'Mirror, mirror, on the wall,
Who is the fairest of us all?'

The mirror always answered that the Queen was the fairest until one fateful day, when it replied:

'Thou Queen art fair and beauteous to see,
But Snow White is fairer far than thee.'

The Queen was so angry she ordered a servant to take Snow White to the forest and kill her.

The servant loved Snow White and could not kill her. Instead he left her in the forest. When he returned to the Queen he said he had obeyed her order

Snow White wandered alone through the forest until she came to a tiny cottage. Inside, everything was arranged in sevens and it was all very untidy. She washed the dishes, scrubbed the floors and dusted all round. Then, feeling tired, she lay on one of the seven beds and fell asleep. She was found by the seven dwarfs, who owned the cottage, when they returned from a day's digging at the mines. The dwarfs took pity on Snow White when she told them her story and they said she could stay with them.

NOVEMBER 25

Snow White and the Seven Dwarfs (Part 2)

The following day, the wicked Queen asked her magic mirror who was the fairest in the land. It replied:

> 'Queen, thou art of beauty rare,
> But Snow White living in the glen,
> With the seven little men,
> Is a thousand times more fair.'

The Queen was very angry because she knew her servant had lied to her. She quickly dressed herself as a pedlar and went to the dwarfs' cottage while they were out.

'Will you buy a pretty petticoat, child?' she asked Snow White, who did not recognise her. The wicked Queen slipped the petticoat over Snow White's head and pulled the tapes so tightly round her waist that Snow White stopped breathing. The dwarfs found her lying on the floor when they got home. At first they thought she was dead, but when they saw the tight lace they guessed what had happened, loosened it, and Snow White began to breathe again

The Queen thought she had killed Snow White. When the magic mirror said that Snow White was still the fairest in the land she turned white with rage. She dressed herself in a different disguise and hurried to the dwarfs' cottage with a poisoned comb in her pedlar's basket. It was so pretty that Snow White couldn't resist trying it in her hair. The instant it touched her head she fell to the floor. When the dwarfs came home they took the comb from her hair and revived her.

'You must not speak to anyone,' they said. 'The wicked Queen is trying to kill you.'

NOVEMBER 26

Snow White and the Seven Dwarfs (Part 3)

When the magic mirror told the Queen that Snow White was still the fairest in the land she decided to kill her or die herself in the attempt. This time she took a poisoned apple to the cottage. Snow White forgot the dwarfs' warning and took a bite from the apple. This time the dwarfs could not revive her.

This time the magic mirror replied to the Queen:

> 'Thou Queen are the fairest in all the land.'

The dwarfs laid Snow White in a crystal case in a forest glade, and kept watch over her day and night, for they had grown to love her.

One day a prince came riding by. When he saw Snow White, whose skin was as white as snow, whose cheeks were as red as roses, whose hair was as black as ebony, he pleaded with the dwarfs to let him take her home to his palace. The Prince looked so sad when they refused, that the dwarfs changed their minds and agreed to his request. Then, just as the Prince was lifting Snow White on to his horse, the piece of apple, which had lodged in her throat all the time, fell from her mouth, and she opened her eyes.

The wicked Queen could not believe it when her mirror said:

> 'Oh Queen, although you are of beauty rare,
> The Prince's bride is a thousand times more fair.'

When she saw that Snow White was the Prince's bride, she choked with rage . . . and died.

Now Snow White had nothing to fear from the wicked Queen. She lived happily with her Prince and often visited the seven dwarfs.

NOVEMBER 27

Ricky and the Strange Insect

Granny had been sewing buttons on Jimmy's coat as she sat in the garden. 'Now I've left my scissors indoors,' she said impatiently. She pushed her needle into the reel of thread but she didn't notice the reel drop on to the ground as she got up and went indoors.

Popsy the kitten found it and dragged the reel through the hedge. Then the needle pricked her and she ran off.

Next Ricky the stagbeetle found it. 'What a strange insect! Only one eye!' he said, looking at the top of the needle. 'That tail looks sharp,' he said, looking at the other end of the needle. His insect didn't speak and it didn't

move. Ricky jumped on top of it.

Just then a dog, digging for a bone, sent earth and stones over Ricky and the reel of thread, knocking them into the stream. Ricky tried to fly off but a loose thread had wound round his back leg.

'Think you're smart, eh?' grumbled Ricky, as they were swept into a huge pipe carrying water under a road. Then out they came on the other side into a wider stream.

'I'm travelling the world,' shouted Ricky. He tried to forget he was trapped by the damp thread. As they floated along, Ricky closed his eyes and dozed. When he woke up he found they had reached a firm sandy beach. The thread was dry and had loosened. Ricky wriggled free.

'Well thanks for the ride,' he said to the reel of thread. 'I'm flying off home now.' The reel of

thread said nothing as Ricky waved goodbye.

A little boy, gathering sea shells, saw the reel of thread. 'Granny,' he shouted as he carefully picked it up, 'you can sew my buttons on now.'

NOVEMBER 28

Lionel the Lazy Lion

Lions are playing Rhinos Athletic in the Jungle Cup Final. Lionel is the Lions' goalie. He hasn't touched the watermelon ball yet. With any luck he will not have anything to do. His team-mates are far more skilful than the Rhinos. They are running the other team ragged. Rhinos are so slow to move.

'Come on, you Rhinos!' shouts someone in the crowd. Other animals start to sing: 'You'll Never Walk-A-lion.'

Lions are on the attack once more. Leo passes the ball to Larry. Just as Larry is about to score, Roger Rhino stamps on the ball. Splat! The watermelon ball is splattered into squidgy pieces. 'Penalty!' roar the crowd.

A fresh watermelon is rolled on and captain Len prepares to take the penalty kick. He hits the ball to the right and Ringo, the Rhinos' goalie, flops to the left. Goal! One – nil. 'Easy! Easy!' the animals chant.

As the game continues, Lions do all the attacking. They run rings round Rhinos but they can't score. The sun beats down. Lionel the lazy lion feels sleepy. He rests his head on his front paws and before you can say 'hippopotamus' he is fast asleep.

With one minute left in the game, Rugged Ronald Rhino gets the ball and charges upfield, heading the ball along

the ground. He barges through the Lions' defence at full speed. Nobody can stop him. He thunders towards Lionel.

'Wake up, Lionel!' Too late! Rugged Ronald heads the ball past Lionel and into the net. 'Goal!'

Lionel lifts his head. 'Did someone call my name? Have we won?' he asks his team-mates.

The ref blows his whistle. The final score is Lions 1 Rhinos 1. Now why do you think the Lions are chasing Lionel around the pitch? They don't look very happy. They're snarling and growling . . .

NOVEMBER 29

Jumping Frogs (Part 1)

Once there was a young frog who would not jump. His mother tried to make him jump. His father tried to make him jump. His brothers tried. His sisters tried. But whenever they jumped or hopped, he walked. And of course that meant everyone was always having to stop and wait for him. His mother was always begging him to hurry. So were his brothers and sisters.

'Jump . . . Francis . . . JUMP!' they would call impatiently, every time they had to stop and wait for him.

'I don't want to jump,' Francis would reply.

'Perhaps he can't jump,' said Mother Frog. She took him along to see the frog doctor. He made Francis lie on the couch and examined his legs carefully.

'Stretch . . . bend . . . stretch . . . bend . . .' he said. Francis did it perfectly. Or rather his legs did. Then the doctor tapped his knees with a rubber hammer to make sure his legs jerked

properly. They did. They jerked perfectly.

'Nothing wrong with him at all,' said the doctor .

'I knew there wasn't,' said Francis.

'Then why won't you jump?' asked his mother tearfully.

'Because I don't want to,' said Francis.

'Because he doesn't want to,' said the frog doctor and shook his head wisely. 'I'm afraid there's no medicine to cure that.' That evening the frog family sent Francis out on an errand and had a family conference.

NOVEMBER 30

Jumping Frogs (Part 2)

Francis Frog refused to jump so his family held a meeting and they decided they would make Francis feel silly by walking like him. They found it a very difficult thing to do for it is as natural for a frog to jump as it is for a tree to grow. How tired their legs got. How short their tempers became.

Francis was used to walking. His legs never got tired and although it took him a long time to walk everywhere, he always got there much quicker than the rest of the family. Now it was his turn to stand and wait while everyone caught up with him.

'Oh do hurry up!' he said one morning, when there had been a shower of rain and they were all on their way to the puddle patch. 'The sun will dry up the puddles before we get there.' Father Frog signalled secretly to the rest of the family to slow down even more. The sun was warm. Francis could feel it drying his back. He wanted to get into some cool water.

'We'll all dry up and frizzle away!' he grumbled. 'If you can't walk any faster than that,

why don't you jump?'

'What was that you said?' asked Father Frog.

'Jump . . . JUMP!' shouted Francis, losing his temper, because he was dry and hot, and everyone else was being silly. 'Look, like this . . . I'll show

you . . . jump . . . JUMP . . .' There he was, jumping like a proper frog should. His brothers and sisters raced him to the puddle patch. From that day onwards Francis jumped everywhere and to his surprise he found he enjoyed it.

173

DECEMBER

DECEMBER 1

The Magic Key

Nippy the gnome was walking home one day when he saw something glinting in the grass. He stopped and picked it up. It was a silver key. 'Someone has lost this,' he thought. 'I'd better take it to the police station.' He popped it into his pocket and was just about to go along to the police station when he began to sneeze. 'Atishoo! Atishoo! Atishoo!' At the same time his feet began to go in the opposite direction to where he wanted them to go.

He was so bewildered by all the sneezing that he couldn't think properly at all. Try as he might he could not make his feet go in the direction of the police station. Eventually, he found himself on Old Witchy Winnie's doorstep. He stood there, dazed and sneezing. His feet had come to a stop. 'Atishoo! Atishoo!' he sneezed. He didn't have to ring the bell. The door opened and out came Witchy Winnie.

'Ha-ha,' she cackled. 'You must have my key.

Give it to me.' Between gasps and sneezes, Nippy took the key from his pocket and gave it to her. To his relief, his sneezing stopped at once.

'Come in,' said Witchy Winnie. 'I'm sorry it was you who found my key, Nippy. You're an honest little gnome but I put that spell on it, you see, so that if I ever lost it, it would come back to me. Come and have a piece of my special chocolate cake with fresh cream, as a reward.'

'Sneezing was awful, but the chocolate cake was delicious,' chuckled Nippy an hour later, as he made his way home.

DECEMBER 2

Chuffa in Trouble (Part 1)

'Oh, these mountain railways are so old,' said Mr Driver. He and Chuffa were struggling along a track that ran up the steep sides of a South American mountain. Pieces of the track would fall off into the valley below as they made their daily journey with wood and food. 'Come on, old friend. Soon be there,' said Mr Driver. 'Then we can have a rest.'

At the very top of the mountain, Mr Driver jammed on the brakes. There by a waterfall were Chuffa's animal friends waiting for him. There was Rabbitito, the Andes bunny, some large-eyed llamas and a whole family of chuckling chinchillas.

Chuffa and Mr Driver couldn't resist stopping for a game or two, even if they were a bit late. But when they finally reached Alto-Passo station, old Grumpito, the station master, didn't think much of their playing games on company time.

Grumpito reported Chuffa and Mr Driver for being late. The Railway Managers had a meeting and they decided:
1 That they must have some new trains.
2 That Chuffa should be broken up for scrap.
3 That they should all have some more money.
4 That it was time for lunch.

The next day Mr Driver was given his orders. Chuffa was to be driven to the End-of-the-Line and left there.

DECEMBER 3

Chuffa in Trouble (Part 2)

Chuffa had been late once too often and now Mr Driver had been told to take Chuffa to the End-of-the-Line and to leave him there.

'Cher-uff, cher-uff, cher-uff,' went Chuffa. 'Sniff, Sniff,' went Mr Driver, as they drove along the track together for the last time. When they reached the waterfall in the High Andes, their animal friends were waiting for them as usual. 'Where have you been?' asked Rabbitito.

'We've been in trouble,' said Mr Driver. 'I'm afraid we shan't be seeing you any more or playing any more games. I have to take Chuffa to the End-of-the-Line and leave him there.' The chinchillas stopped chuckling when they heard this. The llamas' eyes were full of tears.

Mr Driver waved goodbye to the sad animals as he and Chuffa went on their way. As they disappeared from view, Rabbitito called the animals together. 'Listen,' he said. 'I have a plan and I need all of you and many more to help.'

Meanwhile Mr Driver drove Chuffa to the End-of-the-Line. It was a very sad place. All around were old trains that were either broken-down or broken-up. 'Goodbye, old friend,' said Mr Driver, as he walked away. Chuffa couldn't raise a single puff of steam or a whistle in reply.

DECEMBER 4

Chuffa in Trouble (Part 3)

Chuffa had been taken to the End-of-the-Line to be scrapped but his animal friends had made a plan. That night Mr Driver was woken up by Rabbitito. 'Get dressed and come quickly,' he whispered. Mr Driver couldn't believe his eyes as he saw a llama and a chinchilla pulling Chuffa out of the scrapyard shed. They led him away without making a sound.

'Come with us,' said Rabbitito. 'We're going to save Chuffa.' Mr Driver followed them along the track.

Up in the mountains there was a wooden ramp running from the railway track. 'I don't remember seeing that before,' said Mr Driver.

'We've just built it,' said Rabbitito. They heaved Chuffa off the track and on to the ramp which led into a cave. 'Chuffa will be safe here,' said Rabbitito as they left Chuffa in the cave and began to take the ramp apart. 'No one will know where Chuffa is,' said the wise old bunny. Soon there was no sign that the ramp had ever been there. 'Now we really get to work,' said Rabbitito. Mr Driver followed him up the mountain. As they turned a corner, Mr Driver found hundreds of animals all sawing wood and hammering nails.

'What ever are you all building?' he asked.

'Wait and see,' said Rabbitito.

In a few days they had finished. They brought Chuffa out of his hiding place and they set Mr Driver at Chuffa's controls. The animals had built their very own scenic railway, high in the mountains, and this was the first of many journeys.

Now no one cares if Chuffa is late; no one stops Chuffa's games with the animals and all the rides on Chuffa's railway are free. 'Chuffa-chuff, chuffa-chuff, wooo-wooo!'

DECEMBER 5

Rumpelstiltskin (Part 1)

Once there was a miller who had a beautiful daughter. He was always boasting about her. One day he said, 'My daughter is so clever she can spin straw into gold.'

The King heard about the miller's daughter and sent for her. 'You shall spin straw into gold for me,' he said. The miller's daughter wanted to say it was impossible, but she was afraid to speak. The King took her to a room where there was a spinning wheel and a pile of straw. 'If you value your life,' he said sternly, 'you will spin all that straw into gold by morning.' Then he left the room and locked the door.

The miller's daughter began to cry. She didn't know what to do. Then she saw a tiny man with a long white beard, standing beside the spinning wheel.

'What will you give me if I spin the straw into gold for you?' he asked.

'I will give you my necklace,' she said.

The next morning, when the King unlocked the door, the straw was gone. In its place was a heap of gold.

DECEMBER 6

Rumpelstiltskin (Part 2)

The King had ordered the miller's daughter to spin straw into gold. A strange little man had appeared and had spun the gold for her.

That night the King led her back to the same room. This time the straw stretched from wall to wall. 'If you value your life,' said the King, 'spin all that into gold by morning.'

As soon as the door was locked the little man appeared. 'What will you give me if I help you this time?' he asked.

'My ring,' replied the miller's daughter.

When the King saw the huge pile of gold next morning he was very pleased. He led the miller's daughter straight to a room where the straw was piled so high it touched the ceiling. 'Spin all that into gold and you shall be my queen,' he said.

As soon as the door was locked the little man appeared. 'I have nothing left to give you,' said the miller's daughter sadly.

'Give me the first child born to you when you are Queen,' said the little man. The miller's daughter agreed and the little man began to spin. A few days later the miller's daughter married the King.

DECEMBER 7

Rumpelstiltskin (Part 3)

A whole year went by and the new Queen forgot about the little man who had come to help her. Then, one day, there was great excitement at the palace. A baby had been born. The excitement quickly changed to weeping and wailing when the little man appeared.

'I will give you all the treasure in the treasure house, if only you will let me keep my baby,' wept the Queen.

'You made a promise. You must keep it,' said the little man. But the Queen held the baby so tightly that at last he said, 'You may keep the child if you can guess my name within the next three days.'

The Queen lay awake all night thinking. 'Is your name Grizzlebeard?' she asked next morning. 'Is it Firkin? Is it Bodkin?' The little man shook his head.

On the second day, after another sleepless night, the Queen asked, 'Is your name Shortlegs? Is it Longears? Is it Pipkin?' The little man shook his head again.

The Queen sent her servants far and wide across the land in search of strange names. One of her grooms was riding through a wood when he heard someone singing. He stopped his horse and got

off. He crept closer and saw a little man dancing round a fire of twigs and leaves. He was singing to himself:

> 'Today I bake, tomorrow brew.
> What a clever thing I do.
> Soon a baby I will claim
> For Rumpelstiltskin is my name.'

The servant galloped back to the palace as fast as he could. He told the Queen all that he had seen and heard.

The next day, when the little man appeared at the palace, the Queen asked, 'Is your name Harry?'

'No!'

'Is it Timothy?'

'No!'

'Could it be . . . Rumpelstiltskin?'

'A witch must have told you that!' shouted the little man in a rage. He was so angry he stamped his foot too hard and it went through the floor. But he had made a promise and he kept it. The baby was safe.

DECEMBER 8

The Fable of the Hound and the Lion

A hound was exploring in the bush when he saw a lion walking some distance ahead of him. The hound had never seen a lion before but he was used to chasing and catching other animals and he supposed that a lion, though bigger than most, would be just as easy to catch.

At first he stalked the lion cautiously. Then as he drew closer he became bolder and followed more openly. Presently he broke into a trot. He was almost in a position to pounce when the lion stopped. The lion realised that he was being followed and looked back lazily over his shoulder to see who was daring to stalk him in this way.

'I've got you now,' thought the hound, and prepared to spring.

The lion looked the hound straight in the eye, then opened his mouth and roared.

It was the hound's turn to stop. He was frozen in his tracks. He had never heard such a noise before! He had never seen such teeth before! He sprang into action, but not in the way he had planned. He turned, and ran in the opposite direction with his heart beating wildly and with his tail between his legs.

DECEMBER 9

An Old Horse for an Old King

It was the day of the Royal Procession. The King trotted at the head on a splendid young stallion but his legs were too short to fit into the stirrups. Up and down he bounced unable to control his horse.

'Why do I have to put up with all this jiggling and joggling?' he muttered to himself. 'Everyone says I have to ride the finest horse but they don't have my bad back or my old bones. I need a good slow horse.'

The King's son was riding behind his father in the procession. He rode a pony and his long legs dangled almost to the ground. 'How foolish I look,' he muttered to himself. 'Everyone says I'm too young to ride a horse but I'm eighteen tomorrow. I need a full-size horse.'

Coming along the street towards the procession was a gipsy caravan pulled by a very old, very slow horse. 'You're too old to pull this caravan now,' muttered the gipsy to his horse. 'What I need is a fresh young animal.'

The Royal Procession and the gipsy caravan met one another face to face. The King raised his sword. 'Stop the procession,' he shouted. What was he going to do? 'That's the animal for me,' he said, pointing to the gipsy's horse. 'My son shall have my horse as an early birthday present and you shall have his pony,' he told the gipsy.

The gipsy harnessed the Prince's pony to his caravan, the Prince sat proudly on the King's horse and the King, sitting comfortably on the old horse, raised his sword and happily set the procession in motion again – at a very slow pace.

DECEMBER 10

The Organ Man

Grandma thinks of years ago,
When, playing in the street,
The Organ Man with his monkey, Max,
Gave boys and girls a treat.

There's no TV – no radio;
No cars to knock them down;
And when they hear the magic notes
They race to gather round.

Their games can wait; some bring a coin
Saved up from pocket-money;
They give it gladly – Max has come!
And Max is very funny.

Max dances to the tinkling sounds,
He'll twist and chase his tail;
When the children clap and laugh
He bows and holds the rail.

His tiny hands will clap like them,
To make the children cheer.
His master turns the handle
And grins from ear to ear.

Then suddenly the organ stops
And Max is shut inside;
The Organ Man is on his way
To a street they've not yet tried.

The children go back home again;
A few will follow on;
And Grandma hears the music still
Long after it has gone.

DECEMBER 11

The Fable of the Birds, Beasts and Bat

The birds and the beasts were at war. The war had been going on for a long time and many battles had been fought. Sometimes the birds won and the beasts lost. Sometimes the beasts won and the birds lost. But there was one creature who was always on the winning side, whichever it might be, and that was the bat. If the bat thought the side he was fighting for was losing, he simply changed to the other side. The birds and beasts noticed, of course. It was hard not to.

Finally an agreement was reached and the war between the birds and the beasts was ended. The bat was sure that now he would be popular with everyone. After all, hadn't he helped to win every battle? 'They might even make me king,' he thought proudly. But things didn't work out quite the way he expected.

'You are a two-faced traitor,' said the birds and the beasts. 'You are loyal to no one. You let down both sides. We want nothing more to do with you.'

From that day onwards the bat was an outcast, shunned by both birds and beasts.

DECEMBER 12

Adventures of *The Tulip* – The Tunnel

'Tunnel ahead!' called Wilbur to Thomas and Minty from the deck of *The Tulip*.

'It's very long,' said Minty.

'And very dark,' said Wilbur.

'And very narrow,' said Minty.

'Will it be dangerous?' asked Wilbur.

'No, I shouldn't think so,' said Thomas. They headed into the tunnel very slowly. They lit all the lanterns and put them on deck.

'It's as dark as night in here,' said Minty. 'It's as dark as night in here,' said Minty's echo very loudly.

'We'd better whisper,' whispered Thomas. Suddenly Minty saw some eyes watching them from out of the dark.

'What's that?' he whispered. 'It's a monster!' he cried. 'It's a monster!' shouted his echo.

'Help!' cried Wilbur. 'Help!' cried his echo.

'Stop shouting, you two,' said Thomas, but they couldn't be calmed. So Thomas picked them up, one under each arm, and carried them, yelling and crying, across the deck and down below. He slammed the door shut and rolled two barrels against it.

Thomas ran back on deck in time to steer *The Tulip* just to one side of the "monster", which was another boat coming in the other direction.

'What's all the noise about?' called someone from behind the boat's lights, the monster's "eyes".

'Nothing,' said Thomas. 'Everything under control.' Thomas didn't let Wilbur and Minty out until *The Tulip* was well out of the tunnel.

'Are you sure it wasn't a monster?' asked Minty, rubbing his eyes in the sunshine.

'Quite sure,' said Thomas patiently.

DECEMBER 13

Alvin's Quest (Part 1)

Of all the animals in Africa, Alvin the Aardvark was the most humble. He knew that the other animals thought him ugly and odd, with his bald tail, big ears and funny eating habits. So when he returned home just before dawn, covered in earth but full of tasty, tickly ants, he was surprised to find a note pinned to his burrow door.

Dear Alvin, said the note, *I want you to discover who is first among all the animals. I shall return tonight for your answer.* It was signed: *The Lord of All Animals.*

Alvin was very surprised. He knew that the Lord of All Animals was fond of giving his subjects tasks to do. But he never dreamed that such a humble creature as himself would ever be chosen. Alvin was just sitting thinking about the question when Boris the Boa-constrictor slithered past.

'Well, well!' sighed Boris, in a soft voice that sent shivers right to the tip of Alvin's hairless tail. 'What have we here?'

'P-please,' stammered Alvin, 'it's only me, Alvin the Aardvark. The Lord of All Animals has asked me to discover who is first of all the animals. The trouble is I don't know where to start.'

The big snake laughed silently, his smooth, scaly skin rippling with amusement. 'You are fortunate, little friend,' he breathed, 'for you have found him.'

'Who?' squeaked Alvin, trying not to let Boris see his fear.

'Why, the first of all the animals!' rasped Boris, a little crossly. 'Which creature is longer than I? Or more beautiful?' he added, looking at his coils admiringly. When he looked back again, Alvin had disappeared . . .

DECEMBER 14

Alvin's Quest (Part 2)

Alvin the Aardvark was trying to find out who was the first of all the animals. All the world seemed to be asleep as Alvin walked on. 'Boris is the longest of the Lord's animals,' he thought aloud, 'but does that make him the first?'

'Of course not!' boomed a voice so loud that Alvin tumbled backwards head-over-heels with fright. 'I am!' Alvin found himself looking very closely at what appeared to be a grey, wrinkled tree trunk. In fact it was a leg; a leg attached to a large and very proud-looking elephant.

'Oh, it's you, Ernest!' sighed Alvin.

'It is indeed,' trumpeted Ernest, 'and it is quite obvious that the Lord meant me. I am the biggest and heaviest of all the creatures so I must be first.'

'Oh! Yes! Quite! Thank you, Ernest,' mumbled Alvin, but a little nagging voice inside his narrow, pointed head kept repeating, 'Not the longest, not the heaviest, but the first.' Sighing, he set off across the plain.

By the time he came to a water-hole, Alvin was even more confused. Colin the Cheetah had told him, as he zoomed past at full speed, that he must be first because he was the fastest. Gordon the Giraffe had grunted down to him that he must be the first, being the tallest of the Lord's animals. But still Alvin told himself, 'The Lord said "the first", not the longest, heaviest, fastest or tallest. What could He have meant? Who could it be?'

DECEMBER 15

Alvin's Quest (Part 3)

Alvin the Aardvark seemed no nearer to discovering who was the first of all the animals. Then he bumped into Leroy the Lion.

'Watch where you're going, you aimless aardvark!' snarled Leroy, woken from his sleep.

'I was just wondering,' said Alvin, 'who is the first of the animals?'

'Who is the King of the Jungle?' asked Leroy.

'Why, you, Leroy,' said Alvin.

'Who is the finest of beasts?' said Leroy.

'Why, you, Leroy,' said Alvin.

'There's your answer then,' said the lion with a yawn and went back to sleep.

Alvin set off home. 'Leroy must be right,' thought Alvin. 'He's the first of all the animals.' As he got back to his burrow Alvin saw a book lying on his bed. It was a dictionary of the animal kingdom. Alvin opened it up. The first entry was "aardvark".

'You see, Alvin,' said a deep voice from somewhere above Alvin's head. 'You may not be the longest or the strongest or the proudest animal but in one way you are the first. You are first in the animal alphabet. All my animals are first in some way and I love them all.'

But Alvin was already fast asleep, dreaming of tasty, crunchy, tickly ants . . .

DECEMBER 16

Flewella Goes Supersonic

Flewella the Witch had decided
To clean out her untidy room,
She threw out old potions,
And several pink lotions,
A frog and a moth-eaten broom.

But hidden beneath all the cobwebs,
Forgotten and lost on the shelf,
Was a book, stamped in gold,
Called 'Spells New and Old:
A Guide to Brew-it-yourself'.

Flewella flicked through all the pages.
It said, 'Is your broom worn away?
When dampness gets in
Broomatism sets in
So magic a new one today.'

She soon had her super brew bubbling.
Her cat hid his eyes from the blast.
But the spell worked a treat,
The new broom was complete,
And Flewella took off, extra fast.

She hurtled past Venus and Saturn,
And flashed by the Moon like a rocket.
She yelled, 'Mix the brew!
It's on page forty-two!
I forget what the spell is to stop it!'

The cat said he'd mix up the potion;
The book would explain what to do.
But the book was no use,
Several pages were loose,
And there wasn't a page forty-two!

Flewella flew on ever faster,
As a spaceship she looked rather comic.
But seven hours later,
She fell in a crater,
And the broom carried on supersonic!

'What a terrible broom!' gasped Flewella.
She jumped on a cloud as it passed,
Then much slower indeed,
At a much safer speed,
She floated home safely at last!

DECEMBER 17

Aladdin (Part 1)

Once upon a time, there was a magician who went to China to find a magic lamp he had heard about. He knew it was hidden in an underground cave, and he knew that the only way to get into the cave was through a narrow passage. He knew too, that if the clothes of anyone passing through the passage touched the walls, they would die. He didn't want to risk his own life, so he found a Chinese boy called Aladdin, and sent him into the cave.

'Wear this ring,' said the magician. 'It will help protect you.'

'Protect me from what?' asked Aladdin.

'Nothing,' said the magician quickly. 'Nothing at all. Down you go and bring me the lamp. It's on the ledge at the back of the cave.'

After a long time the magician saw Aladdin coming towards him. 'Have you got it? Give it to me!' said the magician. He reached down and would have snatched the lamp from Aladdin, but Aladdin had a feeling that the magician was not to be trusted.

'Help me out first,' said Aladdin. 'Then I will give you the lamp.'

'Give me the lamp first,' said the magician.

'Help me out first,' said Aladdin. The magician wouldn't give in, and neither would Aladdin. Finally the magician lost his patience.

'If you won't give me the lamp, then you can stay in the cave for ever!' he shouted, and he closed the entrance to the passage with a short, sharp spell and went away fuming.

DECEMBER 18

Aladdin (Part 2)

Poor Aladdin! He didn't know what to do. He sat, trapped in the dark cave, and tried to think. Then he absent-mindedly rubbed the ring which the magician had given him before he went into the cave. There was a hiss and a strange wispy figure wearing a turban curled up in the air in front of him, like smoke from a fire.

'Who . . . who are you?' he asked.

'I am the genie of the ring. What is your command, master?'

'Can you take me home?' asked Aladdin. Before Aladdin had time to blink he found himself standing outside his own house, wondering if he was asleep or awake. He knew he couldn't be dreaming when he found the lamp tucked inside his sleeve. He took it to his mother.

'We can sell this and buy food,' he said.

'No one will buy a dusty old lamp,' said Aladdin's mother. 'Let me clean it first.' She had rubbed it only once, when there was a hiss and another strange figure appeared.

'Who are you?' asked Aladdin.

'I am the genie of the lamp. What is your command, master?'

Aladdin and his mother soon became rich. Whatever they wanted the genie of the lamp provided, and when Aladdin fell in love with a princess, he was rich enough to marry her and take her to live in a beautiful palace.

Aladdin and his princess lived happily for a long time. They shared all their secrets except one. Aladdin never told the princess about the magic lamp.

DECEMBER 19

Aladdin (Part 3)

Aladdin had discovered a genie in a magic lamp. The genie made Aladdin rich. One day, when Aladdin was out hunting, and the princess was at home, an old man called from the street, 'New lamps for old! New lamps for old!'

Aladdin had never told the princess that his lamp was magic, so she gave Aladdin's lamp to the old man for a shiny new one. Immediately he had the magic lamp in his hand, the magician threw off his disguise.

'Now everything Aladdin has shall be mine,' he cried. He called up the genie of the lamp and ordered him to take him, Aladdin's palace and Aladdin's princess to far-away Africa.

When Aladdin returned home there was nothing but dust. He guessed at once that it was the magician's work. He quickly called up the genie of the ring.

'What is your command, master?' asked the genie.

'Please bring back my princess and my palace,' said Aladdin.

'Only the genie of the lamp can do that.'

'Then take me to my princess, wherever she may be,' commanded Aladdin. The genie of the ring did as he was told. The princess was overjoyed to see Aladdin.

'I've come to take you home,' said Aladdin. 'But first we must outwit the magician and get back the lamp. Slip this powder into his wine when he is not looking.' The powder made the magician sleep, and while he slept, Aladdin was able to take the lamp from his pocket. Aladdin rubbed the lamp. The genie appeared.

'What is your command, master?' asked the genie.

'Leave the magician here in the middle of Africa, and take the palace and everyone in it, back to China,' said Aladdin. That is what the genie of the lamp did, and everyone, except the magician, lived happily ever after.

DECEMBER 20

The Fable of the Oak and the Reeds

An oak tree grew beside a river. It was big and beautiful and very proud of its strength. One day a fierce wind blew across the land. It howled and roared. It tore branches from the trees. The oak tree stood strong and defiant and dared the wind to do its worst. It had always proved to be stronger than the wind before. But that day, the wind was even stronger than the oak tree, and it tore the tree up by its roots as if it were a sapling. The oak fell across the river and lay in a bed of reeds. It looked at the reeds and wondered why the wind didn't seem to be worrying them.

'I don't understand,' said the tree at last. 'How is it that you who are so frail and slender have escaped the wrath of the wind, while I, so big and strong, have been torn up by my roots?'

'You were too stubborn for your own good,' said the reeds. 'You fought with the wind when he was stronger than yourself and he was sure to win. We know we are weak and frail so we bend before the wind which passes over our heads without harming us. Unlike you, we live to fight another day.'

DECEMBER 21

The Surprise Prize (Part 1)

There was once a knight who wore black armour and owned a fine black charger. He should have looked splendid but he didn't have the knightly knack of staying on his horse. As fast as he got on, he fell off again.

All the other knights laughed at him as he sat in the mud. 'He doesn't look like a bright knight in shining armour at all. He looks more like a black night in darkest winter!' they jeered. But the black knight didn't mind how much the knights teased him. He was always merry and just laughed with them.

One day a grand tournament was announced and knights came from near and far to fight for the prize of a brilliant diamond. The tournament was to end with a surprise prize which the Princess would award. Every knight hoped to win this prize for the Princess was loved by them all.

The Black Knight practised and practised his jousting. 'If I can

only win one or two rounds then I might impress the Princess,' he thought.

Then came the news of the tournament order of play. 'In the first round,' proclaimed a courtier, 'the Black Knight will fight Sir Winalot.' Sir Winalot was the bravest and fiercest fighter in the land. The Black Knight sighed. He knew he didn't stand a chance.

DECEMBER 22

The Surprise Prize (Part 2)

The Black Knight wasn't very good at being a knight but he wanted to impress the Princess at the Grand Tournament. She had announced that after the tournament she would award a surprise prize.

The day of the tournament arrived. The Black Knight was drawn to fight the brave Sir Winalot. Their horses thundered towards each other. As the Black Knight lowered his lance he accidentally knocked down the visor on his helmet. He couldn't see where he was going. His lance dug into the ground and threw him off his horse. The Black Knight landed on the ground with a thud. The crowd laughed and clapped. Sir Winalot had won and, as he sat there in front of the crowds, the Black Knight couldn't help giggling.

Sir Winalot won every contest that day and it was he who collected the precious diamond. The crowd cheered as he raised it in salute.

Then came a fanfare of trumpets. An excited hush came over the crowd. The Princess announced, 'The winner of the surprise prize is . . . the Black Knight.' The crowd gasped. That *was* a surprise. The other knights began to jeer. The Princess waved her hand for silence.

'I have chosen the Black Knight because he makes us all laugh. He even makes himself laugh. His prize is to live in my castle. He shall be my very own knight and keep me merry all day.'

Sir Winalot then spoke:
'Hooray for the Knight
Who gives us good cheer.
Hooray for the Black Knight,
The Knight of the Year!'

All the other knights gave a cheer and everyone laughed but now they were laughing with the Black Knight, not at him. The Princess smiled and the Black Knight went very red.

DECEMBER 23

The Snowy House

It was a very hot day as Jasmin sat in the garden looking at her book. She was feeling too hot. As she turned the page she saw a picture of a snowy house. Jasmin had never seen real snow. She lived in a country where it was nearly always warm.

'I wish I could be there with that snow,' she said.

'I'm going that way myself,' said a voice beside her, 'if you want to come along.' She turned to look and was surprised to see a little pixie. Before she had time to reply he had taken hold of her hand and they were spinning in space. It grew colder and colder until at last they came down softly by a snowy house, like the one in Jasmin's book.

The pixie flew off. 'I'll be back soon,' he shouted. Jasmin found that she was wrapped in a warm red cloak so she was able to play in the snow. It was fine at first but then she began to feel cold. She was afraid to knock at the house so she went round the back and found a little shed where it was dry and out of the wind.

'I wish I could go home now,' she sighed, longing for the warm sunshine. At once the little pixie appeared, followed by a little bird.

'We can go now,' he said. 'This little bird's mother sent me over here to find him. He had hurt his wing and couldn't fly away with them when the winter came. Now we can all go back together.' Soon they were whirling through the air.

Back in Jasmin's garden, the pixie flew off. 'Thank you,' shouted Jasmin. Then she smiled to see the little bird with his mother sitting on a tree singing together in the sunshine.

DECEMBER 24

Mother Christmas Saves the Day

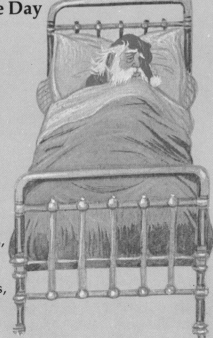

Dear Santa Claus, a busy man,
Worked hard by night and day
To make the toys the children want
When it is time for play.

With lots of happy little elves
To help the work along,
The workrooms soon began to ring
With laughter and with song.

One lively group made fluffy toys
Like teddy bears and dogs,
Grey elephants with huge pink ears,
White pussy cats and frogs.

Another group made wooden trains,
Farm tractors and big bears –
While others carved a Noah's Ark
With animals in pairs.

Computer games and dolls and cars
All piled up on the shelves –
And Santa Claus worked just as hard
As all those little elves.

When Mother Christmas came to see
If all their work was done,
She found the elves had all gone home
And Santa Claus was gone!

On tiptoe then she crept upstairs,
And there upon the bed
Poor Santa Claus lay fast asleep,
His night-cap on his head.

'We cannot let the children down,'
She thought in great dismay.
'Whatever will they do without
Their toys on Christmas Day?'

And so it was, one Christmas time,
By driving Santa's sleigh,
Mother Christmas did the work
And saved our Christmas Day.

DECEMBER 25

The Nutcracker Prince (Part 1)

There was to be a Christmas party at Clara's house. Everyone would be there, including Hermann and his family. Hermann was going to marry Clara's sister, Louise. At least that's what Clara's mother hoped.

Suddenly Clara's brother ran in with a dead mouse. 'Take it away,' cried the two girls. He threw it into the fire.

Soon the first guests arrived. There was Doctor Drosselmeyer and his young friend, Karl, carrying a chest between them.

'What's in there?' asked Clara.

'Presents of course,' said the doctor.

'And these are for you, Louise,' said Karl, presenting Clara's sister with some roses.

'They're beautiful,' said Louise. She and Karl sat down together.

'Louise,' her mother shouted. 'Hermann has arrived.' Louise didn't notice her mother calling. Her mother walked over to her, snatched the roses and threw them on the floor.

'Mother!' cried Louise. But the door-bell rang again and more guests came in. Soon the room was full of laughing children.

'Come, children,' called Doctor Drosselmeyer. 'Come and see what's in my magic chest.' Clara and all the other children gathered round. First the doctor pulled out a beautiful Spanish fan, then an Arabian prince's hat, then two more hats, one from China, one from Russia. Next came some wooden soldiers. Soon all the children had presents.

'What's for me?' asked Clara.

'Here's yours,' said the doctor giving her a box of sweets, 'and there's something else.' He held up a wooden doll with a smiling face. He put a nut in its mouth, pulled its legs and the nut broke in half.

'It's a nutcracker prince,' cried Clara in delight.

DECEMBER 26

The Nutcracker Prince (Part 2)

Clara had been given a nutcracker prince as a Christmas present. She danced round the room with it. But Hermann grabbed it and pulled its legs. One of the legs came off.

'You've broken it,' cried Clara. The doctor took the doll and fitted the leg back in place.

Finally everyone went home, wishing one another a happy Christmas. Clara and Louise went

to bed, but a few minutes later they came back downstairs.

'I forgot my Nutcracker Prince,' said Clara sitting down nursing the doll.

'I've come for Karl's roses,' said Louise. The two girls talked about the evening and soon they fell asleep.

As the clock struck twelve, Clara saw a mouse, the size of a man, jump out of the fire. 'He looks like Hermann,' she gasped. More mice jumped out of the fire. The mice moved towards Louise who was still asleep. 'Don't hurt her,' cried Clara.

'We'll save her,' said a voice. A tall nutcracker prince, followed by his soldiers, marched towards the mice.

'He looks like Karl,' thought Clara.

A battle was fought between the mice and the soldiers. Suddenly the Mouse King picked up Louise and ran off with her. The Nutcracker Prince ran after them. Now Clara stood alone and in tears.

'Don't cry,' said Doctor Drosselmeyer, coming up to her. 'I'll help you find Louise and Karl.'

They sailed together in a magical ship to the Land of Sweets. They sat in a huge box of sweets watching dancers from Spain, Arabia, China and Russia. Then as Clara joined in the dance of the flowers, two people danced towards her.

'Louise! Karl!' she shouted. 'At last I've found you.'

'Wake up! Wake up! What are you two doing down here?' It was Clara's mother.

'Oh, Mother,' said Clara. 'You'll never believe where I've been in my dreams.'

DECEMBER 27

Around the World in an Afternoon

Jonathin Spindle had long legs, long arms, long feet and a long nose. One day, he put some bread and cheese into a paper bag and said, 'I shall go round the world today.'

Jonathin jumped on his bicycle and, following his long nose, he set off round the world. He sped along the lane and into the wood.

'This must be the jungle where the elephants live,' he said. A little brown rabbit hopped up in front of him. 'An elephant,' shouted Jonathin. 'So elephants live under the ground,' he said as the rabbit scurried away down a burrow.

Jonathin steered out of the wood into a ploughed field. 'This must be the desert,' he cried as mud spattered his boots and trousers. A tiny bird flew up from one of the furrows. 'A flying camel,' gasped Jonathin, steering his bicycle into a hedge.

'What a prickly place the world is,' he sighed. 'I wish it would look where it's going.' He decided to eat his bread and cheese but the bag was caught high in the hedge. 'I suppose hedges get hungry too,' he said. 'Be sure and put the bag away tidily when you've finished,' Jonathin shouted as he cycled off. He swished through a duck pond. 'I see the sea,' he shouted, 'and three white sailing ships.' He splashed three ducks as he went by.

Jonathin's long nose led him in a circle and soon took him back home. He propped his bicycle against the wall and offered it a clump of grass, which it refused to eat.

'Meow,' said the cat, wondering why Jonathin had been gone all afternoon.

'I've been round the world, puss,' he said, 'and that always takes a long time.'

DECEMBER 28

The Sticky Nose

Pom-Pom, a little American Indian boy, watched his father carving a wooden face on a totem-pole. 'If that's Grandfather's face,' thought Pom-Pom, 'his nose is too long.'

Later, Pom-Pom decided to chop a bit off Grandfather's wooden nose. He took his tomahawk and climbed the totem-pole. But a bee kept buzzing about him. 'Shooo!' cried Pom-Pom, waving his tomahawk about. Then . . . Oh no! The tomahawk hit the wooden nose and chopped it all off!

'I must stick Grandfather's nose back on before Father finds out!' cried Pom-Pom. But with what? Sticky maple syrup! Just the thing! Pom-Pom stuck the nose back on with the syrup and went home, keeping very quiet about it.

But Bear was about, his nose twitching. While Pom-Pom was away, Bear climbed the totem-pole. 'Yum . . . yum.' He licked off all the syrup and Grandfather's nose fell off again! Again and again, Pom-Pom stuck the nose back on, but Bear always came back and licked off all the syrup.

'I'll get even with that bear!' cried Pom-Pom. He found Bear fishing in the river. Pom-Pom crawled out on an overhanging branch and tried to lasso him, but he lost his balance and fell into the river. Kind-hearted Bear lifted him out of the water, hung him up to dry and trotted off.

Pom-Pom's father found him and said. 'You were lucky that bear didn't eat you, Pom-Pom. Someone saw him up the totem-pole, chewing on Grandfather's nose!'

Pom-Pom couldn't let the bear take the blame and he told his father the whole story. His father laughed. He thought it would make Grandfather laugh too.

DECEMBER 29

Sleeping Beauty (Part 1)

There was once a king and a queen who longed for a child. After many years of waiting they at last had a daughter. They invited all seven fairies who lived in their kingdom to be godmothers.

The day of the christening came and a splendid banquet was prepared. The King and Queen had seven golden caskets made, each one containing a golden knife, fork and spoon.

As the King and his guests were taking their places at the table, an old fairy arrived unexpectedly. The King immediately ordered another place to be set, but there were eight fairies and only seven caskets, and the old fairy had to eat with a silver knife, fork and spoon. The old fairy was very angry. First she hadn't received an invitation and now she wasn't to have a golden casket.

The time came for the fairies to bestow their gifts upon the baby Princess.

'She shall be very beautiful,' said the first.

'She shall have the nature of an angel,' said the second.

'She shall be graceful,' said the third.

'She shall dance to perfection,' said the fourth.

'She shall sing like a nightingale,' said the fifth.

'She shall play the sweetest music,' said the sixth.

'She shall prick her finger on a spindle . . . and DIE!' cackled the old fairy.

Everyone gasped. But before anyone could think what to say or do, the seventh fairy said, 'The Princess will prick her finger but she will not die. Instead she will sleep for a hundred years.'

DECEMBER 30

Sleeping Beauty (Part 2)

The King and Queen were told that their daughter would prick her finger on a spindle and fall asleep for a hundred years. The King ordered all the spinning wheels in the kingdom to be destroyed.

Sixteen years passed. Then one day, the Princess found an old tower. In the room at the very top she found an old woman spinning.

'What are you doing?' asked the Princess.

'I'm spinning,' said the old woman.

'May I try?' asked the Princess. She took the spindle from the old woman. Everything came about as the fairy had predicted. The Princess pricked her finger and fell into a sleep from which she did not wake. Everyone in the castle fell asleep too.

As time went by, thick thorns and brambles grew up around the castle and made it impossible for anyone to get near it. A hundred years passed. Many tried to get into the castle, but no one succeeded. And then one day a king's son happened to pass that way. He asked about the castle and an old woodcutter told him about the Princess and the magic spell.

The Prince was curious and decided to look for himself. He unbuckled his sword and prepared to hack through the thorns, but before he could touch them they seemed to melt away, and a path appeared which led to the castle gate.

The castle was very still. There wasn't a sound to be heard anywhere. He found the Princess on the couch where she had fallen a hundred years before. She looked so beautiful that he bent to kiss her.

The Prince's kiss woke the Princess and as she woke, so did everyone else in the castle. The Prince married the Princess and they both lived happily ever after.

188

DECEMBER 31

Twinkle Twinkle Little Star

Twinkle, twinkle, little star,
How I wonder what you are!
Up above the world so high,
Like a diamond in the sky.

When the blazing sun is gone,
When he nothing shines upon,
Then you show your little light,
Twinkle, twinkle, all the night.

Then the traveller in the dark,
Thanks you for your tiny spark.
He could not see which way to go,
If you did not twinkle so.

In the dark blue sky you keep,
And often through my curtains peep,
For you never shut your eye,
Till the sun is in the sky.

As your bright and tiny spark
Lights the traveller in the dark,
Though I know not what you are,
Twinkle, twinkle, little star.